# Student Study Guide

Kevin Bodden
Randy Gallaher
Kathy Kopelousos

Lewis and Clark Community College

# Prealgebra

## Fourth Edition

K. Elayn Martin-Gay

PEARSON

Prentice Hall

Upper Saddle River, NJ 07458

Editor-in-Chief: Chris Hoag
Project Manager: Mary Beckwith
Assistant Editor: Christina Simoneau
Supplement Editor: Elizabeth Covello
Assistant Managing Editor: John Matthews
Production Editor: Donna Crilly
Supplement Cover Manager: Paul Gourhan
Supplement Cover Designer: Joanne Alexandris
Manufacturing Buyer: Ilene Kahn

© 2004 Pearson Education, Inc.
Pearson Prentice Hall
Pearson Education, Inc.
Upper Saddle River, NJ 07458

Pearson Prentice Hall® is a trademark of Pearson Education, Inc.

The author and publisher of this book have used their best efforts in preparing this book. These efforts include the development, research, and testing of the theories and programs to determine their effectiveness. The author and publisher make no warranty of any kind, expressed or implied, with regard to these programs or the documentation contained in this book. The author and publisher shall not be liable in any event for incidental or consequential damages in connection with, or arising out of, the furnishing, performance, or use of these programs.

Printed in the United States of America

10 9 8 7 6 5 4 3 2 1

ISBN 0-13-144538-3

Pearson Education Ltd., *London*
Pearson Education Australia Pty. Ltd., *Sydney*
Pearson Education Singapore, Pte. Ltd.
Pearson Education North Asia Ltd., *Hong Kong*
Pearson Education Canada, Inc., *Toronto*
Pearson Educación de Mexico, S.A. de C.V.
Pearson Education—Japan, *Tokyo*
Pearson Education Malaysia, Pte. Ltd.

# TABLE OF CONTENTS

**EXERCISES**

**SOLUTIONS**

# Preface

Congratulations! Your purchase of this Student Study Guide which supplements your textbook <u>Prealgebra, 4e</u>, K. Elayn Martin-Gay, will provide you with various resources that will help you succeed in your prealgebra course.

This first portion of this Student Study Guide presents some strategies for success. These tips are arranged into three areas: Classroom Strategies, Study/Homework Strategies, and Test-taking Strategies.

The second portion of this Guide provides supplemental materials that align with each chapter in the textbook. For each section within a chapter, examples with detailed solutions are presented. These examples are followed by exercise sets containing twenty problems each. At the end of each chapter, a twenty-five-question practice test is provided. All of the examples, exercise sets, and practice tests are similar to those in the textbook. Each practice test is followed by a set of Helpful Hints and Insights that include important facts, helpful hints, and tips for avoiding common errors. Finally, at the end of all the chapters, two 100-question practice final examinations are given.

In the third and final portion of this Guide, complete step-by-step solutions for the exercise sets, practice tests, and final examinations are provided. Once again, the methods used to solve the problems are the same as those presented within the textbook.

Good luck in your prealgebra course! To ultimately succeed in this course, you must be responsible and take advantage of all available resources. We are confident that this Student Study Guide, if used correctly, will contribute to your success.

Randy Gallaher
Kevin Bodden
Kathy Kopelousos
Lewis & Clark Community College

## Strategies for Success

**Important Information:**

- On the first day of class, obtain the following information for future use:

Instructor:  Name: _____

Office location: _____

Office hours: _____

_____

Phone number: _____

Email address: _____

Obtain the names of at least two students whom you can contact for information or study questions.

1. Name: _____

Phone number: _____

Email address: _____

2. Name: _____

Phone number: _____

Email address: _____

Determine if your campus has a math lab.

Location: _____

Hours: _____

Phone number: _____

Determine if your campus has tutoring available.

Location: _____

Hours: _____

Phone number: _____

Which textbook supplements does your instructor recommend?

_____

_____

## Classroom Strategies

- Attend class every day. If you must be absent, copy the notes from another student. Call the instructor or another student to obtain homework assignments so you will not get behind. Watch the video that accompanies the material you missed.

- Choose a seat where you have a good view of the board or projector screen and where you can hear the instructor clearly.

- Be prepared for class. Keep a notebook specifically for this class, preferably consisting of a section for notes and a section for homework. Maintain a supply of writing utensils.

- Since a lecture can move rapidly, you are often forced to take notes quickly. Set up your own abbreviation system. Take notes as thoroughly as possible and after class rewrite your notes more legibly and fill in the gaps.

- Do not be afraid to ask questions. If something is unclear, ask for a further explanation. More often than not, other students in the class have the same questions.

- Before you leave class, make sure you know what is assigned for homework and what assignments, if any, are due for the next session.

## Study/Homework Strategies

- Study your mathematics daily, even if it is just for 10 or 15 minutes. Do not wait until test time to do a cram session. You should learn the material for understanding, not just memorize it long enough to take the exam. Most likely, you will have additional mathematics courses after this one. You are gaining tools in this class that will be essential for subsequent courses. Retaining what you learn is essential!

- Choose an environment for studying that will allow you to maximize your concentration. Avoid areas where frequent distractions will arise.

- When reading the textbook, do not just read the examples. The text between the examples is important to your overall understanding of the material.

- As you read the textbook and work the exercises, write down any questions that arise. If you rely on your memory for this, you may very likely forget some of the questions once you are in class.

- Complete your homework as soon after the lecture as possible. This way, the information will still be fresh in your mind.

- Create a glossary of important terms. Understanding the mathematical terminology is an important aspect of any math course. Writing out a word's definition can help you remember that word's meaning.

- Practice will improve your skills. Practice will make you feel more comfortable with the material and build your confidence. If you are having difficulty with a certain type of assigned problems, do more of that type until you can do them easily. Remember that this Student Study Guide provides many additional problems. Once you do them, check them against the completely worked-out solutions.

- Try each homework problem that is assigned. As you watch your instructor work a problem, it may appear to be simple. However, when you are on your own, it may suddenly seem more difficult.

- When working homework problems, allow plenty of paper. Show every step of a problem in an organized and systematic manner. This will help to reduce the number of careless mistakes. When you look back at the problem at a later date, you will be able to follow your work more easily.

- When two different approaches are available for solving a problem, use one approach to solve the problem and the second approach to check your answer. If your two answers do not agree, you will know that you have made an error.

- When your instructor returns an assignment or quiz, be sure to review it and understand your mistakes. Do not simply file away old papers without first making an effort to learn from your mistakes.

- Make use of the resources that accompany the textbook. Watch the videos, use the MathPro Tutorial Software, and utilize the companion website.

- Look for other sources of help. See your instructor during office hours, work with fellow classmates, form a study group, go to the math lab if one exists at your school, and/or find a tutor.

- Do not lose points needlessly. Have all assignments in on time. Take advantage of all extra-credit opportunities if they exist.

**Test-taking Strategies**

- Once again, prepare daily for a test, not just the night before the test. Do not let difficulties get out of hand, get early help well before the test date. At least three days prior to the test, begin to prepare more intensely.

- Many times, students can do their homework assignments, but "freeze-up" on tests. One way to prevent this from happening to you is to use practice tests. When studying for a test, actually make yourself a test. Find a quiet location and take the test just as though you were in class. Generally, the more you practice taking tests, the more comfortable and confident you will feel during the actual event. Remember that this Student Study Guide provides practice tests. Once you use them, you can check your answers and your work because the step-by-step solutions are provided.

- When preparing for a test, complete an overall review of the chapter(s), focusing on the objectives and the examples.

- Complete the review exercises and test at the end of the chapter(s). Check your answers with the back of the textbook. Review any missed items.

- On the night before the test, be sure to get a good night's sleep. If you are well rested, your brain will work more effectively than if you are tired.

- While taking the test, do not get bogged down on one question. If there is a problem that you do not know how to work, skip it and move on to problems you can work. Then, return to that problem later on if time permits.

- Pay attention to the point value on test questions. Instructors frequently assign heavier weights to more difficult problems.

- Be sure to answer every question on the test. Leaving a question blank will automatically result in zero points for that problem. Do as much work as you can, even if it is just righting down the first step.

- When using a calculator on a test (assuming you are allowed to do so), be sure that you are familiar with the model of calculator you are using. Because button sequences may vary from calculator to calculator, using a "new" calculator for the first time on an exam can be problematic.

- Use all of the allowed test time. Leaving early without checking over all your answers can be a very costly habit. Do not worry about the first person who "finishes" the test and leaves. A test is not a race to see who can finish first.

- When your instructor hands back a graded test, make correction to any problems you missed. It is important to clear up these mistakes now, because you will generally be using these concepts again.

- When final exam time comes around, your old tests are a great study resource. Also, remember the two practice final examinations along with complete solutions that are provided in this Student Study Guide. Use them to help prepare for the final.

## 1.1 TIPS FOR SUCCESS IN MATHEMATICS

The list below summarizes many of the tips offered in textbook.
- Maintain a positive attitude as you progress through the course.
- Make sure your schedule (school, work, family, etc.) allows you the best chance for success in the course.
- Exchange names and phone numbers with other student in the class
- Attend all class periods and be on time.
- Do your homework.
- Check your work.
- Learn from your mistakes and be patient with yourself.
- Know how to get help if you need it.
- Organize your class materials.
- Read your textbook before class.
- Do not be afraid to ask questions.
- Hand in all assignments on time.
- Utilize the resources in the text.

## 1.1 EXERCISES

*Suggestions for **Getting Ready for This Course** and **General Tips for Success** are provided in the textbook. For each statement below, fill in the blank(s) with the appropriate word(s) to finish the suggestion from the textbook.*

1. Remember that your _____ is your best source for information.

2. Make sure that you are ready for this course by having the time and _____ attitude that it takes to succeed.

3. Exchange names and _____ _____ with at least one other person in class.

4. Choose to attend _____ class periods and be on time.

5. Sit near the _____ of the classroom.

6. Do your _____.

7. Check your work and _____ your mistakes.

8. _____ from your mistakes.

9. Be _____ with yourself.

10. Know how to get _____ if you need it.

11. _____ your class materials.

12. Read your textbook _____ class.

13. As you read, you should _____ _____ any questions that you want to ask in class.

14. Don't be afraid to _____ _____.

15. Hand in assignments _____ _____.

16. When taking a test, read the _____ on the test carefully.

17. When taking a test, read each problem carefully and make sure that you _____ the question asked.

18. When taking a test, watch your time and _____ yourself so that you can attempt each problem.

19. When taking a test, if you have time, check your _____ and _____.

20. When taking a test, do not turn your test in _____. If you have extra time, spend it double-checking your work.


## 1.2 PLACE VALUE AND NAMES FOR NUMBERS

**Example 1:**   Write 124,503,978 in words.

**Solution:**   $\underbrace{\text{one hundred twenty-four}}_{\text{number in period}}$ $\underbrace{\text{million}}_{\text{name of period}}$ , $\underbrace{\text{five hundred three}}_{\text{number in period}}$ $\underbrace{\text{thousand}}_{\text{name of period}}$ , $\underbrace{\text{nine hundred seventy-eight}}_{\text{number in period}}$

**Example 2:**   Write nine hundred fifteen thousand, three hundred thirty-two in standard form.

**Solution:**   915,332

**Example 3:**   Write 4,507,237 in expanded form.

**Solution:**   $4,000,000 + 500,000 + 7000 + 200 + 30 + 7$

**Example 4:**   Insert < or > to make a true statement:  1273   997

**Solution:**   Since 1273 is larger than 997, we obtain $1273 > 997$.


## 1.2 EXERCISES

*Determine the place value of the digit 6 in each whole number.*

  1. 3267        2. 769,532        3. 16,005,278,129        4. 672,958,010

*Write each whole number in words.*

  5. 9371        6. 80,029        7. 148,552        8. 8070

*Write each whole number in standard form.*

  9. Six thousand, seventy eight

10. Fifteen million, six hundred thirty-one thousand, eight hundred ninety

11. Eighty thousand, seven hundred two

12. Seven billion, four thousand, twenty-one

*Write each whole number in expanded form.*

13. 891        14. 78,094        15. 82,348,975        16. 8,002,507,406

*Insert < or > to make a true statement.*

17. 8   14        18. 240   204        19. 121   97        20. 1268   1286

## 1.3 ADDING WHOLE NUMBERS AND PERIMETER

**Example 1:**  Add: $252,654 + 83,826$.

**Solution:**
$$
\begin{array}{r}
\overset{1\;\;\;1\;\;\;1}{2\,5\,2\,,\,6\,5\,4} \\
+\,8\,3\,,\,8\,2\,6 \\
\hline
3\,3\,6\,,\,4\,8\,0
\end{array}
$$

**Example 2:**  Add: $14 + 21 + 6 + 8 + 9$.

**Solution:**   Use the commutative and associative properties of addition to reorder and regroup the addends in such a way as to obtain sums of 10, 20, 30, etc.

$$
\begin{aligned}
14 + 21 + 6 + 8 + 9 &= 14 + 6 + 21 + 9 + 8 \\
&= (14 + 6) + (21 + 9) + 8 \\
&= 20 + 30 + 8 \\
&= 58
\end{aligned}
$$

**Example 3:**  Find the perimeter of the given triangle.

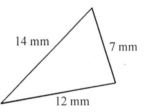

**Solution:**   Add the lengths of the three sides: $14 \text{ mm} + 7 \text{ mm} + 12 \text{ mm} = 33 \text{ mm}$. Thus, the perimeter of the triangle is 33 mm.

**Example 4:**  According to the 2000 U. S. census, the two states with the smallest populations are Wyoming with 493,782 and Vermont with 608,827. What is the total population of these two states?

**Solution:**
$$
\begin{array}{ll}
\text{Wyoming's population} \;\rightarrow & \overset{1\;1\,1\;\;1}{\;\;493,782} \\
\text{Vermont's population} \;\rightarrow & +608,827 \\
\hline
& 1,102,609
\end{array}
$$

The total population of the two states (Vermont and Wyoming) is 1,102,609 people.

## 1.3 EXERCISES

*Add.*

1.  $23 + 48$

2.  $76 + 89$

3.  $527 + 917$

4.  $\begin{array}{r} 37 \\ +\,49 \\ \hline \end{array}$

5.  $\begin{array}{r} 354 \\ +\,538 \\ \hline \end{array}$

6.  $\begin{array}{r} 1485 \\ +\,347 \\ \hline \end{array}$

7.  $4238 + 427$

8.  $3472 + 2541$

9.  $27 + 60 + 58$

10.  $\begin{array}{r} 51,243 \\ +\,32,548 \\ \hline \end{array}$

11.  $\begin{array}{r} 43 \\ 632 \\ +\,2726 \\ \hline \end{array}$

12.  $\begin{array}{r} 3074 \\ 305 \\ +\,2043 \\ \hline \end{array}$

*Add. Use the commutative and associative properties of addition to help.*

13. $12 + 15 + 8$

14. $16 + 23 + 12 + 17 + 8$

*Find the perimeter of each figure.*

15.

4 in.

11 in.    11 in.

12 in.

16.

5 feet

8 feet

*Solve.*

17. An owner of a construction company bought two parcels of land. One parcel contained 537 acres and the other contained 264 acres. How much land did he buy altogether?

18. Three attendants are selling tickets at a box office. The first attendant sold 378 tickets, the second sold 543 tickets, and the third sold 488 tickets. How many tickets were sold altogether?

19. A basic auto tune-up costs $89, tire rotation costs $16, and an oil change costs $24. Find the total cost for all the services.

20. Benjamin and Ethan are brothers who are going to pool their money in order to buy a new video game costing $59. Benjamin has $32 and Ethan has $29. Determine whether the two have enough money to buy the game.

## 1.4 SUBTRACTING WHOLE NUMBERS

**Example 1:**   Subtract: $38 - 17$. Check the answer by adding.

**Solution:**      $38 - 17 = 21$ because $21 + 17 = 38$.

**Example 2:**   Subtract: $7469 - 3255$. Check the answer by adding.

**Solution:**
$$\begin{array}{r} 7469 \\ -3255 \\ \hline 4214 \end{array}$$
*Check:*
$$\begin{array}{r} 4214 \\ +3255 \\ \hline 7469 \end{array}$$

**Example 3:**   Subtract: $8274 - 4579$. Check the answer by adding.

**Solution:**
$$\begin{array}{r} {}^{11\ 16} \\ 7\ \cancel{1}\ \cancel{6}\ 14 \\ \cancel{8}\cancel{2}\cancel{7}\cancel{4} \\ -4\ 5\ 7\ 9 \\ \hline 3\ 6\ 9\ 5 \end{array}$$
*Check:*
$$\begin{array}{r} {}^{1\ 1\ 1} \\ 3695 \\ +4579 \\ \hline 8274 \end{array}$$

**Example 4:** A football stadium has 24,849 seats. Attendance for one game was 19,825. How many seats were empty for that game?

**Solution:**

Total number of seats        $\rightarrow$
Number of occupied seats   $\rightarrow$
$$\begin{array}{r} {}^{1\ 14} \\ 2\cancel{4},849 \\ -1\ 9,825 \\ \hline 5,024 \end{array}$$

The game had 5024 empty seats.

## 1.4 EXERCISES

*Subtract.  Check by adding.*

1. $67 - 52$
2. $86 - 56$
3. $947 - 532$

4. $\begin{array}{r} 83 \\ -\ 29 \\ \hline \end{array}$
5. $\begin{array}{r} 60 \\ -\ 34 \\ \hline \end{array}$
6. $\begin{array}{r} 63 \\ -\ 19 \\ \hline \end{array}$

7. $\begin{array}{r} 854 \\ -\ 658 \\ \hline \end{array}$
8. $\begin{array}{r} 485 \\ -\ 347 \\ \hline \end{array}$
9. $\begin{array}{r} 700 \\ -\ 251 \\ \hline \end{array}$

10. $\begin{array}{r} 928 \\ -\ 863 \\ \hline \end{array}$
11. $\begin{array}{r} 4738 \\ -\ 2851 \\ \hline \end{array}$
12. $\begin{array}{r} 51,243 \\ -\ 32,548 \\ \hline \end{array}$

13. Subtract 12 from 76.

14. Find the difference of 52 and 29.

15. What is 134 decreased by 75?

16. Find the number that is 17 fewer than 38.

*Solve.*

17. A television that normally sells for $589 is discounted by $97.  What is the sale price?

18. For her associate's degree, Julie needs a total of 60 credit hours.  At present, she has completed 42 credit hours.  How many more credit hours does Julie need?

19. When Karen began her trip, the odometer of her van read 43,761.  At the end of her trip, the odometer read 48,643.  How many miles did Karen drive on her trip?

20. According to the 2000 U. S. census, the population of California was 33,871,648 and the population of Texas was 20,851,820.  How many more people live in California than Texas?

## 1.5 ROUNDING AND ESTIMATING

**Example 1:** Round 57,632 to the nearest thousand.

**Solution:**     5 7 , 6 3 2     The digit to the right of the thousands place is the hundreds place,
         ↑       which is underlined.
    thousands place

         5 7 , 6 3 2     Since the underlined digit is 5 or greater, add 1 to the 7 in the
         Add   Replace     thousands place and replace each digit to the right of it with 0.
         1    with zeros

57,632 rounded to the nearest thousand is 58,000.

**Example 2:**   Round 164,986 to the nearest ten-thousand.

**Solution:**       1 6 <u>4</u> , 9 8 6       The digit to the right of the ten-thousands place is the thousands
                      ↑                         place, which is underlined.
              ten-thousands
                 place

              1 6 <u>4</u> , 9 8 6       Since the underlined digit is less than 5, replace it and the each
              Do    Replace              digit to the right of it with 0.
              not   with zeros
              add
               1

       163,986 rounded to the nearest ten-thousand is 160,000.

**Example 3:**   Round each number to the nearest thousand to find an estimated sum.
                 3295
                 1784
                 6121
                +4879

**Solution:**       3 2 9 5   rounds to     3 0 0 0
                    1 7 8 4   rounds to     2 0 0 0
                    6 1 2 1   rounds to     6 0 0 0
                   +4 8 7 9   rounds to    +5 0 0 0
                                          ‾‾‾‾‾‾‾‾
                                           1 6 0 0 0

       The estimated sum is 16,000.  (The exact sum is 16,079).

## 1.5 EXERCISES

*Round each whole number to the given place.*

1.  873 to the nearest hundred

2.  1564 to the nearest ten

3.  438 to the nearest hundred

4.  16,825 to the nearest thousand

5.  9849 to the nearest thousand

6.  2449 to the nearest hundred

7.  43,648 to the nearest hundred

8.  134,670 to the nearest thousand

9.  142,049 to the nearest ten-thousand

10.  69,999 to the nearest ten

11.  The speed of light in a vacuum is 299,792,458 meters per second.  Round this number to the nearest hundred thousand.

*Estimate the sum or difference by rounding each number to the nearest ten.*

| 12. | 62 | 13. | 78 | 14. | 824 |
|-----|----|-----|----|-----|-----|
|     | 51 |     | 83 |     | − 196 |
|     | 27 |     | 52 |     |     |
|     | + 38 |   | + 98 |   |     |

*Estimate the sum or difference by rounding each number to the nearest hundred.*

| 15. | 884 | 16. | 832 | 17. | 2892 |
|-----|-----|-----|-----|-----|------|
|     | 531 |     | − 267 |   | − 1781 |
|     | + 378 |   |     |     |      |

10

*Solve.*

18. Matt, Ethan, and Drew have $483, $1142, and $687, respectively. Round each amount to the nearest hundred to estimate the total amount of money they have.

19. Enrollment figures at the local university showed an increase from 58,735 credit hours in 2002 to 60,791 credit hours in 2003. Round each number to the nearest thousand to estimate the increase in credit hours.

20. Jerome is trying to quickly estimate the distance from Springfield, MO to Rolla, MO. Round each distance provided to the nearest ten to estimate the total distance.

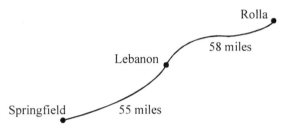

## 1.6 MULTIPLYING WHOLE NUMBERS AND AREA

**Example 1:** Multiply: $62 \times 3$.

**Solution:**
$$\begin{array}{r} 62 \\ \times\ 3 \\ \hline 186 \end{array}$$

**Example 2:** Rewrite $8(3+7)$ using the distributive property.

**Solution:** $8(3+7) = 8 \cdot 3 + 8 \cdot 7$

**Example 3:** Multiply: $236 \times 68$.

**Solution:**
$$\begin{array}{r} 236 \\ \times\ 38 \\ \hline 1888 \\ 7080 \\ \hline 8968 \end{array}$$
$\leftarrow 8(236)$
$\leftarrow 30(236)$
Add.

**Example 4:** Bill and Beverly Meyers plan to take their three children to the movies. The ticket price for each child is $5 and for each adult is $8. How much money is needed for their admission?

**Solution:** The price for the three children will be $3 \cdot \$5 = \$15$. The price for the two adults will be $3 \cdot \$8 = \$16$. The total price will be $\$15 + \$16 = \$31$.

**Example 5:** Find the area of the rectangle shown below.

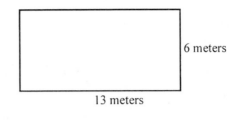

13 meters

**Solution:**     Area  = length · width
                       = (13 meters)(6 meters)
                       = 78 square meters

## 1.6 EXERCISES

*Use the distributive property to rewrite each expression.*

1. $4(6+1)$  2. $9(2+7)$  3. $15(30+2)$

*Multiply.*

4.  39
    × 3

5.  31
    × 8

6.  328
    × 7

7.  342
    × 31

8.  589
    × 67

9.  3142
    × 82

10.  978
     × 30

11.  153
     × 321

12.  2754
     × 372

13. $(70)(60)$  14. $(23)(1)(40)$  15. $(378)(52)(0)$

*Estimate the products by rounding each factor to the nearest hundred.*

16. $578 \times 327$  17. $324 \times 478$

*Find the area of the given rectangle.*

18.  19.

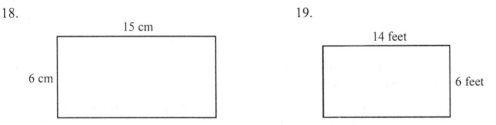

*Solve.*

20. Jeremiah bought four tires at $76 each and two seat covers at $49 each. What is the total amount that he spent?

## 1.7 DIVIDING WHOLE NUMBERS

**Example 1:**   Find the quotient: $32 \div 4$. Check the answer by multiplying.

**Solution:**   $32 \div 4 = 8$ because $4 \cdot 8 = 32$.

**Example 2:**   Divide $3258 \div 6$. Check the answer by multiplying.

**Solution:**

$$
\begin{array}{r}
543 \\
6\overline{)3258}
\end{array}
$$

$\underline{30}$       $5(6) = 30$

$25$       $32 - 30 = 2$, bring down the 5.

$\underline{24}$       $4(6) = 24$

$18$       $25 - 24 = 1$, bring down the 8.

$\underline{18}$       $3(6) = 18$

$0$       $18 - 18 = 0$

*Check :*

$$
\begin{array}{r}
543 \\
\times\ 6 \\
\hline
3258
\end{array}
$$

**Example 3:**   Divide $5143 \div 17$. Check the answer.

**Solution:**

$$
\begin{array}{r}
302\ \text{R}\ 9 \\
17\overline{)5143}
\end{array}
$$

$\underline{51}$       $3(17) = 51$

$04$       Subtract and bring down the 4.

$\underline{\ 0}$       $0(17) = 0$

$43$       Subtract and bring down the 3.

$\underline{34}$       $2(17) = 34$

$9$       Subtract. The remainder is 9.

*Check :*

$$
\begin{array}{r}
302 \\
\times\ 17 \\
\hline
2114 \\
3020 \\
\hline
5134 \\
+\ \ 9 \\
\hline
5143
\end{array}
$$

**Example 4:**   How many buses are needed to take 163 vacationers to Branson, MO if 45 people will fit on each bus?

**Solution:**   (number of buses) = (total number of people) $\div$ (number of people per bus)

$$= \qquad 163 \qquad \div \qquad 45$$

$$
\begin{array}{r}
3\ \text{R}\ 28 \\
45\overline{)163}
\end{array}
$$

$\underline{135}$       $3(45) = 135$

$28$       Subtract. The remainder is 28.

Three full buses with 28 people left over, so 4 buses will be needed.

## 1.7 EXERCISES

*Divide and then check by multiplying.*

1.  $104 \div 8$

2.  $85 \div 5$

3.  $252 \div 6$

4.  $329 \div 5$

5.  $239 \div 3$

6.  $989 \div 23$

7.  $425 \div 6$

8.  $801 \div 5$

9.  $5209 \div 13$

10.  $6907 \div 21$

11.  $3839 \div 38$

12.  $2056 \div 38$

13. $\dfrac{5696}{178}$          14. $\dfrac{17,476}{257}$          15. $\dfrac{14,442}{130}$

*Find the average of each list of numbers.*

16. 84, 79, 67, 92, 108

17. 35, 28, 19, 31, 38, 41

*Solve.*

18. Twenty-seven people pooled their money and bought lottery tickets. One ticket won a prize of $12,366,000. If the prize is shared evenly, how many dollars will each person receive?

19. A dump truck can haul 16 tons per trip. How many trips will the truck have to make in order to deliver 200 tons of rock to a worksite?

20. A phone company bought 13 identical utility vans for a total of $224,055. Find the cost of each utility van.

## 1.8 EXPONENTS AND ORDER OF OPERATIONS

**Example 1:**   Write using exponential notation: $5 \cdot 5 \cdot 5 \cdot 5 \cdot 5 \cdot 5$.

**Solution:**      $5 \cdot 5 \cdot 5 \cdot 5 \cdot 5 \cdot 5 = 5^6$          The base 5 is multiplied by itself 6 times.

**Example 2:**   Evaluate $6^4$.

**Solution:**      $6^4 = 6 \cdot 6 \cdot 6 \cdot 6 = 1296$

**Example 3:**   Simplify $(8-6)^3 + 4^2 \cdot 3$.

**Solution:**
$$
\begin{aligned}
(8-6)^3 + 4^2 \cdot 3 &= 2^3 + 4^2 \cdot 3 && \text{Simplify inside parentheses.}\\
&= 8 + 16 \cdot 3 && \text{Write } 2^3 \text{ as 8 and } 4^2 \text{ as 16.}\\
&= 8 + 48 && \text{Multiply.}\\
&= 56 && \text{Add.}
\end{aligned}
$$

**Example 4:**   Find the area of the square whose side measures 14 yards.

14 yards

**Solution:**
$$
\begin{aligned}
\text{Area of a square} &= (\text{side})^2\\
&= (14 \text{ yards})^2\\
&= 196 \text{ square yards}
\end{aligned}
$$

## 1.8 EXERCISES

*Write using exponential notation.*

1. $7 \cdot 7 \cdot 7 \cdot 7 \cdot 7 \cdot 7$                        2. $4 \cdot 4 \cdot 4 \cdot 4 \cdot 4 \cdot 4 \cdot 4$

3. $2 \cdot 2 \cdot 2 \cdot 2 \cdot 5 \cdot 5$                        4. $3 \cdot 3 \cdot 7 \cdot 8 \cdot 8 \cdot 8 \cdot 8 \cdot 8$

*Evaluate.*

5. $9^2$                        6. $7^3$                        7. $4^5$

8. $2^8$                        9. $347^1$                        10. $100 \div 4 \cdot 5$

11. $12 - 3 + 8$                        12. $19 + 3 \cdot 6$                        13. $8 \cdot 7 - 23$

14. $24 \div 4 + 7 \cdot 3$                        15. $100 - 5(30 - 2^4)$                        16. $3 + 2[10 - (2 + 4)]$

17. $\dfrac{27 - 3}{23 - 19}$                        18. $\dfrac{15 + 3 \cdot 9 - 6}{5 + 2^2}$                        19. $7^2 - \{9 + 3[2 + 3(14 - 9)] - 13\}$

*Find the area of the square.*

20.

25 mm

## 1.9 INTRODUCTION TO VARIABLES AND ALGEBRAIC EXPRESSIONS

**Example 1:**    Evaluate $x + 8$ for $x = 9$.

**Solution:**        $x + 8 = 9 + 8$        Replace $x$ with 9.
                        $= 17$            Add.

**Example 2:**    Evaluate $7x - 2y$ for $x = 3$ and $y = 5$.

**Solution:**        $7x - 2y = 7(3) - 2(5)$        Replace $x$ with 3 and $y$ with 5.
                        $= 21 - 10$        Multiply.
                        $= 11$        Add.

**Example 3:**    Evaluate $\dfrac{3x^2 + y}{y - x}$ for $x = 5$ and $y = 3$.

**Solution:**        $\dfrac{3x^2 + y}{y - x} = \dfrac{3(5)^2 + 7}{7 - 5}$        Replace $x$ with 5 and $y$ with 7.

$= \dfrac{3 \cdot 25 + 7}{7 - 5}$        Evaluate the exponent.

$= \dfrac{75 + 7}{7 - 5}$        Multiply.

$= \dfrac{82}{2}$        Add and subtract.

$= 41$        Divide.

**Example 4:**   Write as an algebraic expression.  Use $x$ to represent "a number."
Fifteen less than the product of seven and a number

**Solution:**      The product of seven and a number is $7x$.  We want 15 less than $7x$, so $7x - 15$.

## 1.9 EXERCISES

*Evaluate the following expressions for $x = 4$, $y = 3$, and $z = 7$.*

1.  $5 + 6y$

2.  $2xz - 5y$

3.  $x + 2y - z$

4.  $xy^2 + 8$

5.  $21 - (z - x)$

6.  $6z - 2(x^2 - y)$

7.  $\dfrac{x + 28}{z - y}$

8.  $\dfrac{6xz}{8y}$

9.  $\dfrac{3z + x}{5}$

10.  $x^3 + y^2 - z$

11.  $\dfrac{5x}{2} + \dfrac{21}{y}$

12.  $x^2 - (y + z)$

13.  $(xy - z)^2$

14.  $\dfrac{5z + 3y}{z + x}$

15.  $y^4 - (5z + 2x)$

*Write the following phrases as variable expressions.  Use x to represent "a number."*

16.  The difference of fifteen and a number

17.  The quotient of a number and ten

18.  A number increased by twenty-seven

19.  The quotient of a number and seven, decreased by forty

20.  Five times the sum of a number and twelve

## CHAPTER 1 PRACTICE TEST

*Evaluate.*

1.  $37 + 56$

2.  $725 - 248$

3.  $375 \times 34$

4.  $52,037 \div 56$

5.  $5^2 \cdot 2^4$

6.  $7^1 \cdot 3^4$

7.  $237 \div 1$

8.  $0 \div 12$

9.  $31 \div 0$

10.  $\dfrac{2^5 - 5}{9}$

11.  $17 + 20 \div 2 \cdot 5 - 15$

12.  $4\left[(7 - 5)^3 + (25 - 22)^2\right] + 12$

13.  Round 1,937,216 to the nearest ten-thousand.

*Estimate each sum or difference by rounding each number to the nearest hundred.*

14. $3481 + 6228 + 2949$                    15. $3827 - 1692$

*Solve.*

16. A new motel that will have 58 rooms is under construction. The manager recently bought 58 identical television sets for the rooms. She paid a total $14,094 for the television sets. What is the price of one television set?

17. Twenty-four members of the Drama Club are planning to attend a play. The tickets cost $38 each. What is the total cost of their tickets?

18. Darius is planning to purchase a new washer and dryer for his house. The washer he likes costs $569 and the matching dryer costs $479. What is the total cost for the washer and dryer?

19. Evaluate the expression $6\left(2x^2 - 15\right)$ for $x = 5$.

20. Evaluate the expression $\dfrac{7x - 5y}{4}$ for $x = 13$ and $y = 7$.

21. Translate the following phrases into mathematical expressions. Use $x$ to represent "a number."

    a.   The difference of a thirty-two and a number

    b.   Fourteen less than the product of twelve and a number

*Find the perimeter and the area of each figure.*

22.  Square — 8 meters

23.  Rectangle — 7 inches, 16 inches

*The following table shows the diameters of the nine planets (in miles).*

| Planet | Diameter (in miles) |
|--------|--------------------|
| Mercury | 3,031 |
| Venus | 7,520 |
| Earth | 7,926 |
| Mars | 4,221 |
| Jupiter | 88,846 |
| Saturn | 74,898 |
| Uranus | 31,763 |
| Neptune | 31,329 |
| Pluto | 1,423 |

24. Which planet has the largest diameter? What is that diameter?

25. How much larger is the diameter of Earth than the diameter of Mars?

## CHAPTER 1 HELPFUL HINTS AND INSIGHTS

- The name of the ones period is not used when reading and writing whole numbers.

- A comma may or may not be inserted in a four-digit number.

- One way to remember the meaning of the symbols < and > is to think of them as arrowheads that "point" towards the smaller number.

- Perimeter measures the *distance* around a geometric figure while area measures the *surface* of the geometric figure. The units for perimeter will be units of length such as inches, feet, yards, miles, meters, millimeters, centimeters, and kilometers. The units for area will typically be *square units* such as square inches, square feet, square yards, square miles, square meters, square millimeters, square centimeters, and square kilometers. The only commonly used measure of area that is not a "square unit" is *acres*.

- A square inch is literally a square that measures one inch on each side. Likewise, a square centimeter is a square that measures one centimeter on each side. And so on . . . .

- A nonzero number divided by 0 is undefined.

- An exponent applies only to its base.

## 2.1 INTRODUCTION TO INTEGERS

**Example 1:**   Insert < or > between the pair of numbers to make a true statement.
$$-18 \qquad -10$$

**Solution:**   $-18$ is to the left of $-10$ on a number line, so $-18 < -10$.

**Example 2:**   Simplify: $\left|-5\right|$.

**Solution:**   $\left|-5\right| = 5$, because $-5$ is 5 units away from 0 on a number line.

**Example 3:**   Find the opposite of $-36$.

**Solution:**   The opposite of $-36$ is $-(-36) = 36$.

**Example 4:**   Simplify: $-\left|-3\right|$.

**Solution:**   $-\left|-3\right| = -3$. The absolute value of $-3$ is 3 and the opposite of 3 is $-3$.

**Example 5:**   The lowest point in the state of Louisiana is at New Orleans which lies 8 feet below sea level. Express this amount as an integer.

**Solution:**   If 0 represents sea level, then 8 feet below sea level can be represented by $-8$.

## 2.1 EXERCISES

*Represent each quantity by an integer.*

   1.  The Purdue Boilermakers gained 45 yards on their first play.

   2.  The temperature in Happy Valley is 16 degrees (Fahrenheit) below zero.

*Graph each integer in the list on the same number line.*

   3.  $-5, -1, 0, 4$          4.  $-4, -2, 1, 3$

*Insert < or > between each pair of integers to make a true statement.*

   5.  $-15 \quad -14$        6.  $-3 \quad 0$         7.  $5 \quad -5$         8.  $7 \quad -9$

*Simplify.*

   9.  $\left|35\right|$               10.  $\left|-12\right|$               11.  $\left|-68\right|$

*Find the opposite of each integer.*

   12.  23                    13.  $-22$                    14.  132

*Simplify.*

   15.  $-\left|-8\right|$               16.  $-(-6)$               17.  $-\left|34\right|$

*Insert $<$, $>$, or $=$ between each pair of numbers to make a true statement.*

18. $-|14|$      $-|-14|$      19. $-|-4|$      $-|-7|$      20. $-28$      $-(-30)$

## 2.2 ADDING INTEGERS

**Example 1:** Add: $-3+(-22)$.

**Solution:**     *Step 1.*    $|-3|=3$, $|-22|=22$, and $3+22=25$.

                     *Step 2.*    Their common sign is negative, so the sum is negative:
$$-3+(-22)=-25$$

**Example 2:** Add: $15+(-7)$.

**Solution:**     *Step 1.*    $|15|=15$, $|-7|=7$, and $15-7=8$

                     *Step 2.*    15 has the larger absolute value and its sign is positive:
$$15+(-7)=+8 \text{ or } 8$$

**Example 3:** Add: $10+(-5)+(-21)+13$.

**Solution:**
$$\begin{aligned}
10+(-5)+(-21)+13 &= 5+(-21)+13 \\
&= -16+13 \\
&= -3
\end{aligned}$$

**Example 4:** Evaluate $x+y$ if $x=-5$ and $y=29$.

**Solution:**
$$\begin{aligned}
x+y &= -5+29 \\
&= 24
\end{aligned}$$

## 2.2 EXERCISES

*Add.*

1. $31+17$             2. $-5+(-2)$           3. $43+(-43)$        4. $11+(-9)$

5. $14+(-41)$         6. $-17+(-50)$       7. $-20+13+(-4)$    8. $12+(-1)+(-7)$

9. $12+4+(-8)+(-30)$ 10. $(-19)+20+(-12)+8$ 11. $-112+(-63)$      12. $141+(-38)$

13. $-71+16$          14. $-7+(-15)+28+(-6)$

*Evaluate $x+y$ given the following replacement values.*

15. $x=-3$ and $y=12$                   16. $x=-40$ and $y=-23$

17. $x=18$ and $y=-42$                   18. $x=-34$ and $y=-79$

*Solve.*

19. The temperature at 5 p.m. was $-15°$ Celsius. By 11:30 p.m. the temperature had fallen 12 degrees. Find the temperature at 11:30 p.m.

20. Suppose a deep-sea diver dives from the surface to 150 feet below the surface. If the diver swims down 30 feet more, find her depth.

## 2.3 SUBTRACTING INTEGERS

**Example 1:**   Subtract:  $-18-4$

**Solution:**    $-18-4=-18+(-4)=-22$

**Example 2:**   Simplify:  $17-6-(-8)-3$

**Solution:**    $17-6-(-8)-3=17+(-6)+8+(-3)$
$$=11+8+(-3)$$
$$=19+(-3)$$
$$=16$$

**Example 3:**   Evaluate  $x-y$  if  $x=-7$  and  $y=15$ .

**Solution:**    $x-y=-7-15$
$$=-7+(-15)$$
$$=-22$$

**Example 4:**   A bus driver begins a route with 10 passengers. He picks up 5 passengers at the first stop and drops off 3. At the next stop, 4 passengers get on the bus and none get off. Express the final number of passengers as an integer.

**Solution:**    $10+5-3+4=10+5+(-3)+4$
$$=15+(-3)+4$$
$$=12+4$$
$$=16$$
There are 16 passengers on the bus after the second stop.

## 2.3 EXERCISES

*Subtract.*

1. $-37-(-37)$         2. $12-4$                    3. $14-17$

4. $-17-(-19)$         5. $6-8$                      6. $-28-49$

7. Subtract 12 from $-51$.      8. Find the difference of $-20$ and $-25$ .

*Simplify.*

9. $40-25-15$         10. $-7-11-(-16)$         11. $5-(-7)+12$

12. $-(-8)-16+21$     13. $-10-10-14$           14. $-31-(-31)-5$

*Evaluate* $x - y$ *given the following replacement values.*

15. $x = -22$ and $y = 14$ $\qquad$ 16. $x = -42$ and $y = -27$

*Evaluate each express for the given replacement values.*

17. $x - y + z$ if $x = -5$, $y = 8$, and $z = 14$.

18. $-x - y + z$ if $x = 60$, $y = -30$, and $z = -50$.

*Solve.*

19. Payton has $400 in her checking account. She writes a check for $132, makes a deposit of $75, and then writes another check for $212. Find the amount she has left in her account.

20. The boiling point of pure oxygen is $-182°C$ and the freezing point is $-218°C$. Find the difference between the boiling point and the freezing point of oxygen.

## 2.4 MULTIPLYING AND DIVIDING INTEGERS

**Example 1:** Multiply: $-6(-5)$

**Solution:** $-6(-5) = 30$

**Example 2:** Multiply: $4(-10)(-2)$

**Solution:** $4(-10)(-2) = (-40)(-2) = 80$

**Example 3:** Evaluate $xy$ and $\dfrac{x}{y}$ if $x = -16$ and $y = -8$.

**Solution:** $xy = (-16)(-8) = 128$

$\dfrac{x}{y} = \dfrac{-16}{-8} = 2$

**Example 4:** Divide: $\dfrac{-40}{5}$

**Solution:** $\dfrac{-40}{5} = -8$

**Example 5:** Divide: $27 \div (-3)$

**Solution:** $\dfrac{27}{-3} = -9$

**Example 6:** Evaluate: $(-8)^2$

**Solution:** $(-8)^2 = (-8)(-8) = 64$

## 2.4 EXERCISES

*Multiply or divide the following.*

1. $(-6)(-2)$         2. $0(-8)$         3. $(-54)(3)$         4. $\dfrac{-39}{-3}$

5. $\dfrac{42}{-6}$         6. $\dfrac{217}{0}$         7. $(3)(-4)(-5)$         8. $(-8)(-10)(-2)$

9. $(-2)(5)(-3)(-1)$    10. $(-9)^2$         11. $(-7)^3$         12. $-45 \div 5$

*Evaluate* $ab$ *for the given replacement values.*

13. $a = -7$ and $b = -7$         14. $a = -30$ and $b = -8$         15. $a = 75$ and $b = -4$

*Evaluate* $\dfrac{x}{y}$ *for the given replacement values.*

16. $x = 120$ and $y = -40$         17. $x = -196$ and $y = -14$         18. $x = 0$ and $y = 77$

*Solve.*

19. Eric's stock portfolio lost $3000 for 5 consecutive months. Represent the total loss as a product of integers, and find the total loss.

20. The weather forecast states that the high temperature will drop 4 degrees each day for the next 7 days. Represent this drop in temperature as a product of integers and find the total drop in temperature.

## 2.5 ORDER OF OPERATIONS

**Example 1:**   Find the value of each expression.
        (a) $(-5)^2$         (b) $-5^2$

**Solution:**   (a) $(-5)^2 = (-5)(-5) = 25$
        (b) $-5^2 = -(5 \cdot 5) = -25$

**Example 2:**   Simplify: $12 + 30 + (-4)^2$

**Solution:**   $12 + 30 + (-4)^2 = 12 + 30 + 16$     Simplify exponents first.
                $= 58$                              Add left to right.

**Example 3:**   Simplify: $(-3) \cdot |-9| - (-2) + 8^2$

**Solution:**   $(-3) \cdot |-9| - (-2) + 8^2 = (-3) \cdot (9) - (-2) + 8^2$     Write $|-9|$ as 9 (grouping symbols first).
                $= (-3) \cdot (9) - (-2) + 64$     Write $8^2$ as 64 (exponents next).
                $= -27 - (-2) + 64$               Multiplication next.
                $= 39$                            Add or subtract from left to right.

**Example 4:** Simplify: $24 \div 4 + 2 \cdot 9$

**Solution:**
$$24 \div 4 + 2 \cdot 9 = 6 + 18 \qquad \text{Divide and multiply from left to right}$$
$$= 24 \qquad \text{Add}$$

**Example 5:** Evaluate $2x - y^2 \cdot z$ if $x = -6$, $y = 2$, and $z = -3$.

**Solution:**
$$2x - y^2 \cdot z = 2(-6) - (2)^2 \cdot (-3) \qquad \text{Substitute.}$$
$$= 2(-6) - 4 \cdot (-3) \qquad \text{Evaluate exponents first.}$$
$$= -12 - (-12) \qquad \text{Multiplication from left to right.}$$
$$= 0 \qquad \text{Addition and subtraction from left to right.}$$

## 2.5 EXERCISES

*Simplify.*

1. $7 + (-18) \div 3$

2. $11 + 5(8)$

3. $9(-2) + 4$

4. $25 + 3^3$

5. $\dfrac{26 - 11}{-5}$

6. $\dfrac{92}{-9 + 32}$

7. $\left[ 3 + (-5) \right]^4$

8. $60 - (-7)^2$

9. $|13 - 17| \cdot (-4)^2$

10. $4 \cdot 2^2 + 35$

11. $8 + 4^2 - 3^3$

12. $(12 - 24) \div 4$

13. $(64 - 36) \div (27 - 41)$

14. $(-30 - 6) \div 12 - 11$

15. $-8^2 - (-7)^2$

16. $4(-7) \div \left[ 2(-6) - 8(-5) \right]$

17. $\dfrac{(-4)(-8) - 6(2)}{2[7 + (9 - 6)]}$

18. $\dfrac{40(-1) - (-4)(-5)}{3[-10 \div (-7 + 2)]}$

*Evaluate the following expressions if $x = 2$, $y = -4$, and $z = -3$.*

19. $5x - y^2$

20. $\dfrac{6x}{z} - 3y$

## CHAPTER 2 PRACTICE TEST

*Simplify each expression.*

1. $12 - 27$

2. $-18 + 11$

3. $5 \cdot (-20)$

4. $(-21) \div (-7)$

5. $(-31) + (-11)$

6. $-14 - (-38)$

7. $(-30) \cdot (-5)$

8. $\dfrac{-105}{-7}$

9. $|-79| + (-65)$

10. $40 - |-70|$

11. $|13| \cdot |-5|$

12. $\dfrac{|-52|}{-|-13|}$

13. $(-15) + 70 \div (-10)$        14. $-7 + (-81) \div (-9)$        15. $(-3)^3 - 52 \div (-13)$

16. $(3-5)^2 \cdot (9-5)^3$        17. $18 \cdot (-2) - (-7)^2$        18. $48 - (24 - 26)^3$

19. $\dfrac{12}{6} - \dfrac{8^2}{16}$        20. $\dfrac{|45 - 50|^2}{8(-3) + 19}$        21. $\dfrac{30 - 8(-2)}{(-15 - 8)}$

*Evaluate the following when* $x = 3$, $y = 0$, *and* $z = -5$.

22. $3x - 2y$        23. $|x| - |y| - |z|$        24. $\dfrac{18z}{-2x}$

*Solve.*

25. Shawn is at the top of Taum Sauk Mountain at an elevation of 1,772 feet. He moves down the mountain a distance of 734 feet. Represent is final elevation as a sum and find the sum.

26. The Purdue football team's leading rusher has a total of 675 yards rushing. On his next three carries, he gained 12 yards, lost 3 yards, and gained 5 yards. Find his total rushing yards after these carries.

27. The temperature in St. Louis was 72°F at noon when a cold front moved in. Over the next three hours the temperature dropped a total of 28 degrees. What was the temperature at 3pm?

## CHAPTER 2 HELPFUL HINTS AND INSIGHTS

- The symbol " – " has two meanings:

    1. It can be read as "minus" and means the operation of subtraction.

    2. It can be read as "negative" and means that the number is less than 0.

- When simplifying expressions with exponents, notice that the parentheses make an important difference. For example, $(-2)^2$ and $-2^2$ do not mean the same thing.

- When two sets of parentheses are next to each other, it is implied multiplication. For example, $(3)(5)$ means $3 \cdot 5$.

- When substituting values in for a variable, put the value in parentheses to avoid making mistakes with order of operations.

- Proper use of order of operations is necessary when simplifying expressions. Use of a mnemonic device can aid in remembering the proper order. For example: "**P**lease **E**xcuse **M**y **D**ear **A**unt **S**ally" can be used to remember **P**arentheses, **E**xponents, **M**ultiplication, **D**ivision, **A**ddition, and **S**ubtraction.

## 3.1 SIMPLIFYING ALGEBRAIC EXPRESSIONS

**Example 1:**   Find the numerical coefficient of the variable term, $-27x^2y^3z$

**Solution:**    The numerical coefficient of $-27x^2y^3z$ is $-27$.

**Example 2:**   Simplify: $12x - 7 + 5x - 8$

**Solution:**    $12x - 7 + 5x - 8 = 12x + (-7) + 5x + (-8)$

$$= 12x + 5x + (-7) + (-8) \quad \text{Commutative property of addition}$$
$$= (12 + 5)x + (-7) + (-8) \quad \text{Distributive property.}$$
$$= 17x - 15 \quad \text{Simplify.}$$

**Example 3:**   Use the distributive property to multiply: $3(x + 4)$

**Solution:**    $3(x + 4) = 3 \cdot x + 3 \cdot 4 \quad \text{Distributive property.}$

$$= 3x + 12 \quad \text{Multiply.}$$

**Example 4:**   Simplify: $7(x - 2) + 5(3x - 9)$

**Solution:**    $7(x - 2) + 5(3x - 9) = 7 \cdot x + 7 \cdot (-2) + 5 \cdot 3x + 5 \cdot (-9) \quad \text{Distributive property.}$

$$= 7x - 14 + 15x - 45 \quad \text{Multiply.}$$
$$= 7x + 15x - 14 - 45 \quad \text{Rearrange terms.}$$
$$= 22x - 59 \quad \text{Combine like terms}$$

**Example 5:**   Find the area of the rectangular garden:

$(4x + 5)$  feet

15  feet

**Solution:**    $A = \text{length} \cdot \text{width}$

$$= 15(4x + 5) \quad \text{Let length} = 15 \text{ and width} = (4x + 5)$$
$$= 15 \cdot 4x + 15 \cdot 5 \quad \text{Distribute.}$$
$$= 60x + 75 \quad \text{Simplify.}$$

The area of the rectangular garden is $(60x + 75)$ square feet.

**Example 6:** Find the perimeter of the region:

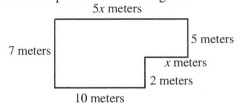

5x meters

7 meters

5 meters

x meters

2 meters

10 meters

**Solution:** The perimeter of the region is the sum of the lengths of all the sides.

$$P = 5x + 5 + x + 2 + 10 + 7$$
$$= 5x + x + 5 + 2 + 10 + 7$$
$$= 6x + 24$$

The perimeter of the region is $(6x + 24)$ meters.

## 3.1 EXERCISES

*Find the numerical coefficient of each variable term.*

1.  $53x$

2.  $-y$

3.  $-17x^2y^2z^3$

*Simplify the following by combining like terms.*

4.  $13x - 4x$

5.  $2c - 4c + 7c$

6.  $12y + 9y - 2y + 7$

*Multiply.*

7.  $-2(21x)$

8.  $2(3x - 1)$

9.  $5(3x - 10)$

*Simplify the following.*

10.  $4(x - 11) + 16$

11.  $3(8 - 5b) - 12b$

12.  $-5(2x + 7) + 4(x - 6)$

13.  $-2y - 12y + 8y + 3y$

14.  $-12(1 + 2v) + 4v$

15.  $2(k + 3) - 7(2k - 1)$

16.  $22x + 6(2x - 5)$

17.  $2(5xy - 4) + (8xy - 3)$

*Find the perimeter.*

18.

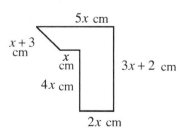

5x cm

x + 3 cm

x cm

3x + 2 cm

4x cm

2x cm

19. Each side: $2x + 1$ inches

Hexagon

*Find the area of the figure.*

20.

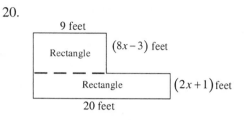

## 3.2 SOLVING EQUATIONS: THE ADDITION PROPERTY

**Example 1:**    Is $-5$ a solution of the equation $7(x+2)=15$ ?

**Solution:**         $7(x+2)=15$

$7(-5+2)=15$ ?        Replace $x$ with $-5$

$7(-3)=15$ ?

$-21=15$ ?      False

Since $-21=15$ is false, $-5$ is <u>not</u> a solution of the equation.

**Example 2:**    Solve for $x$:  $x-5=9$

**Solution:**         $x-5=9$

$x-5+5=9+5$        Add 5 to both sides of the equation

$x=14$            Simplify.

To check, replace $x$ with 14 in the original equation.

$x-5=9$            Original equation.

$14-5=9$            Replace $x$ with 14.

$9=9$            True.

Since $9=9$ is a true statement, 14 is the solution of the equation.

**Example 3:**    Solve for $z$:  $z-9=-3+8$

**Solution:**         $z-9=-3+8$

$z-9=5$                Simplify the right side of the equation.

$z-9+9=5+9$        Add 9 to both sides of the equation.

$z=14$            Simplify.

Check to see that 14 is the solution of the equation.

**Example 4:**  Solve for $x$:  $5x + 9 - 4x = 18 - 28$

**Solution:**   $5x + 9 - 4x = 18 - 28$

$5x - 4x + 9 = 18 - 28$      Simplify each side separately.

$x + 9 = -10$

$x + 9 - 9 = -10 - 9$      Subtract 9 from both sides.

$x = -19$

Check to see that $-19$ is the solution.

## 3.2 EXERCISES

*Decide whether the given number is a solution to the given equation..*

1.  Is 5 a solution to $x + 3 = 8$ ?

2.  Is $-3$ a solution to $x - 7 = -10$ ?

3.  Is 0 a solution to $4(m - 2) = 8$ ?

4.  Is $-2$ a solution to $4h + 2 = 23 - h$ ?

*Solve the following.*

5.  $x - 3 = 19$

6.  $t - 14 = 21$

7.  $x - 4 = 7 + 9$

8.  $-9 - 2 = -5 + y$

9.  $2x + 3 - x = -4 - 7$

10.  $11 - 11 = 9x - 8x$

11.  $34 + (-12) = 5x + 6 - 4x$

12.  $78 = w + 78$

13.  $z - 3 = -16$

14.  $m + 20 = 22$

15.  $-14 + x = -29$

16.  $-17n - 10 + 18n = -6$

17.  $7w + 8 - 6w = 37 - 18$

18.  $-19x + 13 + 20x = -1 - 5$

19.  $x + 32 = -17$

20.  $15x + 20 - 14x = -51$

## 3.3 SOLVING EQUATIONS: THE MULTIPLICATION PROPERTY

**Example 1:**  Solve for $x$:  $3x = 27$

**Solution:**   $3x = 27$      Original equation.

$\dfrac{3x}{3} = \dfrac{27}{3}$      Divide both sides by 3.

$\dfrac{3}{3} \cdot x = \dfrac{27}{3}$      Simplify.

$x = 9$

To check, replace $x$ with 9 in the original equation.

$3x = 27$      Original equation.

$3(9) = 27$      Let $x = 9$.

$27 = 27$      True.

The solution is 9.

**Example 2:**   Solve for $x$:   $-6x = 48$

**Solution:**          $-6x = 48$          Original equation.

$$\frac{-6x}{-6} = \frac{48}{-6}$$          Divide both sides by $-6$.

$$\frac{-6}{-6} \cdot x = \frac{48}{-6}$$          Simplify.

$$x = -8$$

To check, replace $x$ by $-8$ in the original equation.

$$-6x = 48$$          Original equation.

$$-6(-8) = 48$$          Let $x = -8$.

$$48 = 48$$          True.

The solution is $-8$.

**Example 3:**   Solve for $x$:   $12x - 10x = -19 + 33$

**Solution:**          $12x - 10x = -19 + 33$          Original equation.

$$2x = 14$$          Combine like terms on each side.

$$\frac{2x}{2} = \frac{14}{2}$$          Divide both sides by 2.

$$x = 7$$          Simplify.

Check to see that the solution is $7$.

**Example 4:**   Solve for $m$:   $14m - 19m = -20 + 45$

**Solution:**          $14m - 19m = -20 + 45$          Original equation.

$$-5m = 25$$          Combine like terms on each side.

$$\frac{-5m}{-5} = \frac{25}{-5}$$          Divide both sides by $-5$.

$$m = -5$$          Simplify.

Check to see that the solution is $-5$.

### 3.3 EXERCISES

*Solve the following equations.*

1.  $4x = 72$                          2.  $-9z = 99$                          3.  $-7y = -35$

4.  $2m = 24$                          5.  $6b - 9b = -42$                 6.  $18 = -6t - 3t$

7.  $9x - 4x = -15 + (-10)$     8.  $-13y = 13$                       9.  $11n - 5n = 54$

10.  $-8x = -8$                        11.  $y - 3y = 18$                   12.  $21a - 4a = 34$

13.  $28x - 17x = -17 - 27$    14.  $7v + 11v = 36$              15.  $48y - 8y = -70 - 10$

*Translate each phrase to an algebraic expression.*

16. Six more than three times a number.

17. Eight added to the product of 9 and a number.

18. Four times a number decreased by 18.

19. The quotient of a number and the sum of the number and 4.

20. Twice the difference of a number and 4, all decreased by 8.

## 3.4 SOLVING LINEAR EQUATIONS IN ONE VARIABLE

**Example 1:**   Solve: $4x - 9 = 15$

**Solution:**

$$4x - 9 = 15$$

$$4x - 9 + 9 = 15 + 9 \qquad \text{Add 9 to both sides}$$

$$4x = 24 \qquad \text{Simplify.}$$

$$\frac{4x}{4} = \frac{24}{4} \qquad \text{Divide both sides by 4.}$$

$$x = 6 \qquad \text{Simplify.}$$

Check:   $4x - 9 = 15$

$$4(6) - 9 = 15$$

$$24 - 9 = 15$$

$$15 = 15 \quad \text{True}$$

**Example 2:**   Solve: $4a + 5 = 2a - 5$

**Solution:**

$$4a + 5 = 2a - 5$$

$$4a + 5 - 5 = 2a - 5 - 5 \qquad \text{Subtract 5 from both sides.}$$

$$4a = 2a - 10 \qquad \text{Simplify.}$$

$$4a - 2a = 2a - 10 - 2a \qquad \text{Subtract } 2a \text{ from both sides.}$$

$$2a = -10 \qquad \text{Simplify.}$$

$$\frac{2a}{2} = \frac{-10}{2} \qquad \text{Divide both sides by 2.}$$

$$a = -5 \qquad \text{Simplify.}$$

Check that $a = -5$ is the solution.

**Example 3:** Solve: $8(x-1)=10x+12$

**Solution:**

$$8(x-1)=10x+12$$

$\begin{array}{ll} 8x-8=10x+12 & \text{Distribute.} \\ 8x-8+8=10x+12+8 & \text{Add 8 to both sides.} \\ 8x=10x+20 & \text{Simplify.} \\ 8x-10x=10x+20-10x & \text{Subtract } 10x \text{ from both sides.} \\ -2x=20 & \text{Simplify.} \\ \dfrac{-2x}{-2}=\dfrac{20}{-2} & \text{Divide both sides by } -2. \\ x=-10 & \text{Simplify.} \end{array}$

Check that $x=-10$ is the solution.

**Example 4:** Solve: $2(x-4)+16=0$

**Solution:**

$$2(x-4)+16=0$$

$\begin{array}{ll} 2x-8+16=0 & \text{Distribute.} \\ 2x+8=0 & \text{Simplify.} \\ 2x+8-8=0-8 & \text{Subtract 8 from both sides.} \\ 2x=-8 & \text{Simplify.} \\ \dfrac{2x}{2}=\dfrac{-8}{2} & \text{Divide both sides by 2.} \\ x=-4 & \text{Simplify.} \end{array}$

Check that $x=-4$ is the solution.

## 3.4 EXERCISES

*Solve each equation.*

1. $7x-56=0$       2. $2b-6=8$       3. $2y+11=-5y-17$

4. $9-a=11$       5. $12m+19=79$       6. $8y-3=-19$

7. $6m-24=0$       8. $5t+2=37$       9. $10z+9=5z-6$

10. $-y-11=5y-17$       11. $-4m+2=-5m+3$       12. $14-5y=14+2y$

13. $2(x-7)=4x+8$       14. $7(4c+2)-1=26c+5$       15. $-6(2-x)=3(x-3)$

16. $20+8(y-1)=6y+32$

*Write each sentence as an equation.*

17. The sum of $-18$ and 5 is $-13$.

18. Four times the difference of $-10$ and 3 amounts to $-52$.

19. Forty subtracted from $-18$ equals $-58$.

20. The quotient of 150 and twice 5 is equal to 15.

## 3.5 LINEAR EQUATIONS IN ONE VARIABLE AND PROBLEM SOLVING

**Example 1:**   Write the following sentences as equations. Use $x$ to represent "a number".

        (a)  Eight more than a number is 17.

        (b)  Four times a number is 96.

**Solution:**   (a)  In words:    Eight    more than    a number    is    17

              Translate:    8    +    $x$    =    17

        (b)  In words:    Four    times    a number    is    96

              Translate:    4    ·    $x$    =    96

**Example 2:**   Twice a number decreased by 4 is the same as the number increased by 7. Find the number.

**Solution:**   Let $x =$ the unknown number

    In words:  Twice a number  decreased by  4  is the same as  the number  increased by  7

    Translate:    $2x$    −    4    =    $x$    +    7

    Solve:    $2x - 4 = x + 7$

             $2x - 4 + 4 = x + 7 + 4$      Add 4 to both sides.

                  $2x = x + 11$          Simplify.

             $2x - x = x + 11 - x$       Subtract $x$ from both sides.

                   $x = 11$           Simplify.

    Check:  Twice "11" is 22 and 22 decreased by 4 is 18. This is the same as "11" increased by 7. The unknown number is 11.

**Example 3:**   Patrick sold a used DVD player and a DVD collection for $350, receiving six times as much money for the DVD collection as for the DVD player. Find the price of each.

**Solution:**   Let $x =$ price of DVD player. Then $6x =$ price of DVD collection.

    In words:  DVD player price  plus  DVD collection price  is  350

    Translate:    $x$    +    $6x$    =    350

    Solve:    $x + 6x = 350$

                $7x = 350$          Combine like terms.

              $\dfrac{7x}{7} = \dfrac{350}{7}$       Divide both sides by 7.

                $x = 50$          Simplify.

    Check:  The DVD player sold for $50. The DVD collection sold for $6x = 6(\$50) = \$300$. Since

        $\$50 + \$300 = \$350$, the total price, and $300 is six-times $50, the solution checks. The DVD player sold for $50 and the DVD collection sold for $300.

### 3.5 EXERCISES

*Write the sentences as equations. Use x to represent "a number".*

1.  A number added to $-4$ is $-19$.

2.  Four times a number yields 44.

3.  Six added to twice a number gives 10.

4.  Seven times the difference of 6 and a number amounts to $-14$.

*Solve.*

5.  Four times a number added to fifteen is forty-three. Find the number.

6.  The product of eight and a number gives fifty-six. Find the number.

7.  Seven less than three times a number is twenty-three. Find the number.

8.  Fourteen decreased by some number equals the quotient of twenty and four. Find the number.

9.  The sum of four, five, and a number is ten. Find the number.

10.  The product of eight and a number is one hundred twenty-eight. Find the number.

11.  Seventeen added to the product of five and some number amounts to the product of seven and the same number added to twenty-five. Find the number.

12.  Seventy-one less a number is equal to the product of three and the difference of the number and three. Find the number.

13.  If the sum of three times a number and two times the same number is increased by 1, the result is 16. Find the number.

14.  Four times the sum of twice a number and 6 is $-8$. Find the number.

15.  If 5 is added to the sum of twice a number and three times the number, the result is 25. Find the number.

16.  Shawn is 4 years older than Payton. Five years ago the sum of their ages was 64. How old are they now?

17.  Josh and Bobby collect football cards. Josh has three times the number of cards that Bobby has. Together they have 960 cards. Find how many cards Josh has.

18.  A boat and trailer are worth $7800. The boat is worth five times as much money as the trailer. Find the value of the boat and the value of the trailer.

19.  Angie sold her doll collection and accessories for $560. If she received six times as much money for the dolls as she did for the accessories, find how much money she received for the dolls.

20.  Nathan's car is traveling twice as fast as Chad's car. If their combined speed is 60 miles per hour, find the speed of Nathan's car.

### CHAPTER 3 PRACTICE TEST

1.  Simplify: $12x - 4 - 3x + 13$

2.  Multiply: $-5(4y - 5)$

3. Simplify: $5(3z+5)-4z+16$

4. Find the perimeter.

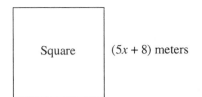

Square    $(5x + 8)$ meters

5. Find the area.

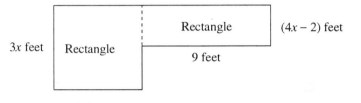

3x feet    Rectangle

Rectangle    $(4x - 2)$ feet

9 feet

4 feet

*Solve the following equations.*

6. $11x+5x=-48$

7. $29=2x-31x$

8. $3z-8=31$

9. $42+5z=12$

10. $11x+21-10x-18=30$

11. $3-2d+3d=25$

12. $6x-9=-57$

13. $-5y+10=-10$

14. $4(x-3)=0$

15. $7(1+3y)=112$

16. $11x-5=x+25$

17. $9a-7=7a+19$

18. $4+5(2m-3)=9$

19. $6(3x+8)=10(2x-3)$

*Write each sentence as an equation.*

20. The product of $-18$ and 3 yields $-54$.

21. Twice the sum of $-8$ and 11 amounts to 6.

*Solve the following.*

22. The sum of four times a number and six times the same number is thirty. Find the number.

23. Three times the sum of a number and 1 is 18. Find the number.

24. In a local basketball game, Brian made three times as many free throws as Jeff. If the total number of free throws made by both men was twenty-four, find how many free throws Brian made.

25. In a bowling league, there are eighteen more men than women. Find the number of women in the league if the total number of league members is 120.

**CHAPTER 3 HELPFUL HINTS AND INSIGHTS**

- When solving an equation, it does not matter on which side of the equation the variable is isolated.

- It is always a good idea to check the solution of an equation that we have solved to see that it makes the equation a true statement.

- When solving an equation, check to see whether a side of the equation can be simplified before applying a property of equality.

- When translating a word statement, it often helps to underline each part as it is translated.

## 4.1 INTRODUCTION TO FRACTIONS AND EQUIVALENT FRACTIONS

**Example 1:**   Graph $\dfrac{7}{4}$ on the number line.

**Solution:**

**Example 2:**   Write $\dfrac{5}{8}$ as an equivalent fraction whose denominator is 32.

**Solution:**   Since $8 \cdot 4 = 32$, multiply the numerator and denominator by 4.

$$\frac{5}{8} = \frac{5 \cdot 4}{8 \cdot 4} = \frac{20}{32}$$

Then $\dfrac{5}{8}$ is equivalent to $\dfrac{20}{32}$.

**Example 3:**   Write $\dfrac{5}{9x}$ as an equivalent fraction whose denominator is $27x$.

**Solution:**   Since $9x \cdot 3 = 27x$, multiply the numerator and denominator by 3.

$$\frac{5}{9x} = \frac{5 \cdot 3}{9x \cdot 3} = \frac{15}{27x}$$

Then $\dfrac{5}{9x}$ is equivalent to $\dfrac{15}{27x}$.

**Example 4:**   Simplify $\dfrac{-15}{-5}$ by dividing the numerator by the denominator.

**Solution:**   $\dfrac{-15}{-5} = 3$

## 4.1 EXERCISES

*Represent the shaded part of each geometric figure by a proper fraction.*

1.
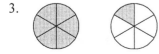

2.

*Represent the shaded part of each geometric figure by an improper fraction.*

3.

4.

*Graph each fraction on a number line.*

5. $\dfrac{3}{8}$                          6. $\dfrac{5}{7}$                          7. $\dfrac{8}{5}$

*Write each fraction as an equivalent fraction with the given denominator.*

8. $\dfrac{7}{9}$; denominator of 45         9. $\dfrac{3}{5}$; denominator of 75         10. $\dfrac{6a}{11}$; denominator of 33

11. $\dfrac{9x}{17}$; denominator of 51      12. $\dfrac{4}{9b}$; denominator of $36b$    13. 8; denominator of 7

14. 2; denominator of 15

*Write each fraction as an equivalent fraction with the given denominator.*

15. $\dfrac{12}{12}$                         16. $\dfrac{-9}{-9}$                         17. $\dfrac{24}{6}$

18. $\dfrac{-36}{12}$                        19. $\dfrac{14}{-14}$                        20. $\dfrac{30}{1}$

## 4.2 FACTORS AND SIMPLEST FORM

**Example 1:**   Write the prime factorization of 60.

**Solution:**

The prime factorization of 60 is $2 \cdot 2 \cdot 3 \cdot 5$ or $2^2 \cdot 3 \cdot 5$.

**Example 2:**   Write the prime factorization of 1836.

**Solution:**

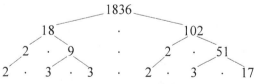

The prime factorization of 1836 is $2 \cdot 2 \cdot 3 \cdot 3 \cdot 3 \cdot 17$ or $2^2 \cdot 3^3 \cdot 17$.

**Example 3:**   Simplify: $\dfrac{28}{84}$.

**Solution:**   Write out the prime factorization of the numerator and the denominator. Then divide out all of the common factors.

$$\frac{28}{84} = \frac{\boxed{2} \cdot \boxed{2} \cdot \boxed{7}}{\boxed{2} \cdot \boxed{2} \cdot 3 \cdot \boxed{7}} = \frac{1}{3}$$

**Example 4:** Simplify: $\dfrac{12m}{18mn}$ .

**Solution:** Write out the prime factorization of the numerator and the denominator. Then divide out all of the common factors.

$$\frac{12m}{18mn} = \frac{\boxed{2} \cdot 2 \cdot \boxed{3} \cdot \boxed{m}}{\boxed{2} \cdot \boxed{3} \cdot 3 \cdot \boxed{m} \cdot n} = \frac{2}{3n}$$

**Example 5:** Simplify: $\dfrac{50x^3 y}{45x^2 y^3}$ .

**Solution:** Write out the prime factorization of the numerator and the denominator. Then divide out all of the common factors.

$$\frac{50x^3 y}{45x^2 y^3} = \frac{2 \cdot 5 \cdot \boxed{5} \cdot \boxed{x} \cdot \boxed{x} \cdot x \cdot \boxed{y}}{3 \cdot 3 \cdot \boxed{5} \cdot \boxed{x} \cdot \boxed{x} \cdot \boxed{y} \cdot y \cdot y} = \frac{10x}{9y^2}$$

## 4.2 EXERCISES

*Write the prime factorization of each number.*

1. 84
2. 200
3. 120
4. 756

*Simplify each fraction.*

5. $\dfrac{14}{21}$

6. $\dfrac{90}{100}$

7. $\dfrac{15}{35}$

8. $\dfrac{30}{8}$

9. $\dfrac{70}{42}$

10. $\dfrac{144}{60}$

11. $\dfrac{18b}{45b}$

12. $\dfrac{12xy}{45x}$

13. $\dfrac{19x^2}{38x}$

14. $\dfrac{68x}{85xy}$

15. $\dfrac{90m^2}{350mn}$

16. $\dfrac{9xy}{54wx}$

17. $\dfrac{144ab}{84b^2}$

18. $\dfrac{432x}{120x^2}$

19. There are 1760 yards in a mile. What fraction of a mile is represented by 220 yards?

20. Jacob works 45 hours per week. What fraction of his work week is represented by 12 hours.

## 4.3 MULTIPLYING AND DIVIDING FRACTIONS

**Example 1:** Multiply: $\dfrac{3}{5} \cdot \dfrac{4}{7}$ .

**Solution:** $\dfrac{3}{5} \cdot \dfrac{4}{7} = \dfrac{3 \cdot 4}{5 \cdot 7} = \dfrac{12}{35}$  ← Product of numerators
← Product of denominators

**Example 2:** Multiply and simplify: $\dfrac{21}{8} \cdot \dfrac{12}{35}$.

**Solution:**     Notice that 21 and 35 have a common factor of 7 and that 8 and 12 have a common factor of 4.

$$\frac{21}{8} \cdot \frac{12}{35} = \frac{21 \cdot 12}{8 \cdot 35} = \frac{3 \cdot \boxed{7} \cdot \boxed{4} \cdot 3}{2 \cdot \boxed{4} \cdot 5 \cdot \boxed{7}} = \frac{9}{10}$$

**Example 3:** Multiply and simplify: $\dfrac{7x}{9} \cdot \dfrac{15}{28x}$.

**Solution:**     Notice that 7 and 21 have a common factor of 7 and that 9 and 15 have a common factor of 3.

$$\frac{7x}{9} \cdot \frac{15}{28x} = \frac{7x \cdot 15}{9 \cdot 28x} = \frac{\boxed{7} \cdot \boxed{x} \cdot \boxed{3} \cdot 5}{\boxed{3} \cdot 3 \cdot 4 \cdot \boxed{7} \cdot \boxed{x}} = \frac{5}{12}$$

**Example 4:** Evaluate: $\left(\dfrac{3}{4}\right)^4$.

**Solution:**     $\left(\dfrac{3}{4}\right)^4 = \dfrac{3}{4} \cdot \dfrac{3}{4} \cdot \dfrac{3}{4} \cdot \dfrac{3}{4} = \dfrac{3 \cdot 3 \cdot 3 \cdot 3}{4 \cdot 4 \cdot 4 \cdot 4} = \dfrac{81}{256}$

**Example 5:** Divide: $\dfrac{5x}{6} \div \dfrac{2}{9}$.

**Solution:**     $\dfrac{5x}{6} \div \dfrac{2}{9} = \dfrac{5x}{6} \cdot \dfrac{9}{2} = \dfrac{5x \cdot 9}{6 \cdot 2} = \dfrac{5 \cdot x \cdot \boxed{3} \cdot 3}{2 \cdot \boxed{3} \cdot 2} = \dfrac{15x}{4}$

**Example 6:** Evaluate $x \div y$ for $x = \dfrac{6}{7}$ and $y = -4$.

**Solution:**     $x \div y = \dfrac{6}{7} \div -4 = \dfrac{6}{7} \cdot -\dfrac{1}{4} = -\dfrac{6 \cdot 1}{7 \cdot 4} = -\dfrac{\boxed{2} \cdot 3 \cdot 1}{7 \cdot \boxed{2} \cdot 2} = -\dfrac{3}{14}$

## 4.3 EXERCISES

*Perform each indicated operation.*

1.  $\dfrac{7}{10} \cdot \dfrac{4}{21}$

2.  $-\dfrac{5}{6} \cdot \dfrac{4}{7}$

3.  $\dfrac{9x}{11} \cdot \dfrac{22}{15}$

4.  $9 \cdot \dfrac{1}{2}$

5.  $-\dfrac{3}{8} \cdot 16$

6.  $\dfrac{5}{3} \div \dfrac{1}{6}$

7.  $\dfrac{22}{35} \div -\dfrac{55}{14}$

8.  $\dfrac{12y}{13} \div \dfrac{3}{26}$

9.  $-\dfrac{3}{4} \div 12$

10. $\left(-\dfrac{7}{8}\right)^2$

11. $\left(\dfrac{2}{5}\right)^3$

12. $\dfrac{1}{4} \cdot \dfrac{2}{5} \div \dfrac{3}{10}$

13. $\dfrac{3}{4} \div \dfrac{2}{9} \cdot -\dfrac{16}{3}$

14. $12x \div \dfrac{24x}{5}$

15. $\dfrac{3}{16} \cdot \left(35 \div \dfrac{5}{8}\right)$

16. Evaluate (a) $xy$ and (b) $x \div y$ for $x = \dfrac{3}{7}$ and $y = \dfrac{7}{9}$.

17. Determine if $x = -\dfrac{5}{16}$ is a solution of the equation $2x = -\dfrac{5}{8}$.

18. Find the area of the given rectangle.

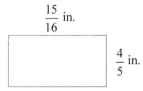

$\dfrac{15}{16}$ in.

$\dfrac{4}{5}$ in.

19. A box full of paperback romance novels weighs 12 pounds. If each book weights $\dfrac{3}{4}$ pounds, how many books are in the box?

20. If $\dfrac{5}{8}$ of a 64-tree orchard are apple trees, find how many apple trees are in the orchard.

## 4.4 ADDING AND SUBTRACTING LIKE FRACTIONS AND LEAST COMMON DENOMINATORS

**Example 1:** Add: $\dfrac{4}{15} + \dfrac{7}{15}$.

**Solution:** $\dfrac{4}{15} + \dfrac{7}{15} = \dfrac{4+7}{15} = \dfrac{11}{15}$    ← Add numerators.
                                         ← Keep the denominator.

**Example 2:** Subtract: $\dfrac{5x}{9} - \dfrac{7}{9}$.

**Solution:** $\dfrac{5x}{9} - \dfrac{7}{9} = \dfrac{5x-7}{9}$

The terms in the numerator are unlike terms and cannot be combined.

**Example 3:** Evaluate $x - y$ for $x = -\dfrac{8}{19}$ and $y = \dfrac{3}{19}$.

**Solution:** Replace $x$ with $-\dfrac{8}{19}$ and $y$ with $\dfrac{3}{19}$ and simplify.

$$x - y = -\dfrac{8}{19} - \dfrac{3}{19} = \dfrac{-8-3}{19} = \dfrac{-11}{19} \text{ or } -\dfrac{11}{19}.$$

**Example 4:** Find the LCD of $-\dfrac{3}{4}, \dfrac{1}{6},$ and $\dfrac{2}{9}$.

**Solution:** $4 = 2 \cdot 2$
$6 = 2 \cdot 3$
$9 = 3 \cdot 3$
$\text{LCD} = 2 \cdot 2 \cdot 3 \cdot 3 = 36$

**Example 5:** Solve: $x + \dfrac{3}{8} = \dfrac{7}{8}$.

**Solution:**

$$x + \frac{3}{8} = \frac{7}{8}$$

$$x + \frac{3}{8} - \frac{3}{8} = \frac{7}{8} - \frac{3}{8} \qquad \text{Add } \frac{3}{8} \text{ to both sides.}$$

$$x = \frac{4}{8}$$

$$x = \frac{1}{2} \qquad \text{Reduce.}$$

## 4.4 EXERCISES

*Add or subtract as indicated.*

1. $\dfrac{1}{8} + \dfrac{5}{8}$

2. $\dfrac{11}{16} + \dfrac{5}{16}$

3. $-\dfrac{1}{3} + \dfrac{1}{3}$

4. $-\dfrac{7}{x} + \dfrac{9}{x}$

5. $\dfrac{7}{10y} + \dfrac{1}{10y}$

6. $\dfrac{4}{21} + \dfrac{8}{21} + \dfrac{5}{21}$

7. $\dfrac{9}{13} - \dfrac{5}{13}$

8. $\dfrac{6}{y} - \dfrac{10}{y}$

9. $\dfrac{5}{22} - \dfrac{3}{22}$

10. $\dfrac{13}{15a} + \dfrac{7}{15a}$

11. $-\dfrac{5}{14} + \dfrac{3}{14}$

12. $\dfrac{11x}{12} - \dfrac{17x}{12}$

*Evaluate each expression for the given replacement values.*

13. $x + y$ ; $x = -\dfrac{1}{8}$, $y = \dfrac{5}{8}$

14. $x - y$ ; $x = -\dfrac{2}{9}$, $y = -\dfrac{5}{9}$

*Find the LCD of each list of fractions.*

15. $\dfrac{1}{6}$, $\dfrac{5}{27}$

16. $-\dfrac{5}{18}$, $\dfrac{17}{30}$

*Solve.*

17. $x + \dfrac{1}{10} = -\dfrac{7}{10}$

18. $5x + \dfrac{1}{7} - 4x = \dfrac{2}{7} - \dfrac{4}{7}$

19. A recipe for Chocolate Divine cake calls for $\dfrac{4}{3}$ cups of flour and later $\dfrac{2}{3}$ cups of flour. Find how much flour is needed to make the recipe.

20. Judy has a piece of material that is $\dfrac{25}{36}$ of a yard long. If she cuts off a piece $\dfrac{15}{36}$ of a yard long to use on a quilt she is making, how much of the material will Judy have left?

## 4.5 ADDING AND SUBTRACTING UNLIKE FRACTIONS

**Example 1:** Add: $\dfrac{7}{24} + \dfrac{5}{12}$.

**Solution:** *Step* 1: The LCD for denominators 12 and 24 is 24.

$\quad$ *Step* 2: $\dfrac{7}{24} = \dfrac{7}{24}, \quad \dfrac{5}{12} = \dfrac{5 \cdot 2}{12 \cdot 2} = \dfrac{10}{24}$

$\quad$ *Step* 3: Add. $\dfrac{7}{24} + \dfrac{5}{12} = \dfrac{7}{24} + \dfrac{10}{24} = \dfrac{7+10}{24} = \dfrac{17}{24}$

**Example 2:** Subtract: $\dfrac{7}{9} - \dfrac{5}{6}$.

**Solution:** *Step* 1: The LCD for denominators 9 and 6 is 18.

$\quad$ *Step* 2: $\dfrac{7}{9} = \dfrac{7 \cdot 2}{9 \cdot 2} = \dfrac{14}{18}, \quad \dfrac{5}{6} = \dfrac{5 \cdot 3}{6 \cdot 3} = \dfrac{15}{18}$

$\quad$ *Step* 3: Subtact. $\dfrac{7}{9} - \dfrac{5}{6} = \dfrac{14}{18} - \dfrac{15}{18} = \dfrac{14-15}{18} = -\dfrac{1}{18}$

**Example 3:** Find: $7 - \dfrac{2x}{5}$.

**Solution:** Recall that $7 = \dfrac{7}{1}$. The LCD for denominators 1 and 5 is 5.

$$7 - \dfrac{2x}{5} = \dfrac{7 \cdot 5}{1 \cdot 5} - \dfrac{2x}{5}$$
$$= \dfrac{35}{5} - \dfrac{2x}{5}$$
$$= \dfrac{35 - 2x}{5}$$

**Example 4:** Solve: $x + \dfrac{5}{12} = -\dfrac{1}{4}$.

**Solution:**

$$x + \dfrac{5}{12} = -\dfrac{1}{4}$$
$$x + \dfrac{5}{12} + \left(-\dfrac{5}{12}\right) = -\dfrac{1}{4} + \left(-\dfrac{5}{12}\right)$$
$$x = -\dfrac{1 \cdot 3}{4 \cdot 3} + \left(-\dfrac{5}{12}\right) \qquad \text{The LCD for denominators 4 and 12 is 12.}$$
$$x = -\dfrac{3}{12} + \left(-\dfrac{5}{12}\right)$$
$$x = -\dfrac{8}{12}$$
$$x = -\dfrac{2 \cdot 4}{3 \cdot 4} = -\dfrac{2}{3} \qquad \text{Write } -\dfrac{8}{12} \text{ in lowest terms.}$$

**4.5 EXERCISES**

*Add or subtract as indicated.*

1.  $\dfrac{1}{8} + \dfrac{7}{16}$

2.  $\dfrac{4}{5} - \dfrac{7}{10}$

3.  $-\dfrac{4}{9} + \dfrac{7}{3}$

4.  $\dfrac{7x}{13} - \dfrac{5}{26}$

5.  $\dfrac{4x}{9} - \dfrac{7}{18}$

6.  $9x - \dfrac{3}{10}$

7.  $\dfrac{2}{5} + \dfrac{1}{4} + \dfrac{3}{10}$

8.  $\dfrac{8}{23} + \dfrac{31}{23} - \dfrac{16}{23}$

9.  $-\dfrac{4}{7} + \dfrac{11}{14} - \dfrac{2}{21}$

10. $\dfrac{y}{2} + \dfrac{y}{6} + \dfrac{5y}{12}$

11. $\dfrac{3}{8} + \dfrac{5}{7x}$

12. $\dfrac{4}{15x} + \dfrac{3}{4}$

13. $\dfrac{7}{15} + \dfrac{11m}{20} - \dfrac{3}{10}$

14. $\dfrac{4x}{13} - \dfrac{3x}{26} - \dfrac{5}{2}$

*Evaluate each expression for* $x = \dfrac{1}{4}$ *and* $y = \dfrac{2}{5}$.

15. $2y - x$

16. $x - y$

*Solve.*

17. $x + \dfrac{11}{15} = \dfrac{2}{3}$

18. $15y - \dfrac{3}{7} - 14y = \dfrac{13}{14}$

19. Find the perimeter of the given rectangle.

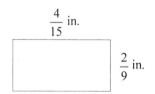

$\dfrac{4}{15}$ in.

$\dfrac{2}{9}$ in.

20. Find the difference in length of two boards if one board is $\dfrac{5}{6}$ of a foot long and the other is $\dfrac{3}{4}$ of a foot long.

**4.6 COMPLEX FRACTIONS AND REVIEW OF ORDER OF OPERATIONS**

**Example 1:**  Simplify: $\dfrac{\dfrac{2}{3}}{\dfrac{7}{12}}$.

**Solution:**  $\dfrac{\dfrac{2}{3}}{\dfrac{7}{12}} = \dfrac{2}{3} \div \dfrac{7}{12} = \dfrac{2}{3} \cdot \dfrac{12}{7} = \dfrac{2 \cdot 12}{3 \cdot 7} = \dfrac{2 \cdot \boxed{3} \cdot 4}{\boxed{3} \cdot 7} = \dfrac{8}{7}$

**Example 2:** Simplify: $\dfrac{\dfrac{5x}{6}-4}{\dfrac{3}{8}}$ .

**Solution:**    $\dfrac{\dfrac{5x}{6}-4}{\dfrac{3}{8}} = \dfrac{24\left(\dfrac{5x}{6}-2\right)}{24\left(\dfrac{3}{8}\right)}$        Multiply both the numerator and denominator by the LCD, 24.

$= \dfrac{24\left(\dfrac{5x}{6}\right)-24(2)}{24\left(\dfrac{3}{8}\right)}$        Apply the distributive property.

$= \dfrac{20x-48}{9}$        Multiply.

**Example 3:** Simplify: $\left(\dfrac{1}{4}+\dfrac{1}{6}\right) \div \left(\dfrac{1}{2}-\dfrac{2}{3}\right)$.

**Solution:**    $\left(\dfrac{1}{4}+\dfrac{1}{6}\right) \div \left(\dfrac{1}{2}-\dfrac{2}{3}\right) = \left(\dfrac{3}{12}+\dfrac{2}{12}\right) \div \left(\dfrac{3}{6}-\dfrac{4}{6}\right)$

$= \dfrac{5}{12} \div \left(-\dfrac{1}{6}\right)$

$= \dfrac{5}{12}\left(-\dfrac{6}{1}\right)$

$= \dfrac{5\cdot(-1)\cdot\boxed{6}}{2\cdot\boxed{6}\cdot1}$

$= \dfrac{-5}{2}$  or  $-\dfrac{5}{2}$

## 4.6 EXERCISES

*Simplify.*

1.  $\dfrac{\dfrac{8}{27}}{\dfrac{1}{9}}$

2.  $\dfrac{\dfrac{6x}{13}}{\dfrac{9}{4}}$

3.  $\dfrac{\dfrac{3}{8}+\dfrac{1}{4}}{\dfrac{2}{5}+\dfrac{7}{10}}$

4.  $\dfrac{\dfrac{2x}{5}}{5-\dfrac{3}{10}}$

5.  $\dfrac{\dfrac{6}{11}+1}{\dfrac{3}{8a}}$

6.  $\dfrac{8-\dfrac{1}{3}}{6+\dfrac{3}{5}}$

7.  $\left(-\dfrac{3}{8}-\dfrac{9}{8}\right) \div \dfrac{5}{16}$

8.  $3^2-\left(\dfrac{2}{3}\right)^2$

9.  $\left(3-\dfrac{5}{2}\right)^2$

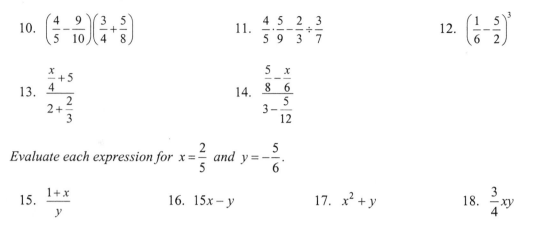

10. $\left(\dfrac{4}{5}-\dfrac{9}{10}\right)\left(\dfrac{3}{4}+\dfrac{5}{8}\right)$

11. $\dfrac{4}{5}\cdot\dfrac{5}{9}-\dfrac{2}{3}\div\dfrac{3}{7}$

12. $\left(\dfrac{1}{6}-\dfrac{5}{2}\right)^{3}$

13. $\dfrac{\dfrac{x}{4}+5}{2+\dfrac{2}{3}}$

14. $\dfrac{\dfrac{5}{8}-\dfrac{x}{6}}{3-\dfrac{5}{12}}$

*Evaluate each expression for* $x=\dfrac{2}{5}$ *and* $y=-\dfrac{5}{6}$.

15. $\dfrac{1+x}{y}$

16. $15x-y$

17. $x^{2}+y$

18. $\dfrac{3}{4}xy$

*Find the average of each pair of numbers.*

19. $\dfrac{4}{9},\ \dfrac{7}{18}$

20. $\dfrac{7}{9},\ \dfrac{5}{6}$

## 4.7 SOLVING EQUATIONS CONTAINING FRACTIONS

**Example 1:** Solve for $x$:  $\dfrac{7}{8}x=\dfrac{21}{32}$

**Solution:**

$$\dfrac{7}{8}x=\dfrac{21}{32}$$

$$\dfrac{8}{7}\cdot\dfrac{7}{8}x=\dfrac{8}{7}\cdot\dfrac{21}{32} \qquad \text{Multiply both sides by }\dfrac{8}{7}.$$

$$1x=\dfrac{8\cdot 21}{7\cdot 32} \qquad \text{Multiply.}$$

$$x=\dfrac{3}{4} \qquad \text{Simplify.}$$

**Example 2:** Solve for $y$:  $\dfrac{y}{10}+2=\dfrac{3}{5}$

**Solution:**

$$\dfrac{y}{10}+2=\dfrac{3}{5}$$

$$10\left(\dfrac{y}{10}+2\right)=10\left(\dfrac{3}{5}\right) \qquad \text{Multiply both sides by the LCD, 10.}$$

$$10\left(\dfrac{y}{10}\right)+10(2)=10\left(\dfrac{3}{5}\right) \qquad \text{Apply the distributive property.}$$

$$y+20=6 \qquad \text{Simplify.}$$

$$y+20-20=6-20 \qquad \text{Subtract 20 from both sides.}$$

$$y=-14 \qquad \text{Simplify.}$$

**Example 3:**  Solve for $m$:  $\dfrac{m}{3} = \dfrac{m}{7} + 2$

**Solution:**

$$\dfrac{m}{3} = \dfrac{m}{7} + 2$$

$$21\left(\dfrac{m}{3}\right) = 21\left(\dfrac{m}{7} + 2\right) \qquad \text{Multiply both sides by the LCD, 21.}$$

$$21\left(\dfrac{m}{3}\right) = 21\left(\dfrac{m}{7}\right) + 21(2) \qquad \text{Apply the distributive property.}$$

$$7m = 3m + 42 \qquad \text{Simplify.}$$

$$7m - 3m = 3m + 42 - 3m \qquad \text{Subtract } 3m \text{ from both sides.}$$

$$4m = 42 \qquad \text{Simplify.}$$

$$\dfrac{4m}{4} = \dfrac{42}{4} \qquad \text{Divide both sides by 4.}$$

$$m = \dfrac{21}{2} \qquad \text{Simplify.}$$

## 4.7 EXERCISES

*Solve.*

1.  $12x = 7$

2.  $-6y = 5$

3.  $\dfrac{3}{5}a = 15$

4.  $-\dfrac{5}{6}m = -\dfrac{7}{12}$

5.  $\dfrac{4}{5}x + \dfrac{1}{3} = \dfrac{7}{15}$

6.  $\dfrac{y}{8} - \dfrac{8}{16} = 1$

7.  $\dfrac{7}{8}n - n = -3$

8.  $\dfrac{3}{10} - \dfrac{1}{3} = \dfrac{x}{20}$

9.  $\dfrac{5}{2}b + \dfrac{2}{3}b = \dfrac{13}{6}$

*Add or subtract as indicated.*

10.  $-\dfrac{4}{11} + \dfrac{y}{6}$

11.  $\dfrac{5m}{12} - \dfrac{4m}{9}$

12.  $\dfrac{8a}{5} - \dfrac{7a}{10}$

*Solve. If no equation is given, perform the indicated operation.*

13.  $\dfrac{5}{6}p = \dfrac{10}{21}$

14.  $\dfrac{5}{4} + \dfrac{4}{x} = \dfrac{1}{8}$

15.  $\dfrac{11}{14} - \dfrac{6}{7}$

16.  $-\dfrac{5}{9}x = \dfrac{5}{18} - \dfrac{7}{18}$

17.  $16 - \dfrac{11}{4}$

18.  $\dfrac{y}{4} = -3 + y$

19.  $\dfrac{7}{9}x = \dfrac{4}{5} - \dfrac{1}{2}$

20.  $\dfrac{8}{15}b = -\dfrac{4}{5} + \dfrac{1}{3}$

## 4.8 OPERATIONS ON MIXED NUMBERS

**Example 1:** Write the mixed number $6\dfrac{7}{8}$ as an improper fraction.

**Solution:** $6\dfrac{7}{8} = \dfrac{6 \cdot 8 + 7}{8} = \dfrac{48 + 7}{8} = \dfrac{55}{8}$

**Example 2:** Write the improper fraction $\dfrac{59}{7}$ as a mixed number.

**Solution:**

$$
\begin{array}{r}
8 \\
7\overline{)59} \\
\underline{56} \\
3
\end{array}
$$

Thus, $\dfrac{59}{7} = 8\dfrac{3}{7}$.

**Example 3:** Multiply: $5\dfrac{3}{4} \cdot 6\dfrac{2}{7}$.

**Solution:** $5\dfrac{3}{4} \cdot 6\dfrac{2}{7} = \dfrac{23}{4} \cdot \dfrac{44}{7} = \dfrac{23 \cdot \boxed{4} \cdot 11}{\boxed{4} \cdot 7} = \dfrac{253}{7}$ or $36\dfrac{1}{7}$

**Example 4:** Subtract: $15\dfrac{1}{4} - 9\dfrac{5}{6}$.

**Solution:**

$$
\begin{array}{r}
17\dfrac{1}{4} = \ 17\dfrac{3}{12} \\
-\,9\dfrac{5}{6} = - \ 9\dfrac{10}{12} \\
\hline
\end{array}
$$

The LCD of 4 and 6 is 12.

We cannot subtract $\dfrac{10}{12}$ from $\dfrac{3}{12}$, so we must borrow from the whole number 17.

$$17\dfrac{3}{12} = 16 + 1\dfrac{3}{12} = 16 + \dfrac{15}{12} \text{ or } 16\dfrac{15}{12}$$

$$
\begin{array}{r}
16\dfrac{15}{12} \\
-\,9\dfrac{10}{12} \\
\hline
7\dfrac{5}{12}
\end{array}
$$

Subtract fractions.

Subtract whole numbers

## 4.8 EXERCISES

*Write each mixed number as an improper fraction.*

1. $9\dfrac{1}{4}$

2. $3\dfrac{5}{13}$

3. $12\dfrac{4}{5}$

*Write each improper fraction as a whole number or mixed number.*

4. $\dfrac{17}{6}$

5. $\dfrac{57}{3}$

6. $\dfrac{87}{10}$

*Multiply or divide.*

7. $3\dfrac{4}{5} \cdot \dfrac{1}{8}$

8. $6\dfrac{1}{4} \cdot 3\dfrac{3}{5}$

9. $\dfrac{4}{9} \div 6\dfrac{3}{4}$

10. $10\dfrac{3}{8} \cdot 5$

11. $15\dfrac{2}{7} \div \dfrac{9}{14}$

12. $12 \div 6\dfrac{3}{7}$

*Add or subtract.*

13. $4\dfrac{3}{14} + 2\dfrac{5}{7}$

14. $25\dfrac{7}{10} + 12\dfrac{4}{5}$

15. $9\dfrac{7}{8} - 2\dfrac{1}{4}$

16. $17\dfrac{3}{8} - 11\dfrac{7}{12}$

17. $19 - 18\dfrac{9}{10}$

18. $21\dfrac{1}{6} + 17\dfrac{5}{8} + 11\dfrac{7}{9}$

19. Two packages of sirloin steak weigh $2\dfrac{3}{5}$ pounds and $3\dfrac{1}{4}$ pounds. Find their combined weight.

20. Find both the area and the perimeter of the rectangle shown below.

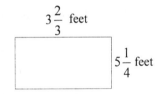

$3\dfrac{2}{3}$ feet

$5\dfrac{1}{4}$ feet

## CHAPTER 4 PRACTICE TEST

*Perform the indicated operations and write the answers in lowest terms.*

1. $\dfrac{13}{15} \div \dfrac{5}{3}$

2. $-\dfrac{5}{7} \cdot \dfrac{9}{5}$

3. $\dfrac{3x}{8} + \dfrac{x}{4}$

4. $\dfrac{1}{10} - \dfrac{2}{x}$

5. $\dfrac{xy^2}{z} \cdot \dfrac{z^3}{x^2 y}$

6. $-\dfrac{4}{9} \cdot -\dfrac{16}{30}$

7. $\dfrac{4m}{7} + \dfrac{5}{14}$

8. $-\dfrac{4}{13m} - \dfrac{6}{13m}$

9. $12xy \div \dfrac{y}{8}$

10. $3\dfrac{1}{8} \div \dfrac{5}{24}$

11. $4\dfrac{5}{6} + 2\dfrac{1}{2} + 8\dfrac{1}{3}$

12. $\dfrac{4x}{7} \cdot \dfrac{14}{8x^4}$

13. $-\dfrac{21}{2} \div -\dfrac{15}{8}$

14. $9\dfrac{1}{5} \cdot 4\dfrac{3}{10}$

15. $30 \div 6\dfrac{1}{4}$

16. $\left(\dfrac{12}{7} \cdot \dfrac{21}{6}\right) \div 8$

17. $\dfrac{7}{8} - \dfrac{2}{3} + \dfrac{5}{12}$

*Simplify each complex fraction.*

18. $\dfrac{\dfrac{4x}{15}}{\dfrac{16x^2}{60}}$

19. $\dfrac{\dfrac{5}{6} - \dfrac{1}{8}}{1 + \dfrac{3}{4}}$

*Solve.*

20. $-\dfrac{7}{8}x = \dfrac{5}{16}$

21. $\dfrac{3}{7}x + \dfrac{1}{2}x = -\dfrac{15}{14}$

22. $\dfrac{1}{4} + \dfrac{x}{3} = \dfrac{5}{6} + \dfrac{x}{2}$

*Evaluate each expression using the given replacement values.*

23. $-8x$ for $x = -\dfrac{5}{12}$

24. $xy$ for $x = \dfrac{2}{3}$ and $y = 4\dfrac{5}{6}$

*Solve.*

25. Cedric has a rope that is $14\dfrac{3}{5}$ feet long. He cuts off a piece $8\dfrac{9}{10}$ feet long. How long is the remaining piece of rope?

## CHAPTER 4 HELPFUL HINTS AND INSIGHTS

- We cannot divide by 0. This means that the denominator of a fraction cannot be 0.

- The number 1 is neither prime nor composite.

- Be careful when all factors of the numerator or denominator are divided out. The result of that numerator or denominator is 1, not 0.

- When the denominator of a fraction contains a variable, such as $\dfrac{7}{9x}$, we assume that the variable does not represent 0.

- Every number except 0 has a reciprocal.

- When dividing by a fraction, do not look for common factors to divide out until you rewrite the division as multiplication.

- When working with signed fractions, remember that $-\dfrac{a}{b} = \dfrac{-a}{b} = \dfrac{a}{-b}$.

- When adding or subtracting fractions, a common denominator is required. When multiplying or dividing fractions, a common denominator is not necessary.

## 5.1 INTRODUCTION TO DECIMALS

**Example 1:**  Write the decimal in standard form:  four hundred seventy-five thousandths

**Solution:**      0.475
                     ↑

                     thousandths place

**Example 2:**  Write 2.67 as a mixed number.

**Solution:**      $2.67 = 2\dfrac{67}{100}$

                     two        two
                  decimal      zeros
                   places

**Example 3:**  Insert <, >, or = to form a true statement.

                  3.099          3.1

**Solution:**      3.099 < 3.1 since 3.1 has a one in the tenths place and 3.099 has a zero in the tenths place;

                  i.e. 0 < 1

**Example 4:**  Round 84.352 to the nearest tenth.

**Solution:**      84.352 rounded to the nearest tenth is 84.4.

                  The digit to the right of the tenths place is 5, so we add 1 to the tenths place and drop all the
                  digits to the right of the tenths place.

**Example 5:**  Write the decimal 4.23 in words.

**Solution:**      four    and    twenty-three hundredths
                              ↓

                           4.23
                              ↑

                     hundredths place

## 5.1 EXERCISES

*Write each decimal in words.*

  1.  3.002                    2.  17.13                    3.  100.25

*Write each decimal in standard form.*

  4.  Ten and twelve hundredths

  5.  Four hundred sixty-five ten-thousandths

  6.  Ninety-six and three tenths

*Write each decimal as a fraction or a mixed number, in lowest terms.*

  7.  0.05                    8.  3.72                    9.  0.45

 10.  14.606                  11.  200.237                 12.  0.3005

13. 0.129       0.131            14. 321.874       321.868

15. 10,000       0.0001          16. 0.67000       0.67

*Round the decimal to the given place.*

17. 2.467, nearest hundredth          18. 0.53, nearest tenth

19. 0.5686, nearest thousandth        20. 145.827, nearest ten

## 5.2 ADDING AND SUBTRACTING DECIMALS

**Example 1:** Add: $1.35 + 23.163$

**Solution:**   Line up the decimal points and add.

$$\begin{array}{r} \overset{1}{1.350} \\ + 23.163 \\ \hline 24.513 \end{array}$$

**Example 2:** Evaluate the expression $y - x$ given $x = 7$ and $y = 0.879$.

**Solution:**   $0.879 - 7 = 0.879 + -7$

$$\begin{array}{r} \overset{6\;\;\overset{9}{\cancel{10}}\;\overset{9}{\cancel{10}}\;10}{\cancel{7}.\cancel{0}\,\cancel{0}\,\cancel{0}} \\ -\;0\,.\,8\;7\;9 \\ \hline 6\,.\,1\;\;2\;\;1 \end{array}$$   Subtract the absolute values.

$0.879 + -7 = -6.121$   The answer has the same sign as the number with the larger absolute value.

**Example 3:** Is 5.2 a solution to the equation $7.8 - x = -2.6$?

**Solution:**   $7.8 - x = -2.6$

$7.8 - 5.2 = -2.6$   Replace $x$ with 5.2.

$2.6 = -2.6$        False.

Since $2.6 = -2.6$ is a false statement, 5.2 is not a solution.

**Example 4:** Simplify by combining like terms: $-3.2x - 4.26x + 1.5x$

**Solution:**   To simplify, we add and/or subtract the coefficients.

$-3.2 - 4.26 + 1.5 = -3.2 + -4.26 + 1.5 = -7.46 + 1.5 = -5.96$
$-3.2x - 4.26x + 1.5x = -5.96x$

## 5.2 EXERCISES

*Perform the indicated operations.*

1. $17.03 + 5.682$
2. $7.6 + 9.5$
3. $-10 + 4.5$

4. $-14 + (-2.37)$
5. $4 - 0.0932$
6. $-3.2 - 55.7$

7. $23.9 - 50$
8. $-33.81 + 60.3$
9. Subtract 4.9 from 17.

10. $-2.35 + 7.3$

*Find the following when* $x = 14, y = 2.1, and\ z = 0.412.$

11. $y - x$             12. $x - y + z$             13. $z + x + y$

*See if the given values are solutions to the given equations.*

14. $x + 7.3 = 9.8;\ \ \ x = 2.6$            15. $51.7 - y = 92;\ \ \ x = -40.3$

16. $a + 9.3 = 7.2 - a;\ \ \ a = -1.8$

*Simplify by combining like terms.*

17. $12.3y - 3 - 6.13y + 7.2$             18. $4x - 0.45 - 8.3x - 2$

*Solve.*

19. If you pay for a pizza that costs $12.99 plus a $3 tip, how much change will you have from a $20 bill.

20. Find the perimeter of a triangle whose sides measure 14.2 cm, 8.95 cm, and 10 cm.

## 5.3 MULTIPLYING DECIMALS AND THE CIRCUMFERENCE OF A CIRCLE

**Example 1:**    Multiply $15.1 \times 0.23$

**Solution:**
$$
\begin{array}{rl}
15.1 & \text{1 decimal place} \\
\underline{\times\ 0.23} & \text{2 decimal places} \\
453 & \\
\underline{3020} & \\
3.473 & \text{3 decimal places}
\end{array}
$$

**Example 2:**    Multiply $4.2863 \times 100$

**Solution:**    To multiply a decimal number by 100 we move the decimal point to the right two places (since there are two zeros).

So, $4.2863 \times 100 = 428.63$

**Example 3:**    Multiply $-2.8 \times 0.5$

**Solution:**
$$
\begin{array}{r}
2.8 \\
\underline{\times\ 0.5} \\
1.40
\end{array}
$$

The product of a negative number and a positive number is negative.
$-2.8 \times 0.5 = -1.4$

**Example 4:**    Evaluate $xy$ when $x = -6$ and $y = -0.43.$

**Solution:**    $xy = (-6)(-0.43)$
$$
\begin{array}{rl}
0.43 & \text{2 decimal places} \\
\underline{\times\ \ 6} & \text{0 decimal places} \\
2.58 & \text{2 decimal places}
\end{array}
$$

The product of two negatives is a positive.

## 5.3 EXERCISES

*Multiply.*

1.  (0.52)(3.76)

2.  $2.19 \times 0.31$

3.  (1.0004)(−6.1)

4.  −24.039(100)

5.  (−32.17)(−2.9)

6.  (452.33)(0.01)

7.  (4.75)(12)

8.  (8.32)(1000)

9.  (−3.33)(3.33)

10.  $5.29 \times -13.7$

*Evaluate xy using the given replacement values.*

11.  $x = -9$ and $y = 0.12$

12.  $x = 4.7$ and $y = 0.001$

13.  $x = -2.5$ and $y = -0.3$

*Determine whether the given value is a solution of each given equation.*

14.  $-2.9x = 9.57;$    $x = -3.3$

15.  $7x = 14.28;$    $x = 2.04$

*Find the circumference of each circle. Then use the approximation 3.14 for $\pi$ and approximate each circumference.*

16.                                17.                                18.

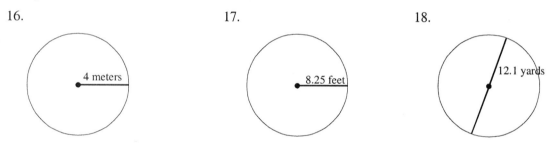

*Solve.*

19. If gas cost $1.69 per gallon, how much would 12.5 gallons cost?

20. Find the area of a rectangular living room that is 14.75 feet long and 13 feet wide.

## 5.4 DIVIDING DECIMALS

**Example 1:**   Divide:    $38.92 \div 5$

**Solution:**

$$
\begin{array}{r}
7.784 \\
5\overline{)38.920} \\
\underline{35}\phantom{.920} \\
39\phantom{.00} \\
\underline{35}\phantom{.00} \\
42\phantom{.0} \\
\underline{40}\phantom{.0} \\
20 \\
\underline{20} \\
0
\end{array}
$$

**Example 2:** Divide: $15.38 \div 1.2$. Round the quotient to the nearest thousandth.

**Solution:** $1.2\overline{)15.38}$   becomes

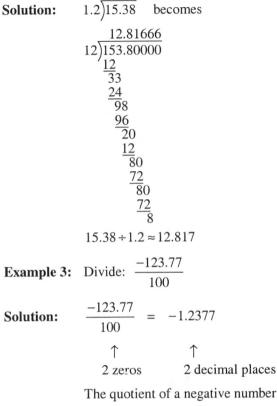

$$
\begin{array}{r}
12.81666 \\
12\overline{)153.80000} \\
\underline{12\phantom{0}} \\
33 \\
\underline{24} \\
98 \\
\underline{96} \\
20 \\
\underline{12} \\
80 \\
\underline{72} \\
80 \\
\underline{72} \\
8
\end{array}
$$

$$15.38 \div 1.2 \approx 12.817$$

**Example 3:** Divide: $\dfrac{-123.77}{100}$

**Solution:** $\dfrac{-123.77}{100} = -1.2377$

$\qquad\qquad\uparrow\qquad\qquad\uparrow$

$\qquad$ 2 zeros $\qquad$ 2 decimal places

The quotient of a negative number and a positive number is always negative.

**Example 4:** Is 890 a solution of the equation $\dfrac{x}{2.5} = 365$?

**Solution:** $\dfrac{x}{2.5} = 365$ $\qquad$ Original equation.

$\dfrac{890}{2.5} = 365$ $\qquad$ Replace $x$ with 890.

$356 = 365$ $\qquad$ False.

Since the statement is false, 890 is not a solution of the equation.

## 5.4 EXERCISES

*Divide. Round the quotients to the nearest thousandth, when necessary.*

1. $4.21 \div 5$

2. $-231.045 \div (-0.02)$

3. $7.488 \div 0.78$

4. $0.093 \div 3$

5. $-9.438 \div 2.7$

6. Divide 36 by 0.04

7. $(-237.14) \div (1000)$

8. $\dfrac{32.45}{-0.011}$

9. $\dfrac{2.004}{-100,000}$

*Evaluate the expression when* $x = 8.92$, $y = -0.4$, *and* $z = -2.7$.

13.  $x \div y$                                  14.  $z \div -0.005$

*Determine whether the given values are solutions of the given equations.*

15.  $\dfrac{x}{6} = 4.02$;   $x = 24.12$          16.  $\dfrac{y}{1000} = 0.204$;   $x = 2040$

*Solve.*

17.  The area of a rectangle is 40.85 square inches.  If the width is 4.3 inches, find the length of the rectangle.

18.  There are approximately 2.54 centimeters in one inch.  Determine how many inches there are in 400 centimeters.

## 5.5 ESTIMATING AND ORDER OF OPERATIONS

**Example 1:**   Add:  $\$24.17 + \$48.31 + \$5.93$   Then estimate the sum to see if the proposed result is reasonable by rounding each decimal to the nearest dollar and then adding.

**Solution:**       Exact                    Estimate

$$
\begin{array}{lll}
\$24.17 & \text{rounds to} & \$24 \\
\$48.31 & \text{rounds to} & \$48 \\
+\ \$\ 5.93 & \text{rounds to} & \$\ 6 \\
\hline
\$78.41 & & \$78 \\
\end{array}
$$

The estimated sum is $78, so $78.41 is reasonable.

**Example 2:**   Multiply  $4.5 \times -62.31$   Then estimate the product to see if the proposed result is reasonable.

**Solution:**       Exact                    Estimate

$$
\begin{array}{ll}
-\ 62.31 & \text{rounds to} \quad -60 \\
\underline{\times\ \ 4.5} & \text{rounds to} \quad \underline{\times 5} \\
31155 & \qquad\qquad -300 \\
\underline{24924} & \\
-280.395 & \\
\end{array}
$$

The estimated product is $-300$, so $-280.395$ is reasonable.

**Example 3:**   Simplify:  $(-2.4)^2 - 7$

**Solution:**   $\begin{aligned}[t]
(-2.4)^2 - 7 &= (-2.4)(-2.4) - 7 \\
&= 5.76 - 7 \\
&= 5.76 + -7 \\
&= -1.24
\end{aligned}$

**Example 4:**   Evaluate  $-3x - 6$ when  $x = 9.1$.

**Solution:**   $\begin{aligned}[t]
-3x - 6 &= -3(9.1) - 6 & & \text{Replace } x \text{ with } 9.1. \\
&= -27.3 - 6 & & \text{Multiply.} \\
&= -33.3 & & \text{Subtract.}
\end{aligned}$

## 5.5 EXERCISES

*Perform each indicated operation. Estimate to see whether the proposed result is reasonable.*

1. $14.9 + 7.2 + 19.5$
2. $48.2 - 37.8$
3. $(32.1)(6.8)$

4. $238.42 \div 9.6$
5. $(-3.3)^3$
6. $(-44.44)(7)$

*Evaluate each expression when $x = -5.6$, $y = 0.4$, and $z = 2.6$.*

7. $x^2 - z$
8. $-4x + 2y$
9. $\dfrac{xz}{y}$

*Determine whether the given value is a solution of the given equation.*

10. $4.6x + 9 = -6.64; \quad x = -3$
11. $7.1x + 0.3 = 2.5x - 4.3; \quad x = -1$

*Perform the indicated operations.*

12. $-3.2(4 - 8.3)$
13. $\dfrac{-4.49 - 1.2}{-0.5}$
14. $(-3.7)^2$

15. $(1 - 0.34)(1 + 0.34)$
16. $\dfrac{2(-3.4) - 6}{5}$
17. $(-2.4 + 3)^2$

*Solve.*

18. Estimate your weekly paycheck if you work 38.5 hours and your hourly rate is $10.75.

19. Use 3.14 for $\pi$ to approximate the circumference of a circle whose radius is 10.3 inches.

20. Estimate the area of a rectangle if the length is 21.3 feet and the width is 18.7 feet.

## 5.6 FRACTIONS AND DECIMALS

**Example 1:** Write $\dfrac{3}{8}$ as a decimal.

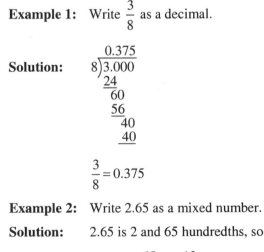

**Solution:**

$$\frac{3}{8} = 0.375$$

**Example 2:** Write 2.65 as a mixed number.

**Solution:** 2.65 is 2 and 65 hundredths, so

$$2.65 = 2\frac{65}{100} = 2\frac{13}{20}$$

**Example 3:** Write the numbers is order from smallest to largest.

$$\frac{4}{9}, \quad \frac{4}{10}, \quad 0.44$$

**Solution:** 

| Original numbers | $\frac{4}{9}$ | $\frac{4}{10}$ | $0.44$ |
|---|---|---|---|
| Decimals | $\approx 0.444$ | $0.4$ | $0.44$ |
| Compare in order | $3^{rd}$ | $1^{st}$ | $2^{nd}$ |

Written from smallest to largest: $\frac{4}{10}, \quad 0.44, \quad \frac{4}{9}$

## 5.6 EXERCISES

*Write each fraction as a decimal.*

1. $\frac{7}{5}$

2. $\frac{9}{4}$

3. $\frac{3}{25}$

*Write each fraction as a decimal. Round to the nearest hundredth.*

4. $\frac{4}{7}$

5. $\frac{1}{9}$

6. $\frac{2}{3}$

*Write each decimal as a fraction.*

7. 0.33

8. 0.002

9. 0.125

*Write each decimal as a mixed number.*

10. 13.5

11. 9.25

12. 5.063

*Insert <, >, or = to form a true statement.*

13. $\frac{8}{9}$   $\frac{7}{8}$

14. $\frac{25}{27}$   $\frac{65}{67}$

15. $\frac{71}{12}$   5.92

*Write each number in order from smallest to largest.*

16. 0.814, 0.836, 0.83

17. $\frac{11}{9}$, 1.22, $\frac{13}{8}$

18. 0.2, 0.20, $\frac{1}{6}$

*Find the value of each expression.*

19. $-4\left(2.5 - \frac{1}{4}\right)$

20. $-4(2.5) - \frac{1}{4}$

## 5.7 EQUATIONS CONTAINING DECIMALS

**Example 1:** Solve for $y$:    $7.3 + y = -10$

**Solution:**

$$7.3 + y = -10$$      Original equation.
$$-7.3 + 7.3 + y = -7.3 + -10$$      Add $-7.3$ to both sides.
$$y = -17.3$$      Simplify.

**Example 2:** Solve for $x$:    $0.25x = -8.5$

**Solution:**

$$0.25x = -8.5$$      Original equation.
$$\frac{0.25x}{0.25} = \frac{-8.5}{0.25}$$      Divide both sides by 0.25.
$$x = -34$$      Simplify.

**Example 3:** Solve for $x$:    $4(x - 0.72) = 2x + 3.8$

**Solution:**

$$4(x - 0.72) = 2x + 3.8$$      Original equation.
$$4x - 2.88 = 2x + 3.8$$      Distributive property.
$$4x - 2.88 - 2x = 2x + 3.8 - 2x$$      Subtract $2x$ from both sides.
$$2x - 2.88 = 3.8$$      Simplify.
$$2x - 2.88 + 2.88 = 3.8 + 2.88$$      Add 2.88 to both sides.
$$2x = 6.68$$      Simplify.
$$\frac{2x}{2} = \frac{6.68}{2}$$      Divide both sides by 2.
$$x = 3.34$$      Simplify.

**Example 4:** Solve for $z$:    $0.4z + 1.6 = 3.84$

**Solution:**

$$0.4z + 1.6 = 3.84$$      Original equation.
$$0.4z + 1.6 - 1.6 = 3.84 - 1.6$$      Subtract 1.6 from both sides.
$$0.4z = 2.24$$      Simplify.
$$\frac{0.4z}{0.4} = \frac{2.24}{0.4}$$      Divide both sides by 0.4.
$$z = 5.6$$      Simplify.

## 5.7 EXERCISES

*Solve the equation.*

1. $x - 4.1 = 5$
2. $y + 3.9 = 21.7$
3. $5x = -7.25$
4. $0.2a = 10.8$
5. $3x - 8 = 2x + 6.5$
6. $5y + 7.2 = 7y - 7.2$
7. $2(x - 3.4) = -10$
8. $7(n + 3.3) = 87.5$

*Solve the equation by first multiplying both sides by the appropriate power of* 10 *so that the equation contains integers only.*

9. $0.6x + 0.12 = -0.24$
10. $6x - 12.5 = x$
11. $3.8a + 7 - 1.2a = 22.6$
12. $-0.005x = 29.65$
13. $y + 15.04 = 11.2$
14. $300x - 0.74 = 200x + 0.9$

*Solve.*

15. $3.2(x-4) = 5.2x$

16. $15x + 14 = 2(5.4x - 7.2)$

17. $0.9x + 42.1 = x - 57.09$

18. $0.004x - 12 = 0.008$

## 5.8 SQUARE ROOTS AND THE PYTHAGOREAN THEOREM

**Example 1:** Find $\sqrt{81}$.

**Solution:** The square root of 81 is 9 because 9 is positive and $9 \cdot 9 = 81$.

**Example 2:** Find $\sqrt{\dfrac{25}{64}}$.

**Solution:** $\sqrt{\dfrac{25}{64}} = \dfrac{5}{8}$ because $\dfrac{5}{8} \cdot \dfrac{5}{8} = \dfrac{25}{64}$.

**Example 3:** Find the length of the hypotenuse of a right triangle with leg lengths 4 meters and 3 meters.

**Solution:** Let $a = 4$ and $b = 3$.
$$a^2 + b^2 = c^2$$
$$4^2 + 3^2 = c^2$$
$$16 + 9 = c^2$$
$$25 = c^2$$
$$\sqrt{25} = c$$
$$5 = c$$
The hypotenuse is 5 meters long.

## 5.8 EXERCISES

*Find the following.*

1. $\sqrt{100}$

2. $\sqrt{1}$

3. $\sqrt{625}$

4. $\sqrt{\dfrac{4}{25}}$

5. $\sqrt{\dfrac{81}{49}}$

6. $\sqrt{\dfrac{1}{64}}$

*Use a calculator to approximate the square root. Round to the nearest thousandth.*

7. $\sqrt{19}$

8. $\sqrt{99}$

9. $\sqrt{40}$

10. $\sqrt{300}$

11. $\sqrt{2}$

12. $\sqrt{82}$

*Find the length of the hypotenuse of each right triangle with given leg lengths. If necessary, approximate the length to the nearest thousandth.*

13. leg = 18, leg = 24

14. leg = 7, leg = 9

15. leg = 20, leg = 20

16. leg = 15, leg = 20

*Solve.*

17. Find the length of the diagonal of the rectangle to the nearest hundredth of a foot.

19 feet

40 feet

18. If the catcher is trying to throw out a runner who is trying to steal second base, how far will the catcher have to throw the ball; i.e. how far is it from home plate to second base? (HINT: The distance between home plate and first base is 90 feet, between first base and second base is 90 feet, between second base and third base is 90 feet, and between third base and home plate is 90 feet.)

## CHAPTER 5 PRACTICE TEST

*Write the decimal as indicated.*

1. 13.013, in words

2. Thirty-five and twelve thousandths, in standard form

*Perform each indicated operation. Round the result to the nearest thousandth if necessary.*

3. $23.912 + 4.77 + 0.8$

4. $-12.8 + 81.2$

5. $-6 - 3.81$

6. $(14.3)(-0.001)$

7. $-80 \div -0.04$

*Round the decimal to the indicated place value.*

8. 47.4747, nearest hundredth

9. 2.0399 nearest thousandth

*Insert <, >, or = to make a true statement.*

10. 2.099    2.1

11. $\dfrac{5}{7}$    0.71

*Write the decimal as a fraction or a mixed number.*

12. 0.225

13. 9.48

*Write the fraction as a decimal.*

14. $\dfrac{29}{80}$

15. $\dfrac{4}{25}$

*Simplify.*

16. $(-0.4)^2 + 2.68$

17. $\dfrac{0.56 + 2.34}{-0.2}$

18. $12.1x - 6.4 - 9.8x - 7.6$

*Find each square root and simplify. Round the square root to the nearest hundredth if necessary.*

19. $\sqrt{36}$

20. $\sqrt{22}$

21. $\sqrt{\dfrac{1}{121}}$

*Solve.*

22. Approximate to the nearest hundredth of an inch the length of the hypotenuse of a right triangle with legs of 7 inches each.

23. Approximate to the nearest hundredth of a meter the length of the hypotenuse of a right triangle with legs of 9 meters and 11 meters.

24. $0.6x + 5.7 = 0.3$

25. $12(x + 1.6) = 10x - 8.4$

## CHAPTER 5 HELPFUL HINTS AND INSIGHTS

- When writing a decimal from words to decimal notation, make sure the last digit is in the correct place by inserting zeros if necessary.

- For any decimal, inserting zeros to the right of the decimal point after the last digit does not change the value of the number.

- When a whole number is written as a decimal, the decimal point is placed to the right of the ones digit.

- When adding decimals, zeros may be inserted to the right of the decimal point after the last digit to help line up place values.

- $\sqrt{43}$ is approximately 6.557. This means that if we multiply 6.557 by 6.557, the product is close to 43.

## 6.1 RATIOS

**Example 1:**  Write the ratio of 10 to 21 using fractional notation.

**Solution:**  $\dfrac{10}{21}$  Remember order is important.

**Example 2:**  Write the ratio of $30 to $45 as a fraction in simplest form.

**Solution:**  $\dfrac{\$30}{\$45} = \dfrac{\cancel{\$}2 \cdot \cancel{15}}{\cancel{\$}3 \cdot \cancel{15}} = \dfrac{2}{3}$

## 6.1 EXERCISES

*Write each ratio using fractional notation.  Do not simplify.*

  1.  17 to 29                       2.  48 to 7

  3.  $\dfrac{3}{5}$ to 9                 4.  $6\dfrac{1}{7}$ to $3\dfrac{8}{11}$

*Write each ratio as a ratio of whole numbers using fractional notation.  Write the fraction in simplest form.*

  5.  14 to 35           6.  40 to 70          7.  42 miles to 160 miles

  8.  33 feet to 15 feet     9.  $100 to $125     10.  99 cm to 102 cm

 11.  4.6 to 9            12.  5.82 to 9.1

*Solve.*

In Mr. Sullivan's Prealgebra class there are 15 women and 10 men present.

 13. Find the ratio of men to women.        14.  Find the ratio of women to total people present.

*Use the given figure to find the ratio for #15 and #16.*

22 feet

40 feet

 15.  Find the ratio of the length to the width of the rectangle.

 16.  Find the ratio of the width to the perimeter of the rectangle.

## 6.2 RATES

**Example 1:**  Write the rate as a fraction in simplest form:  32 students for every 6 teachers

**Solution:**  $\dfrac{32 \text{ students}}{6 \text{ teachers}} = \dfrac{16 \text{ students}}{3 \text{ teachers}}$

**Example 2:**  Write "450 miles every 9 hours" as a unit rate.

**Solution:**  $\dfrac{450 \text{ miles}}{9 \text{ hours}} = \dfrac{50 \text{ miles}}{1 \text{ hour}}$ or 50 miles/hour

**Example 3:**   Approximate each unit price to decide which is the better buy:

$2.95 for 14 ounces of orange juice or $4.99 for 22 ounces of orange juice

**Solution:**   $\dfrac{\$2.95}{14 \text{ ounces}} \approx \$0.211$ per ounce or 21.1 cents per ounce

$\dfrac{\$4.99}{22 \text{ ounces}} \approx \$0.227$ per ounce or 22.7 cents per ounce

Thus the 14 ounce container of orange juice is the better buy.

## 6.2 EXERCISES

*Write each rate as a fraction in simplest form.*

1.  $400 for 12 people

2.  25 pecan trees every 3 acres

3.  12 gallons for 275 miles

4.  40 books for 6 students

5.  400 miles every 8 hours

6.  42 boxes for 200 cookies

*Write each of the following as a unit rate.*

7.  $226 for 40 hours

8.  1000 students for 45 teachers

9.  $1.99 for 8 bagels

10.  65 pages in 4 hours

11.  $14,000,000 for 25 lottery winners

12.  355 milliliters for 12 fluid ounces

*Find each unit rate and decide which is the better buy.  Round to the nearest cent.*

13.  M&M's:        3 ounces for $0.69
                   16 ounces for $2.99

14.  Eggs:   $1.79 for a dozen

$2.88 for $1\dfrac{1}{2}$ dozen

15.  Potato chips:      $3.49 for 32 ounces
                        $0.50 for 6 ounces

## 6.3 PROPORTIONS

**Example 1:**   Is $\dfrac{2}{5} = \dfrac{3}{8}$ a true proportion?

**Solution:**   $\dfrac{2}{5} = \dfrac{3}{8}$

$2 \cdot 8 = 3 \cdot 5$

$16 = 15$

False

Since the cross products are not equal, the proportion is not a true statement.

**Example 2:** Solve for $x$: $\dfrac{4}{9} = \dfrac{x}{27}$

**Solution:**

$$\dfrac{4}{9} = \dfrac{x}{27}$$

$4 \cdot 27 = 9 \cdot x$      Cross multiply.

$108 = 9x$      Multiply.

$\dfrac{108}{9} = \dfrac{9x}{9}$      Divide both sides by 9.

$12 = x$

**Example 3:** Solve for $y$: $\dfrac{2.7}{3.4} = \dfrac{0.8}{y}$. Round the solution to the nearest hundredth.

**Solution:**

$$\dfrac{2.7}{3.4} = \dfrac{0.8}{y}$$

$2.7 \cdot y = 3.4 \cdot 0.8$      Cross multiply.

$2.7y = 2.72$      Multiply.

$\dfrac{2.7y}{2.7} = \dfrac{2.72}{2.7}$      Divide both sides by 2.7.

$y \approx 1.01$

## 6.3 EXERCISES

*Write the sentence as a proportion.*

1. $2\dfrac{1}{4}$ cups of flour is to 36 cookies as $15\dfrac{3}{4}$ cups of flour is to 252 cookies

2. 2 pints is to 1 quart as 46 pints is to 23 quarts

3. 45 females is to 60 males as 180 females is to 240 males

4. 250 Cardinals fans is to 30 Rams fans as 1000 Cardinals fans is to 120 Rams fans

*Determine whether the proportion is a true proportion.*

5. $\dfrac{1}{4} = \dfrac{25}{100}$        6. $\dfrac{30}{80} = \dfrac{300}{800}$        7. $\dfrac{6.25}{2.5} = \dfrac{7.1}{2.84}$

8. $\dfrac{2.8}{1.7} = \dfrac{14}{9}$        9. $\dfrac{\frac{3}{4}}{\frac{7}{3}} = \dfrac{\frac{9}{14}}{\frac{8}{5}}$        10. $\dfrac{3\frac{2}{3}}{\frac{9}{2}} = \dfrac{24}{29\frac{5}{11}}$

*Solve the proportion for the variable. Approximate the solution when indicated.*

11. $\dfrac{4}{3} = \dfrac{x}{33}$        12. $\dfrac{7}{y} = \dfrac{84}{132}$        13. $\dfrac{25}{80} = \dfrac{z}{16}$

14. $\dfrac{3}{5} = \dfrac{y}{55}$        15. $\dfrac{\frac{4}{9}}{18} = \dfrac{x}{9}$        16. $\dfrac{9.4}{3.2} = \dfrac{4.7}{y}$

17. $\dfrac{\dfrac{8}{9}}{\dfrac{26}{27}} = \dfrac{2\dfrac{2}{3}}{z}$                    18. $\dfrac{0.3}{x} = \dfrac{15}{400}$

19. $\dfrac{x}{6.12} = \dfrac{0.91}{0.07}$                    20. $\dfrac{2036}{5694} = \dfrac{3122}{y}$   Round to the nearest hundredth.

## 6.4 PROPORTIONS AND PROBLEM SOLVING

**Example 1:**   On a AAA map of Colorado Springs, 7.5 miles corresponds to 3 inches.  How many miles correspond to 8 inches?

**Solution:**   Let $x =$ the number miles represented by 8 inches

$$\frac{7.5 \text{ miles}}{3 \text{ inches}} = \frac{x \text{ miles}}{8 \text{ inches}}$$

$$7.5 \cdot 8 = 3x \qquad \text{Cross multiply.}$$

$$60 = 3x$$

$$\frac{60}{3} = \frac{3x}{3} \qquad \text{Divide both sides by 3.}$$

$$20 = x$$

20 miles corresponds to 8 inches

**Example 2:**   If 12 loaves of bread cost $21.48, how much will 19 loaves of bread cost?

**Solution:**   Let $x =$ cost of 19 loaves

$$\frac{12 \text{ loaves}}{\$21.48} = \frac{19 \text{ loaves}}{x \text{ dollars}}$$

$$12 \cdot x = 21.48 \cdot 19$$

$$12x = 408.12$$

$$\frac{12x}{12} = \frac{408.12}{12}$$

$$x = 34.01$$

19 loaves should cost $34.01.

## 6.4 EXERCISES

*Solve.*

The ratio of a basketball player's free throws made to free throws attempted is 4 to 9.

1.  If she attempted 45 free throws, how many free throws did she make?

2.  If she made 24 free throws, how many did she attempt?

On an architect's blueprint, 1 inch corresponds to 8 feet.

3.  How long is a wall represented by line $4\dfrac{3}{4}$ inches long on the blueprint?

4.  If a wall is 96 feet long, how long should the blueprint measurement be?

A bag of fertilizer covers 5000 square feet of lawn.

5.  How many bags of fertilizer should be purchased to cover a rectangular lawn 300 feet by 150 feet?

6.  How many bags of fertilizer should be purchased to cover a square lawn 175 feet on each side?

A Florida Marlins baseball player makes 12 hits in every 39 times at bats.

7.  If this player bats 585 times, how many hits would he make?

8.  At this rate, if he made 60 hits, how many times did he bat?

Yearly homeowner property taxes are figured at a rate of $1.95 tax for every $100 of house value.

9.  If George pays $11,700 in property taxes, what is the value of his home?

10.  What are the property taxes on a home valued at $199,000?

A survey reveals that 5 out of 7 people prefer chocolate to vanilla.

11.  In a room of 84 people, how many people are likely to prefer chocolate?

12.  At a college with 14,000 students, how many are likely to prefer vanilla?

A Ford Taurus averages 275 miles on 12 gallons of gas.

13.  At this rate, how far can a Ford Taurus travel on 5 gallons of gas?  Round to the nearest mile.

14.  How many gallons of gas would the Ford Taurus need to travel 1000 miles?  Round to the nearest gallon.

## 6.5 CONGRUENT AND SIMILAR TRIANGLES

**Example 1:**    Determine whether triangle $ABC$ is congruent to triangle $DEF$.

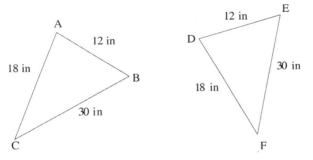

**Solution:**    Since the lengths of all three sides of triangle $ABC$ equal the lengths of the lengths of all three sides of triangle $DEF$, the triangles are congruent.

**Example 2:**    If the following two triangles are similar, find the unknown length $x$.

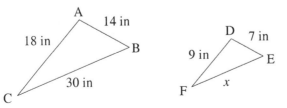

**Solution:** Let $x$ = the length of the unknown side

$$\frac{18}{9} = \frac{30}{x}$$
$$18 \cdot x = 9 \cdot 30$$
$$18x = 270$$
$$\frac{18x}{18} = \frac{270}{18}$$
$$x = 15$$

Therefore, $x$ is 15 inches.

**Example 3:** If a 35-foot pole casts a 45-foot shadow, find the length of the shadow cast by a 50-foot pole. Round to the nearest tenth of a foot.

**Solution:**

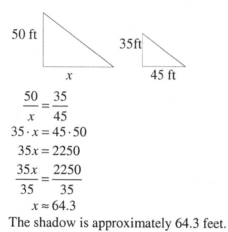

$$\frac{50}{x} = \frac{35}{45}$$
$$35 \cdot x = 45 \cdot 50$$
$$35x = 2250$$
$$\frac{35x}{35} = \frac{2250}{35}$$
$$x \approx 64.3$$

The shadow is approximately 64.3 feet.

## 6.5 EXERCISES

*Determine whether the given pairs of triangles are congruent.*

1.

2.

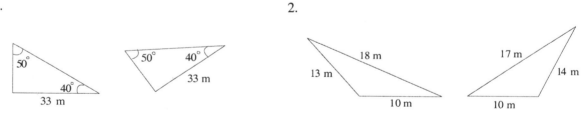

*Find the ratio of the corresponding sides of the similar triangles.*

3.

4.

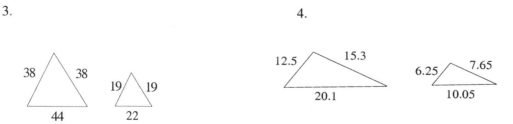

*Given that the pairs of triangles are similar, find the length of the side labeled* x.

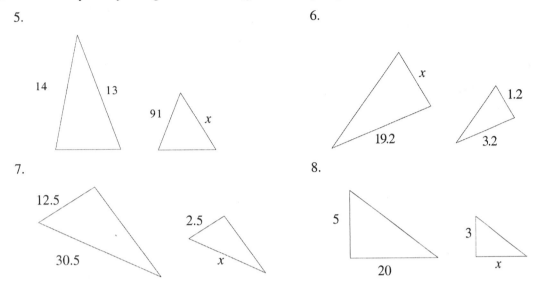

5.

6.

7.

8.

*Solve.*

9. If a 100-foot building casts a 175-foot shadow, find the length of the shadow cast by a 6 foot man.

10. If an 18-foot light pole casts a 25-foot shadow, find the length of a light pole that casts a 20-foot shadow.

## CHAPTER 6 PRACTICE TEST

*Write each ratio using fractional notation. Do not simplify.*

1. 459 Gerber daisies to 132 Gerber daisies

2. On Tuesday the price of MathIsFun stock was $10\frac{3}{8}$ dollars. On Wednesday the stock fell to $8\frac{1}{4}$ dollars.

   Find the ratio of Tuesday's price to Wednesday's price.

*Write each ratio as a ratio of whole numbers using fractional notation. Write each fraction in lowest terms.*

3. 80 to 25                           4. 32 to 50

5. $12 to $90                         6. 42 miles to 84 miles

*Write each rate as a fraction in simplest form.*

7. 10 cars every 3 miles

8. 12 computers for 82 students

*Write each ratio as a unit rate.*

9. 425 miles in 5 hours

10. 22 inches of rain in 30 days

*Compare the unit prices and decide which is the better buy.*

11. Cinnamon rolls:   8 for $1.49 or 12 for $2.28

12. Onions:   $0.99 for a one-pound bag or $4.99 for a five-pound bag

*Write each sentence as a proportion.*

13. 1 cup of sugar is to 3 quarts of iced tea as 4 cups of sugar is to 12 quarts of iced tea

14. 36 inches is to 3 feet as 198 inches is to 16.5 feet

*Determine whether the proportion is true.*

15. $\dfrac{20}{75} = \dfrac{80}{300}$

16. $\dfrac{\frac{2}{5}}{\frac{1}{3}} = \dfrac{\frac{4}{9}}{\frac{1}{4}}$

*Solve the proportion for the variable.*

17. $\dfrac{x}{4} = \dfrac{35}{20}$

18. $\dfrac{\frac{9}{5}}{\frac{7}{11}} = \dfrac{x}{\frac{5}{9}}$

19. $\dfrac{3.6}{4} = \dfrac{9}{y}$

*Solve.*

On a map 1.5 inches corresponds to 75 miles.

20. If Wisconsin is only two inches away from where you are on the map, how many miles away is Wisconsin?

21. If Chicago is 270 miles away from St. Louis, how many inches is it on the map?

22. Given that the following triangles are similar, find the missing length.

23. If 18.5 inches of lace is needed for a set of curtains, how much lace is needed for 12 sets of curtains?

24. Kelly Dawson is trying to estimate the height of a tree. She estimates the length of her shadow to be $3\dfrac{1}{2}$ feet long and the length of the tree's shadow to be 32 feet long. Find the height of the tree if Kelly is $5\dfrac{1}{4}$ feet tall.

## CHAPTER 6 HELPFUL HINTS AND INSIGHTS

- When comparing quantities with different units, write the units as part of the comparison.

- When writing proportions to solve problems, we will place the same units in the numerators and the same units in the denominators.

## 7.1 PERCENTS, DECIMALS, AND FRACTIONS

**Example 1:** Write 45% as a decimal.

**Solution:** $45\% = 0.45$ Move the decimal point two places to the left and drop the % symbol.

**Example 2:** Write 0.248 as a percent.

**Solution:** $0.248 = 24.8\%$ Move the decimal point two places to the right and attach the % symbol.

**Example 3:** Write 21.6% as a fraction in lowest terms.

**Solution:** $21.6\% = \dfrac{21.6}{100}$

$= \dfrac{21.6}{100} \cdot \dfrac{10}{10}$ Multiply numerator and denominator by 10.

$= \dfrac{216}{1000}$

$= \dfrac{27}{125}$ Reduce.

**Example 4:** Write $\dfrac{3}{8}$ as a percent.

**Solution:** $\dfrac{3}{8} = \dfrac{3}{8} \cdot 100\% = \dfrac{300}{8}\% = 37\dfrac{1}{2}\%$ or 37.5%

## 7.1 EXERCISES

*Write each percent as a decimal.*

  1. 38%         2. 3%         3. 50.3%         4. 125%

*Write each decimal as a percent.*

  5. 0.25         6. 0.016         7. 1.05         8. 6

*Write each percent as a decimal.*

  9. 30%         10. 4.7%         11. 150%         12. 0.4%

*Write each fraction as a percent.*

  13. $\dfrac{7}{25}$         14. $\dfrac{7}{8}$         15. $1\dfrac{1}{2}$         16. $\dfrac{49}{50}$

17. If 25 students are enrolled in a class and the attendance today is 100%, determine how many students attended.

18. The Cox family saves 5% of their take-home pay. Write 5% as a decimal.

19. The sales tax rate is 0.0725. Write this is as a percent.

20. A coat is on sale for $\dfrac{1}{2}$ off. Write $\dfrac{1}{2}$ as a percent.

## 7.2 SOLVING PERCENT PROBLEMS WITH EQUATIONS

**Example 1:**   What is 12% of 50?

**Solution:**   What is 12% of 50?

$$\downarrow \quad \downarrow \quad \downarrow \quad \downarrow \quad \downarrow$$

$$x \quad = \quad 12\% \quad \cdot \quad 50$$

$$x = 0.12 \cdot 50 \qquad \text{Write 12\% as 0.12.}$$

$$x = 6$$

6 is 12% of 50.

**Example 2:**   14 is what percent of 90?

**Solution:**

$$14 = x \cdot 90$$

$$\frac{14}{90} = \frac{90x}{90}$$

$$0.155... = x$$

$$15.6\% \approx x$$

14 is approximately 15.6% of 90.

**Example 3:**   2.24 is 3.2% of what number?

**Solution:**

$$2.24 = 3.2\% \cdot x$$

$$2.24 = 0.032x$$

$$\frac{2.24}{0.032} = \frac{0.032x}{0.032}$$

$$70 = x$$

2.24 is 3.2% of 70.

## 7.2 EXERCISES

*Translate each into an equation.  Do not solve.*

1. 35% of 80 is what number?

2. What percent of 10 is 20?

3. 6.2 is 29% of what number?

4. 32% of 912 is what number?

*Solve, Round to the nearest hundredth if necessary.*

5. 5% of 40 is what number?

6. What is 25% of 71.1?

7. 40 is 20% of what number?

8. 0.22 is 40% of what number?

9. 9 is what percent of 36?

10. 3.21 is what percent of 32.1?

11. 0.8 is 20% of what number?

12. 16 is 125% of what number?

13. 14.2 is 8 ¼ % of what number?

14. 400 is what percent of 50?

15. 21.3 is what percent of 100?

16. What is 15% of 25?

## 7.3 SOLVING PERCENT PROBLEMS WITH PROPORTIONS

**Example 1:**   Translate to a proportion: 12% of what number is 20?

**Solution:**   $\underset{\text{percent}}{\underline{12\%}}$ $\underset{\text{base}}{\underline{\text{of what number}}}$ is $\underset{\text{amount}}{\underline{20}}$ ?

$$\frac{\text{amount} \rightarrow}{\text{base} \rightarrow} \quad \frac{20}{b} = \frac{12}{100} \quad \leftarrow \text{percent}$$

**Example 2:**   What number is 30% of 90?

**Solution:**   $\underset{\text{amount}}{\underline{\text{What number}}}$ is $\underset{\text{percent}}{\underline{30\%}}$ of $\underset{\text{base}}{\underline{90}}$ ?

$$\frac{x}{90} = \frac{30}{100}$$
$$100x = 2700$$
$$x = 27$$

**Example 3:**   What percent of 50 is 36?

**Solution:**   $\underset{\text{percent}}{\underline{\text{What percent}}}$ of $\underset{\text{base}}{\underline{50}}$ is $\underset{\text{amount}}{\underline{36}}$ ?

$$\frac{36}{50} = \frac{x}{100}$$
$$50x = 3600$$
$$x = 72$$

## 7.3 EXERCISES

*Translate each to a proportion.  Do not solve.*

1. What percent of 51 is 17?
2. 9% of what number is 10?
3. 44 is 22% of what number?
4. 65% of 100 is what number?

*Solve.  If necessary, round to the nearest hundredth.*

5. 75% of 200 is what number?
6. What is 4.5% of 15?
7. 60 is 8% of what number?
8. 420 is 110% of what number?
9. 5 is what percent of 50?
10. 12 is what percent of 112?
11. 99 is 99% of what number?
12. 3 is 100% of what number?
13. 15.5 is 5.5% of what number?
14. 50 is what percent of 40?
15. 27.6 is what percent of 100?
16. 125% of what number is 4?

## 7.4 APPLICATIONS OF PERCENT

**Example 1:** John counted 5 students absent in his Prealgebra class on a particular day. If this is 20% of the students in his class, how many students are in John's Prealgebra class?

**Solution:** *Method 1.*

$$\underbrace{5}_{} \underbrace{is}_{} \underbrace{20\%}_{} \underbrace{of}_{} \underbrace{\text{what number}}_{}?$$

$$5 = 20\% \cdot x$$
$$5 = 0.2x$$
$$\frac{5}{0.2} = \frac{0.2x}{0.2}$$
$$25 = x$$

There are 25 students in John's class.

*Method 2.*

$$\underbrace{5}_{\text{amount}} \ is \ \underbrace{20\%}_{\text{percent}} \ of \ \underbrace{\text{what number}}_{\text{base}}?$$

$$\frac{5}{b} = \frac{20}{100}$$
$$20b = 500$$
$$\frac{20b}{20} = \frac{500}{20}$$
$$b = 25$$

There are 25 students in John's class.

**Example 2:** Enrollment at the local community college increased from 6500 to 7500 in one year. What is the percent increase? Round to the nearest whole percent.

**Solution:** amount of increase = 7500 − 6500 = 1000

$$\text{percent of increase} = \frac{1000}{6500} \approx 0.15 = 15\%$$

The number of students increased by about 15%.

**Example 3:** Kathy went on a diet. She weighed 160 pounds before the diet and 125 pounds after the diet. What is her percent decrease in weight? Round to the nearest whole percent.

**Solution:** amount of decrease = 160 − 125 = 35

$$\text{percent of decrease} = \frac{35}{160} = 0.21875 \approx 0.22 = 22\%$$

Kathy's weight decreased by about 22%.

## 7.4 EXERCISES

*Solve. If necessary, round to the nearest hundredth.*

1. A 4.5% sales tax is charged on a $1600 copier. 4.5% of $1600 is what number?

2. The Smith household spends $625 a month on a mortgage payment. Their monthly household income is $2500. What percent of their monthly income is spent on their mortgage?

3. The social security taxes an employee pays are 15.02% of total wages. What is the amount of social security tax if wages are $1250?

4. Last year, Dave made $45,500. He got an annual raise of $1000. What percent raise did he receive?

*Solve. If necessary, round all percents to the nearest tenth.*

5. When switching brands of gasoline, Kim increased her car's rate of miles per gallon from 22.4 to 26.2. What is the percent increase?

6. A stereo originally costs $199. It went on sale for $125. What was the percent decrease in price?

7. Roberta went on a diet and decreased her normal calorie intake of 2100 back to 1600. What is the percent decrease?

8. The Kline's bought a house for $125,000 and sold it for $150,000 two years later. What is the percent increase?

9. Gasoline increased in price per gallon from $1.16 to $1.32. What is the percent increase?

10. The number of teachers at the local community college increased from 79 to 89. What is the percent increase?

## 7.5 PERCENT AND PROBLEM SOLVING: SALES TAX, COMMISSION, AND DISCOUNT

**Example 1:** Find the sales tax and the total price on a purchase of $24.95 in a town where the sales tax rate is 7.25%.

**Solution:**     Sales tax = tax rate  ·  purchase price

Sales tax = tax rate  ·  purchase price

$$= 7.25\% \quad \cdot \quad 24.95$$
$$= 0.0725 \cdot 24.95 \qquad \text{Write 7.25\% as a decimal.}$$
$$\approx \$1.81 \qquad \qquad \text{Rounded to the nearest cent.}$$

Total price = purchase price + sales tax

$$= \$24.95 \qquad + \ \$1.81$$
$$= \$26.76$$

The sales tax on $24.95 is $1.81 and the total price is $26.76.

**Example 2:** Jocelyn works at Dress Divine. She earned $96 for selling $1200 worth of merchandise. Find the commission rate.

**Solution:**     commission = commission rate  ·  sales

$$96 \quad = \qquad r \qquad \cdot \ 1200$$
$$96 = 1200r$$
$$\frac{96}{1200} = \frac{1200r}{1200}$$
$$0.08 = r$$
$$8\% = r$$

The commission rate is 8%.

**Example 3:** College tuition of $52.75 per credit hour increased by 4.5%. What is the increase in cost per credit hour, and what is the new cost per credit hour?

**Solution:**

$$\begin{aligned} \text{increase} &= 4.5\% \cdot \$52.75 \\ &= 0.045 \cdot 52.75 \\ &\approx \$2.37 \end{aligned}$$

The increase in tuition is $2.37 per credit hour.

$$\begin{aligned} \text{new cost} &= \text{original cost} + \text{increase} \\ &= \$52.75 \quad\quad + \quad \$2.37 \\ &= \$55.12 \end{aligned}$$

The new tuition is $55.12 per credit hour.

**Example 4:** The price of a $300 VCR is reduced by 30%. What is the decrease and what is the new price?

**Solution:**

$$\begin{aligned} \text{decrease} &= 30\% \cdot \$300 \\ &= 0.3 \cdot 300 \quad\quad \text{Write 30\% as a decimal.} \\ &= \$90 \quad\quad\quad \text{Multiply.} \end{aligned}$$

The decrease in price is $90.

$$\begin{aligned} \text{New price} &= \text{original price} - \text{decrease} \\ &= \$300 - \$90 \\ &= \$210 \end{aligned}$$

The new reduced price is $210.

## 7.5 EXERCISES

*Solve.*

1. What is the sales tax on a coat priced at $150 if the sales tax rate is 6.5%?

2. If the sales tax rate is 5%, find the sales tax on a stove priced at $595.

3. A CD player has a price of $350. What is the sales tax if the sales tax rate is 7%?

4. An area rug is priced at $1200. The sales tax rate is 7.5%. What is the total price?

5. A car is priced at $23,900. The sales tax rate is 6.25%. What is the total price?

6. Ms. Rath bought a sweater for $45, a dress for $75, and a blazer for $120. What is the total price she paid if the sales tax rate was 5.5%?

7. How much commission will Lisa make on a sale of $150,000,000 if her commission rate is 1.2%?

8. A salesperson earned a commission of $2675 for selling $29,722 worth of computer products. What is the commission rate?

9. How much must Andrea sell in order to receive a commission of $1500 if her commission rate is 10%?

10. An $800 chair is on sale for 20% off. What are the discount and the sale price?

11. A $25 book is on sale for 25% off. What are the discount and the sale price?

12. A $25,000 car is on sale for 3.5% off. What are the discount and the sale price?

### 7.6 PERCENT AND PROBLEM SOLVING: INTEREST

**Example 1:**   What is the simple interest on $1000 after 5 years if the interest rate is 2.5%?

**Solution:**   In this example, $P = \$1000$, $R = 2.5\%$, and $T = 5$ years

$$\begin{aligned}
I &= P \cdot R \cdot T & &\text{Simple interest formula.} \\
&= \$1000 \cdot 2.5\% \cdot 5 & &\text{Replace the variables with their values.} \\
&= \$1000 \cdot 0.025 \cdot 5 & &\text{Write 2.5\% as a decimal.} \\
&= \$125 & &\text{Multiply.}
\end{aligned}$$

The simple interest is $125.

**Example 2:**   $9000 is invested at 7% compounded quarterly for 5 years. Find the total amount at the end of 5 years.

**Solution:**   Look in Appendix F of the textbook for the compound interest factor. The compound interest factor for 5 years at 7% in the compounded quarterly section 1.41478.

Total amount = original principal $\cdot$ compound interest factor

$$\begin{aligned}
&= \$9000 \cdot 1.41478 \\
&= \$12733.02
\end{aligned}$$

The total amount at the end of 5 years if $12,733.02.

**Example 3:**   Find the monthly payment for a $15,000 loan for 3 years. The interest in the 3-year loan is $7000.

**Solution:**   Principal + interest = Total amount borrowed
   $15000 + $7000 = $22,000

The number of monthly payments is 3 years $\cdot$ 12 payments/year = 36 payments.

$$\begin{aligned}
\text{Monthly payment} &= \frac{\text{principal} + \text{interest}}{\text{total number of payments}} \\
&= \frac{\$22000}{36} \\
&\approx \$611.11
\end{aligned}$$

### 7.6 EXERCISES

*Find the simple interest for the following situations.*

| | Principal | Rate | Time | | Principal | Rate | Time |
|---|---|---|---|---|---|---|---|
| 1. | $750 | 4% | 5 years | 2. | $80,000 | 7.8% | 10 years |
| 3. | $400 | 13% | 2 ½ years | 4. | $1650 | 20% | 6 months |
| 5. | $1500 | 6 ¼ % | 10 years | 6. | $2500 | 5% | 9 months |

*Solve.*

7.  If you borrow $17,300 for 4 years at a simple interest of 8.5%, what is the simple interest?

8.  A money market fund advertises a simple interest rate of 8 ½ %. What is the simple interest on $3500 for 2 years?

*Find the total amount in each compound interest account.*

9. $9500 is compounded annually at a rate of 12% for 10 years.

10. $1500 is compounded semiannually at a rate of 15% for 5 years.

11. $12,000 is compounded quarterly at a rate of 8% for 15 years.

12. $25,000 is compounded daily at a rate of 7% for 20 years.

13. $950 is compounded annually at a rate of 5% for 15 years.

14. $1250 is compounded quarterly at a rate of 17% for 10 years.

*Solve.*

15. $30,000 is borrowed for 5 years. What is the monthly payment if the interest on the loan is $14,578.42?

16. $133,000 is borrowed for 30 years. What is the monthly payment if the interest on the loan is $300,000?

**CHAPTER 7 PRACTICE TEST**

1. Write 0.371 as a percent.

2. Write 0.371% as a decimal.

3. Write 121% as a fraction in lowest terms.

4. Write $\frac{13}{25}$ as a percent.

5. The sales tax rate if 6.25%. Write this percent as a fraction in lowest terms.

6. What is 35% of 90?

7. 1.2% of what number is 12?

8. 45 is what percent of 90?

9. Write an equation for the statement "14 is 19% of what number?"

10. Write a proportion for the statement "14 is 19% of what number?"

*Solve. Round all dollar amounts to the nearest cent and all percents to the nearest tenth of a percent.*

11. An alloy is 16% copper. How much copper is contained in 180 pounds of this alloy?

12. A 5-pound mixture of a candy corn and peanuts contains 12% candy corn. How many pounds of candy corn does the mixture contain?

13. A real estate agent received a commission rate of 1.5% on a house which sold for $185,000. What is the commission?

14. If the local sales tax rate is 6 ¾ %, what is the total amount charged on a dress that costs $89.99?

15. Jenny borrowed $600 from a bank at 15.5% for 9 months. What is the total simple interest due the bank at the end of the 9-month period?

16. What is the simple interest earned on $4250 saved for 6 ¼ years at an interest rate of 7 ½ %?

17. The price of a gallon of milk increased 16%. It originally costs $2.15 per gallon. What is the new price?

18. Your hourly wage increased from $5.65 to $7.25. What is the percent increase?

19. $5 is invested at a local bank at 8% compounded quarterly. What is the total amount after 20 years?

20. $5260 is compounded semiannually at 6%. What is the total amount after 10 years?

21. The unemployment rate decreased from 10.2% to 8.5%. What is the percent decrease?

22. $8800 is borrowed for 2 ½ years. What is the monthly payment if the interest on the loan is $620.35?

23. Diane's commission rate is 3%. What are her sales if her commission is $12,000?

## CHAPTER 7 HELPFUL HINTS AND INSIGHTS

- Remember that, unless otherwise stated, the interest rate given is per year. A time period given other than years must be converted to years.

- Before solving an equation containing percents, all percents must be converted to decimals.

## 8.1 READING PICTOGRAPHS, BAR GRAPHS, AND LINE GRAPHS

**Example 1:**  The pictograph below shows the annual number of house renovations made by one company for the years 1997-2002.

House Renovations

| | |
|---|---|
| 2002 | ⌂⌂⌂⌂ |
| 2001 | ⌂⌂⌂ |
| 2000 | ⌂⌂⌂⌂ |
| 1999 | ⌂⌂⌂⌂⌂⌂ |
| 1998 | ⌂⌂⌂⌂ |
| 1997 | ⌂⌂ |

Each ⌂ represents 5 houses

a.   How many houses did the company renovate during the year 1998?

b.   During which year were the least number of renovations made?

**Solution:**  a.   (Number of ⌂)   ·   (5 houses)

$= 4 \cdot 5$  houses

$= 20$  houses

20 houses were renovated in 1998.

b.   The least number of symbols appear next to 1997. This is the year in which the least number of renovations were made.

**Example 2:**  The following bar graph shows the profits (in dollars) made by BGK Enterprises during the years 1999 to 2002.

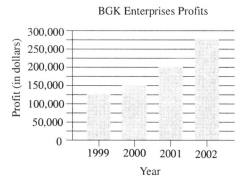

a.   Approximate the profits for the year 2000.

b.   Are profits increasing or decreasing?

**Solution:**  a.   Find the year 2000, go to the top of the bar and then go across to the vertical scale to read the dollar amount of profits. The profit for the year 2000 is $150,000.

b.   As the years increase, the bars are getting taller. This means that profits are increasing.

**Example 3:**    The following line graph shows the temperature highs (in degrees Fahrenheit) for one week during the month of September 2003 in St. Louis.

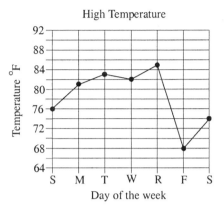

a. What was the high temperature reading on Monday?

b. What day was the temperature the highest? What was the high temperature?

**Solution:**    a. Find Monday on the horizontal scale, go straight up until you reach the line graph then go across to the vertical scale and read the temperature. The high temperature reading on Monday was 81°F.

b. Locate the highest point on the line graph then go down from this point to the horizontal scale and identify the day. Thursday had the highest temperature. Now go from the point on the line graph across to the vertical scale and identify the temperature. The high temperature for Thursday was 85°F.

## 8.1 EXERCISES

*Using the pictograph from Example 1, do the following exercises.*

1. How many houses did the company renovate during the year 2001?

2. How many houses did the company renovate during the year 2002?

3. During which year was the greatest number of renovations made?

4. How many more renovations were made in 1999 than in 1997?

5. Over the years 1997-2002, what was the total number of renovations made?

6. In what year(s) were 15 renovations made?

*Using the bar graph from Example 2, do the following exercises.*

7. Approximate the profits for the year 1999.

8. During what year were the profits $200,000?

9. How much more profit was made during 2002 than in 2000?

10. Between which two consecutive years was the increase in profit the greatest?

11. Over the years 1999-2002, what was the total profit?

12. Which year had the largest profit?

*Using the line graph from Example 3, do the following exercises.*

13.  What was the high temperature reading on Tuesday?

14.  What day was the temperature the lowest?

15.  Between which two consecutive days was there the greatest increase in high temperature?

16.  On what day(s) was the high temperature reading 82°F ?

17.  How many degrees difference was there between the high temperature reading on Sunday and on Saturday?

*Use the given data to answer questions 18-20.*

Koala Kola, Inc. wants feedback on its new product, Platypus Pop. Marketers set up a taste test with 15 people who were asked to rate the product using the following 5-point scale: (worst) 1  2  3  4  5  (best). The 15 ratings are:

2  3  2  1  4  1  5  2  3  3  1  2  4  2  3

18.  Complete the frequency table.

| Rating | Tally | Frequency |
|--------|-------|-----------|
| 1 | | |
| 2 | | |
| 3 | | |
| 4 | | |
| 5 | | |

19.  Which rating was reported the most?

20.  Use the frequency table in problem 18 to make a histogram of the data.

## 8.2 READING CIRCLE GRAPHS

**Example 1:**   The circle graph below is a result of surveying 500 college students. They were asked what type of movie they preferred.

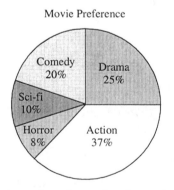

Movie Preference

a.   What type of movie is preferred most by the students in the survey?

b.   Find the number of students out of the survey who prefer comedy.

**Solution:**    a.   Look for the largest sector of the circle, it will be labeled with the largest percent. In this case, the students preferred Action movies more than the other types.

   b.   amount = percent · base

$$= 20\% \cdot 500$$
$$= (0.2)(500)$$
$$= 100$$

100 students prefer comedy.

**Example 2:**   The following table shows the percent of registered voters in a certain county who identify themselves with a particular political party. Draw a circle graph showing the data.

| Political Party | Percent |
|---|---|
| Republican | 50% |
| Democrat | 30% |
| Independent | 15% |
| Other | 5% |

**Solution:**   Find the number of degrees in each sector representing each political party.

| Political Party | Degrees in each sector |
|---|---|
| Republican | $50\% \times 360° = 180°$ |
| Democrat | $30\% \times 360° = 108°$ |
| Independent | $15\% \times 360° = 54°$ |
| Other | $5\% \times 360° = 18°$ |

Now use a protractor to mark off 4 sectors with the degrees shown in the chart above.

Political Party

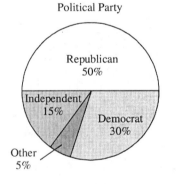

## 8.2 EXERCISES

*Use the circle graph from Example 1 to do problems 1-6.*

1. How many students prefer horror movies?

2. How many students prefer either sci-fi or action movies?

3. How many students prefer drama movies?

4. Find the ratio of students preferring action movies to total students.

5. Find the ratio of students preferring comedy to students preferring drama.

6. Which movie type was preferred the least?

*The circle graph below shows how many campers participated in an activity at Camp Itchyback for a particular session. Use this graph for problems 7-13.*

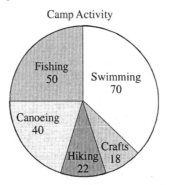

Camp Activity

7.  Which activity had the most participation?

8.  Which activity had the least participation?

9.  What percent of the campers went fishing?

10. What percent of the campers went swimming?

11. Find the ratio of campers that went canoeing to the campers that made crafts.

12. Find the ratio of campers participating in either swimming or hiking to total students.

13. Which category had the second-largest participation?

14. Draw a circle graph to represent the following **data**.

| Type of Glassware in a collection | Percent |
|---|---|
| Fenton | 40% |
| Smith | 5% |
| Mosser | 10% |
| Victorian | 20% |
| Westmoreland | 25% |

*Use the circle graph in Example 2 to answer questions 15-20.*

15. Which category is the largest in that particular county?

16. Which category is the smallest in that particular county?

17. If there are 20,000 registered voters in the county, how many are Independents?

18. If there are 20,000 registered voters in the county, how many are Republicans?

19. If there are 20,000 registered voters in the county, how many are Democrats?

20. Find the ratio of Democrats to Republicans.

## 8.3 THE RECTANGULAR COORDINATE SYSTEM

**Example 1:** Plot each point corresponding to the ordered pairs on the same set of axes.
$$(-3,2),(4,-1),(2,0),(0,-4),(2,5),(-3,-4),(0,0)$$

**Solution:**

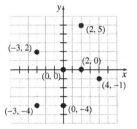

**Example 2:** Is $(3,-1)$ a solution of the equation $2x-3y=9$ ?

**Solution:**
$$2x-3y=9 \qquad \text{Original equation.}$$
$$2(3)-3(-1)=9 \qquad \text{Replace } x \text{ with 3 and } y \text{ with } -1.$$
$$6+3=9 \qquad \text{Multiply.}$$
$$9=9 \qquad \text{True.}$$

Since $9=9$ is a true statement, the ordered pair $(3,-1)$ is a solution of the equation $2x-3y=9$ .

**Example 3:** Complete the ordered pair solutions of the equation $4x-3=y$ .

 a. $(0, \quad )$ b. $( \quad ,5)$ c. $(-3, \quad )$

**Solution:** a. 
$$4x-3=y \qquad \text{Original equation.}$$
$$4(0)-3=y \qquad \text{Replace } x \text{ with 0.}$$
$$0-3=y \qquad \text{Solve for } y.$$
$$-3=y$$

The ordered pair solution is $(0,-3)$ .

 b. 
$$4x-3=y \qquad \text{Original equation.}$$
$$4x-3=5 \qquad \text{Replace } y \text{ with 5.}$$
$$4x-3+3=5+3 \qquad \text{Solve for } x.$$
$$4x=8$$
$$\frac{4x}{4}=\frac{8}{4}$$
$$x=2$$

The ordered pair solution is $(2,5)$ .

c.     $4x - 3 = y$          Original equation.
       $4(-3) - 3 = y$          Replace $x$ with $-3$.
       $-12 - 3 = y$          Solve for $y$.
       $-15 = y$

The ordered pair solution is $(-3, -15)$.

## 8.3 EXERCISES

*Plot points corresponding to the ordered pairs on the same set of axes.*

1. $(4, 1)$          2. $(-4, -6)$          3. $(-1, 5)$

4. $(4, 0)$          5. $(0, -6)$          6. $(2, -5)$

*Find the x- and y-coordinates of each labeled point.*

7.

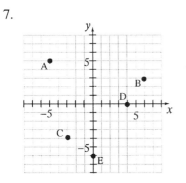

*Determine the quadrant or coordinate axis where each point lies.*

8. $(3, -4)$          9. $(0, 4)$          10. $(-5, -8)$

11. $(-3, 0)$          12. $(-5, 3)$

*Determine whether each ordered pair is a solution of the given linear equation.*

13. $y = 4x$;  $(-1, 4)$          14. $x = -7y$;  $(0, 0)$          15. $3x + 2y = 7$;  $(1, 2)$

*Plot the three ordered-pair solutions of the given equation.*

16. $x - y = 3$;  $(-2, -5)$, $(0, -3)$, $(2, -1)$          17. $x + 2y = -1$;  $(-3, 1)$, $(1, -1)$, $(5, -3)$

*Complete the ordered- pair solutions of the given equations.*

18. $x = 10y$;  $(10, \quad)$, $(\quad, 0)$, $(\quad, -2)$

19. $4x - y = 8$;  $(2, \quad)$, $(3, \quad)$, $(\quad, 8)$

20. $x + 6y = 0$;  $(\quad, 1)$, $(\quad, -2)$, $(0, \quad)$

## 8.4 GRAPHING LINEAR EQUATIONS

**Example 1:**  Graph the equation $-4x = y$ by plotting the following points that satisfy the equation and drawing a line through the points.

$(-1, 4)$,  $(0, 0)$,  $(1, -4)$

**Solution:**  Plot the points and draw a line through them. The line is the graph of the linear equation $-4x = y$.

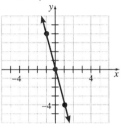

**Example 2:**  Graph $y = -2x + 5$.

**Solution:**  Determine three ordered-pair solutions to the equation. Plot the corresponding points and draw a line through them.

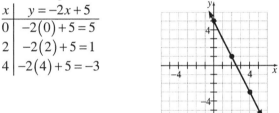

| $x$ | $y = -2x + 5$ |
|---|---|
| 0 | $-2(0) + 5 = 5$ |
| 2 | $-2(2) + 5 = 1$ |
| 4 | $-2(4) + 5 = -3$ |

**Example 3:**  Graph $x = -3$.

**Solution:**  The graph is a vertical line that crosses the x-axis at $-3$.

**Example 4:**  Graph $y = 5$.

**Solution:**  The graph is a horizontal line that crosses the y-axis at 5.

**8.4 EXERCISES**

*Graph each equation.*

1. $x + y = -5$        2. $x + 3y = 1$        3. $3x - y = 6$

4. $y - x = -1$        5. $y = 2x - 4$        6. $x = 2y + 1$

7. $y = x + 3$        8. $x = 2y - 9$        9. $x = 6$

10. $y = 2$        11. $y = -7$        12. $x = -5$

13. $x - 2 = 0$        14. $y + 6 = 0$        15. $x - 4y = 0$

16. $y - 2x = 0$        17. $y = -x - 4$        18. $\dfrac{1}{2}x - y = 1$

19. $x + y = -3$        20. $\dfrac{1}{2}x - \dfrac{1}{3}y = 1$

**8.5 MEAN, MEDIAN, AND MODE**

**Example 1:** Find the mean of the following test scores. Round to the nearest hundredth.
74, 85, 91, 72, 85, 46, 95, 88, 76

**Solution:** To find the mean, find the sum of the numbers and divide by 9, the number of terms.

$$\text{mean} = \frac{74 + 85 + 91 + 72 + 85 + 46 + 95 + 88 + 76}{9} = \frac{712}{9} = 79.11$$

The mean test score is 79.11.

**Example 2:** Find the median of the following list of numbers: 17, 23, 9, 42, 56, 22, 30

**Solution:** First, list the numbers in numerical order and then find the middle number.
9, 17, 22, $\underline{23}$, 30, 42, 56

The median is 23.

**Example 3:** Find the median of the following list of numbers: 41, 32, 78, 90, 64, 54

**Solution:** First, list the numbers in numerical order. Since there are an even number of values, the median is the average of the two middle terms.
32, 41, $\underline{54}$, $\underline{64}$, 78, 90

$$\text{median} = \frac{54 + 64}{2} = \frac{118}{2} = 59$$

The median is 59.

**Example 4:** Find the mode of the following list of numbers: 23, 18, 17, 29, 18, 30, 18

**Solution:** Find the number that occurs most often. The mode is 18.

## 8.5 EXERCISES

*Find the mean for each of the following lists of numbers. Round to the nearest hundredth..*

  1. 18, 24, 16, 31, 19, 26, 30           2. 51, 40, 80, 71, 62, 54, 95, 48

  3. 9.4, 8.6, 11.2, 17.8, 10.1, 3.4         4. 98.6, 98.3, 97.5, 99.1, 98.4, 98.6

  5. −2, 5, 0, 6, −5, 7, 9              6. 5.38, 5.60, 5.53, 5.65, 5.71, 5.42

*Find the median for each of the following lists of numbers.*

  7. 0.1, 0.3, 0.7, 0.6, 0.2, 0.9          8. 62, 81, 9, 27, 54, 71, 11, 90, 65

  9. 576, 419, 328, 637, 505, 491, 387     10. 70, 45, 89, 58, 71, 65, 70, 69

11. 0, 2, 3, 1, 7, 3, 8, 4               12. 0.17, 0.19, 0.12, 0.20, 0.14, 0.16, 0.11

*Find the mode for each of the following lists of numbers.*

13. 11, 15, 9, 11, 15, 10, 20, 15, 10, 8, 9, 15     14. 130, 122, 131, 140, 122, 150, 118, 122

15. 5.4, 3.7, 2.1, 4.5, 4.5, 5.4, 7.3, 5.4, 4.5     16. 3, 7, 2, 9, 6, 2.2, 3, 10, 7.4

17. 0.01, 0.03, 0.06, 0.03, 0.01, 0.05, 0.01

The grades are given for a student during a certain semester. Find the grade point average. Round to the nearest hundredth.

18.

| Grade | Credit Hours |
|-------|--------------|
| A | 4 |
| C | 3 |
| B | 3 |
| B | 4 |

19.

| Grade | Credit Hours |
|-------|--------------|
| C | 4 |
| B | 3 |
| B | 3 |
| A | 4 |
| D | 2 |

20.

| Grade | Credit Hours |
|-------|--------------|
| A | 4 |
| A | 4 |
| B | 4 |
| A | 3 |
| B | 3 |

## 8.6 COUNTING AND INTRODUCTION TO PROBABILITY

**Example 1:**    Draw a tree diagram for the following experiment. Then use the diagram to find the number of possible outcomes.    *Choose a letter (a, b, c, d), and then a number (1 or 2).*

**Solution:**

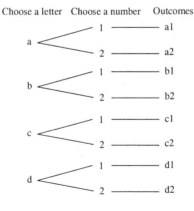

    There are 8 possible outcomes.

**Example 2:**  Using the experiment in Example 1, find the probability of getting c1 or d1.

**Solution:**    probability of c1 or d1 $= \dfrac{2}{8}$   $\rightarrow$  number of ways event can occur
$\phantom{probability of c1 or d1 = \dfrac{2}{8}}$ $\rightarrow$  number of possible outcomes

$\phantom{probability of c1 or d1}= \dfrac{1}{4}$   in simplest form

**Example 3:**  A bag contains 5 red marbles, 4 green marbles, and 11 blue marbles. If a single marble is drawn from the bag, what is the probability that it will be green?

**Solution:**    probability of green $= \dfrac{\text{number of green marbles}}{\text{total number of marbles}}$

$\phantom{probability of green}= \dfrac{4}{20}$

$\phantom{probability of green}= \dfrac{1}{5}$   in simplest form

## 8.6 EXERCISES

*Draw a tree diagram for each experiment. Then use the diagram to find the number of possible outcomes.*

1.  Choose a number (1, 2, 3, or 4) and then toss a coin.

2.  Toss a coin and then choose a number (1, 2, 3, or 4).

3.  Roll a die and then choose a vowel (a, e, i, o, u).

4.  Toss a coin and then choose a number (5, 6, or 7).

*Refer to the tree diagrams in the previous problems to answer these questions.*

5.  For the experiment in problem 1, what is the probability that you get 2H?

6.  For the experiment in problem 2, what is the probability that you get T3?

7.  For the experiment in problem 3, what is the probability that you get 4e?

8.  For the experiment in problem 4, what is the probability that you get H6?

*If a single choice is made from a bag with 6 purple marbles, 4 orange marbles, 2 pink marbles, 3 white marbles, and 5 red marbles, find the probability of each event.*

9.  A white marble is chosen.

10.  A pink marble is chosen.

11.  A purple marble is chosen.

12.  A blue marble is chosen.

13.  A red or orange marble is chosen.

14.  A purple or white marble is chosen.

*Suppose the given spinner is spun once. Find the probability of each event assuming all sectors are the same size.*

15. The result of the spin is an odd number.

16. The result of the spin is 2.

17. The result of the spin is an even number.

*Suppose a single card is drawn from a standard deck of cards. Find the probability of each event.*

18. The card is a spade.

19. The card is the Queen of hearts.

20. The card is a 7.

## CHAPTER 8 PRACTICE TEST

*The circle graph below shows the age groups of students enrolled in a mathematics course during a certain semester. There were a total of 600 students enrolled in the course during that time.*

Students in Mathematics

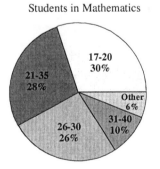

1. Which age group contains the most students?

2. Find the number of students that were in the 31-40 age range.

3. Which age group contained 28% of the students?

*The line graph below shows the closing price for shares of stock in Scandal Corporation for a certain week.*

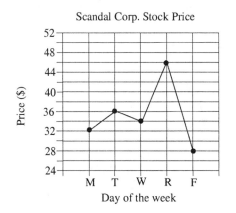

4. What was the price of the stock on Tuesday?

5. On what day was the price the highest? How much did a share of stock cost on that day?

6. On what day was the price the lowest? How much did a share of stock cost on that day?

7. What was the difference in price from Monday to Friday?

8. For which two consecutive days did the price increase the most?

*Find the coordinates of each point.*

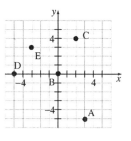

9. A  10. B  11. C  12. D  13. E

*Complete and graph the ordered-pair solutions of the given equation.*

14. $x + 3y = 1$; $(\phantom{x}, 0)$, $(4, \phantom{x})$, $(-5, \phantom{x})$

15. $y = 5x - 2$; $(0, \phantom{x})$, $(1, \phantom{x})$, $(\phantom{x}, -7)$

*Graph each linear equation.*

16. $y = x + 1$   17. $x + 4 = 0$   18. $y + 3 = 0$   19. $5x + 6y = 30$

*Find the mean, median, and mode of each list of numbers.*

20. 54, 71, 88, 47, 64, 67   21. 121, 130, 147, 129, 127, 133, 130

*Find the grade point average. If necessary, round to the nearest hundredth.*

22.

| Grade | Credit Hours |
|-------|--------------|
| D | 3 |
| B | 5 |
| B | 3 |
| A | 4 |

23.

| Grade | Credit Hours |
|-------|--------------|
| C | 3 |
| C | 3 |
| A | 2 |
| B | 4 |

24. If a die is rolled one time, find the probability of rolling a 5 or 6.

25. If a single card is drawn from a standard deck of cards, find the probability that the card is a face-card.

## CHAPTER 8 HELPFUL HINTS AND INSIGHTS

- Remember that each point in the rectangular coordinate system corresponds to exactly on ordered pair and that each ordered pair corresponds to exactly one point.

- An ordered pair that makes an equation in two variables true is a point on the graph of the equation.

- The first coordinate in an ordered pair is associated with the horizontal axis (usually called the x-axis) and tells how many units to move left or right from the vertical axis.

- The second coordinate in an ordered pair is associated with the vertical axis (usually called the y-axis) and tells how many units to move up or down from the horizontal axis.

- If $a$ is a number, then the graph of $x = a$ is a vertical line that crosses the x-axis at $a$.

- If $b$ is a number, then the graph of $y = b$ is a horizontal line that crosses the y-axis at $b$.

- Statistical measures like the mean, median, and mode will have units of measure if the data set has units of measure.

## 9.1 LINES AND ANGLES

**Example 1:** Classify each angle as acute, right, obtuse, or straight.

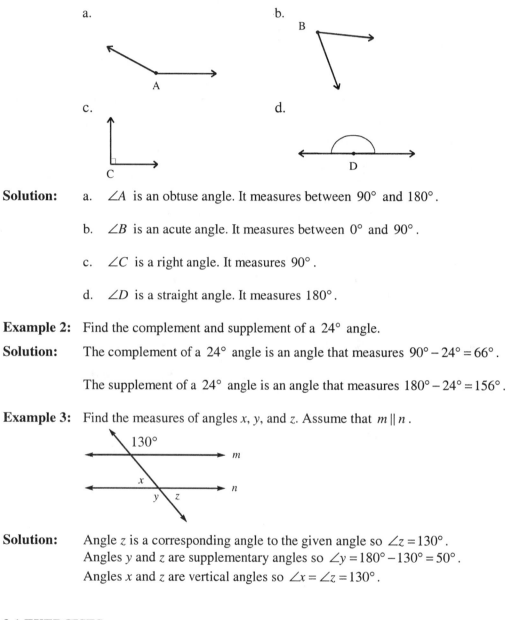

a.

b.

c.

d.

**Solution:**   a.   $\angle A$ is an obtuse angle. It measures between $90°$ and $180°$.

b.   $\angle B$ is an acute angle. It measures between $0°$ and $90°$.

c.   $\angle C$ is a right angle. It measures $90°$.

d.   $\angle D$ is a straight angle. It measures $180°$.

**Example 2:** Find the complement and supplement of a $24°$ angle.

**Solution:**   The complement of a $24°$ angle is an angle that measures $90° - 24° = 66°$.

The supplement of a $24°$ angle is an angle that measures $180° - 24° = 156°$.

**Example 3:** Find the measures of angles $x$, $y$, and $z$. Assume that $m \parallel n$.

**Solution:**   Angle $z$ is a corresponding angle to the given angle so $\angle z = 130°$.
Angles $y$ and $z$ are supplementary angles so $\angle y = 180° - 130° = 50°$.
Angles $x$ and $z$ are vertical angles so $\angle x = \angle z = 130°$.

## 9.1 EXERCISES

*Identify each figure as a line, a ray, a line segment, or an angle.*

1.

2.

3.                                        4.

*Find the measure of each angle in the figure.*

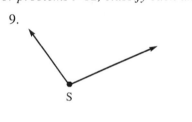

5.  ∠ABD                      6.  ∠ABC

7.  ∠EBC                      8.  ∠DBE

*For problems 9-12, classify each angle as acute, right, obtuse, or straight.*

9.                                        10.

11.                                       12.

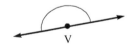

13. Find the supplement of a 43° angle.

14. Find the complement of a 39° angle.

15. Find the supplement of a 121° angle.

16. Find the measure of $x$.

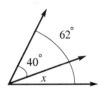

Find the measures of angles *x*, *y*, and *z*.

17.

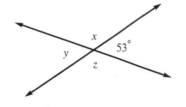

18.  $m \parallel n$

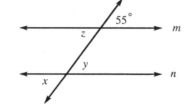

## 9.2 LINEAR MEASUREMENT

**Example 1:**   Convert 7 feet to inches.

**Solution:**    $7 \text{ ft} = 7 \text{ ft} \cdot \dfrac{12 \text{ in.}}{1 \text{ ft}}$

$= 7 \cdot 12 \text{ in.}$

$= 84 \text{ in.}$

**Example 2:**   Convert 4 yards 2 feet to feet.

**Solution:**    $4 \text{ yards} = 4 \text{ yds} \cdot \dfrac{3 \text{ ft}}{1 \text{ yd}}$

$= 4 \cdot 3 \text{ ft}$

$= 12 \text{ ft}$

4 yards 2 feet = 12 ft + 2 ft = 14 ft

**Example 3:**   Add 7 ft 3 in. and 3 ft 11 in.

**Solution:**
```
    7 ft   3 in.
+   3 ft  11 in.
   10 ft  13 in.
```
$= 10 \text{ ft } 1 \text{ ft } 1 \text{ in.}$

$= 11 \text{ ft } 1 \text{ in.}$

**Example 4:**   Convert 72,000 cm to kilometers.

**Solution:**

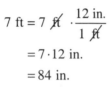

km   hm   dam   m   dm   cm   mm

5 units left

72,000 cm = 0.72 km

**Example 5:**   Multiply 5 m 40 cm by 4.

**Solution:**

$$5 \text{ m } 40 \text{ cm}$$
$$\times \qquad 4$$
$$\overline{20 \text{ m } 160 \text{ cm}}$$

20 m 160 cm = 20 m + 1 m + 60 cm = 21 m 60 cm

## 9.2 EXERCISES

*Convert each measurement as indicated.*

1. 54 in. to feet

2. 17 yd to feet

3. 29,040 feet to miles

4. 2.6 mi to feet

5. 117 ft to yard

6. 97 ft to inches

7. 41 ft = ___ yd ___ ft

8. 53 in. = ____ ft ____ in.

9. 45,000 ft = _____ mi ____ ft

10. 6 ft 4 in. = ____ in

11. 6 yd 1 ft = ____ ft

12. 65 m to centimeters

13. 1300 cm to meters

14. 19.6 mm to decimeters

15. 2.1 km to millimeters

*Perform the indicated operations.*

16. 11 ft 6 in. + 8 ft 9 in.

17. 30 ft 5 in. − 14 ft 7 in.

18. 32 yd 2 ft × 5

19. 12 cm − 37 mm

20. 12.8 m ÷ 4

21. A roll of Bubble Tape bubble gum measures 6 ft 1 in. If Shawn chews 2 ft 5 in of gum, how much would he have left?

22. Payton needs 3 yards of cloth to make a jacket. If she wants to make 4 jackets for gifts, how many inches must she purchase?

## 9.3 PERIMETER

**Example 1:**   Find the perimeter of the rectangle below:

6 feet

13 feet

**Solution:**      Perimeter = 13 feet + 13 feet + 6 feet + 6 feet

= 38 feet

The perimeter of the rectangle is 38 feet.

**Example 2:**   Find the perimeter of a square with sides of length 15 centimeters.

**Solution:**      $P = 4s$

$= 4(15 \text{ cm})$        Let $s = 15$ cm

$= 60$ cm

The perimeter of the square is 60 centimeters.

**Example 3:**   Find the perimeter of a triangle if the sides are 9 meters, 12 meters, and 15 meters.

**Solution:**     $P = a + b + c$

   $= 9$ meters + 12 meters + 15 meters

   $= 36$ meters

The perimeter of the triangle is 36 meters.

**Example 4:**   Find how much lace trim is needed to border a rectangular greeting card that measures 4 inches by 7 inches.

**Solution:**     The border goes along the perimeter.
   $P = 4$ inches + 4 inches + 7 inches + 7 inches

   $= 22$ inches

It will take 22 inches of lace trim to border the card.

## 9.3 EXERCISES

*Find the perimeter of each figure.*

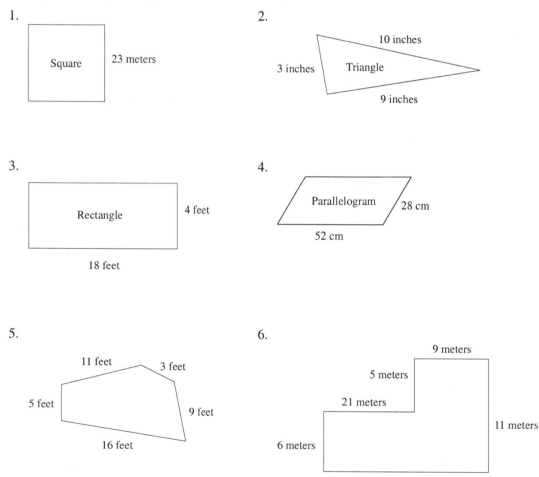

1.

Square   23 meters

2.

10 inches

3 inches   Triangle

9 inches

3.

Rectangle   4 feet

18 feet

4.

Parallelogram   28 cm

52 cm

5.

11 feet   3 feet

5 feet   9 feet

16 feet

6.

9 meters

5 meters

21 meters

6 meters   11 meters

30 meters

7. A polygon has sides of length 20 feet, 25 feet, 8 feet, 6 feet and 4 feet. Find its perimeter.

8. A triangle has sides of 20 centimeters, 30 centimeters, and 50 centimeters. Find its perimeter.

9. A square has a side of length 3 miles. Find its perimeter.

10. A rectangle has dimensions 37 yards by 29 yards. Find its perimeter.

11. A metal strip is being installed around a rectangular cabinet that is 6 feet long and 2 feet wide. Find how much stripping is needed.

12. Find how much fencing is needed to enclose a rectangular garden that measures 110 feet by 60 feet.

13. The perimeter of a rectangular field is 1200 meters. If the field is four times longer than it is wide, find the length of the field.

14. Two sides of a triangle are the same length. The third side is 33 inches. If the perimeter of a triangle is 121 inches, find the length of each equal side.

15. The width of a rectangle is 11 meters less than twice its length. If the perimeter is 38 meters, find its width.

16. Find the perimeter of a square floor tile with a side of 9 inches.

17. The base of a leg of the Gateway Arch in St. Louis is an equilateral triangle measuring 54 feet on each side. What is the perimeter of the leg's base?

18. A mountain lion may hunt in a territory with a radius of up to 25 miles. What is the perimeter of the territory?

## 9.4 AREA AND VOLUME

**Example 1:** Find the area of the triangle.

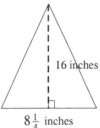

16 inches

$8\frac{1}{4}$ inches

**Solution:**
$$\text{Area} = \frac{1}{2} \cdot \text{base} \cdot \text{height} = \frac{1}{2}\left(8\frac{1}{4} \text{ in.}\right)(16 \text{ in.})$$

$$= \frac{1}{2} \cdot \frac{33}{4} \cdot 16 \text{ sq. in.}$$

$$= \frac{1 \cdot 33 \cdot 2 \cdot 2 \cdot 2 \cdot 2}{2 \cdot 2 \cdot 2 \cdot 1} \text{ sq. in.}$$

$$= 66 \text{ sq. in.}$$

**Example 2:**  Find the area of a circle with a radius of 8 centimeters. Find the exact area and an approximation. Use 3.14 as an approximation for $\pi$.

**Solution:**  $\text{Area} = \pi r^2 = \pi (8 \text{ cm})^2$

$= 64\pi \text{ cm}^2$

To approximate the area, substitute 3.14 for $\pi$.

$64 \text{ cm}^2 \approx 64(3.14) \text{ cm}^2$

$\approx 200.96 \text{ sq. cm.}$

The exact area is $64\pi \text{ cm}^2$, which is approximately 200.96 sq. cm.

**Example 3:**  How much snow is there in a snowball with radius 5 cm? Use 3.14 to approximate $\pi$.

**Solution:**  $\text{Volume} = \dfrac{4}{3}\pi r^3$

$= \dfrac{4}{3}(3.14)(5 \text{ cm})^3$

$\approx 523.33 \text{ cubic cm.}$

The snowball contains about 523.33 cubic centimeters of snow.

**Example 4:**  A box of cereal is 4 inches wide, 8 inches long, and 16 inches tall. How much cereal can the box hold?

**Solution:**  $\text{Volume} = \text{length} \cdot \text{width} \cdot \text{height}$

$= (8 \text{ in})(4 \text{ in})(16 \text{ in})$

$= 512 \text{ cubic inches}$

The box can hold 512 cubic inches of cereal.

## 9.4 EXERCISES

*Find the area of each geometric figure. If the figure is a circle, give an exact area and then give an approximate area using 3.14 for $\pi$.*

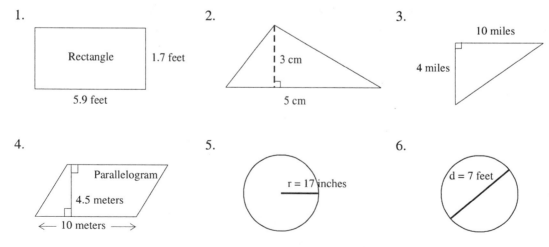

1.

Rectangle   1.7 feet

5.9 feet

2.

3 cm

5 cm

3.

10 miles

4 miles

4.

Parallelogram

4.5 meters

← 10 meters →

5.

r = 17 inches

6.

d = 7 feet

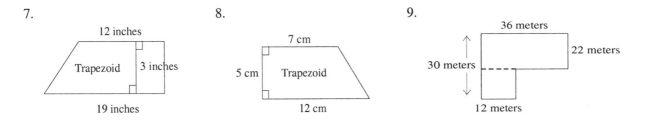

7. 12 inches / Trapezoid / 3 inches / 19 inches

8. 7 cm / 5 cm / Trapezoid / 12 cm

9. 36 meters / 22 meters / 30 meters / 12 meters

*Find the volume of the solid. Use 3.14 as an approximation for $\pi$.*

10. Rectangular box with a length of 2 inches, width of 8 inches, and height of 3 inches.

11. Sphere with radius 7.4 miles.

12. Circular cylinder with base radius 2.2 feet and height 16 feet.

13. Cone with base radius 4 meters and height 31 meters.

14. Square-based pyramid with side 4.7 inches and height 18.6 inches.

*Solve.*

15. A $12\frac{1}{4}$-foot by 40-foot concrete wall is to be built using concrete blocks. Find the area of the wall.

16. A picture frame measures 14 inches by $8\frac{1}{2}$ inches. Find how many square inches of glass the frame requires.

17. An extra-large pizza at Cecil Whittaker's measures 16 inches in diameter. How many square inches of pizza does an extra-large pizza contain? Use 3.14 as an approximation for $\pi$.

18. Find the volume of a cube with edges $2\frac{3}{4}$ inches.

19. Find the volume of a rectangular block of ice 3 feet by $1\frac{1}{2}$ feet by $\frac{1}{2}$ feet.

20. Sand from a conveyor belt forms a conical pile with a base radius of 45 feet and a height of 30 feet. How much sand is in the pile?

## 9.5 WEIGHT AND MASS

**Example 1:**   Convert 1024 ounces to pounds.

**Solution:**    $1024 \text{ oz} = 1024 \text{ oz} \cdot \dfrac{1 \text{ lb}}{16 \text{ oz}} = \dfrac{1024}{16} \text{ lb} = 64 \text{ lb}$

**Example 2:**   Multiply 4 lb 7 oz by 5.

**Solution:**
$$\begin{array}{r} 4 \text{ lb} \quad 7 \text{ oz} \\ \times \qquad\quad 5 \\ \hline 20 \text{ lb } 35 \text{ oz} \end{array}$$

$$\begin{array}{r} 2 \text{ lb 3 oz} \\ 16\overline{)35} \\ -\underline{32} \\ 3 \end{array}$$

Thus, 20 lb 35 oz = 20 lb + 2 lb 3 oz = 22 lb 3 oz.

**Example 3:**   Subtract 58 milligrams from 7.9 grams.

**Solution:**   First convert both numbers to milligrams or grams before subtracting.

58 mg = 0.058 g                    7.9 g = 7900 mg

$$\begin{array}{r} 7.900 \text{ g} \\ -\underline{0.058} \text{ g} \\ 7.842 \text{ g} \end{array} \qquad \begin{array}{r} 7900 \text{ mg} \\ -\underline{\ 58} \text{ mg} \\ 7842 \text{ mg} \end{array}$$

The difference is 7.842 g or 7842 mg.

**Example 4:**   Logan has 5 pounds of ground beef with which she plans to make meatballs. If she needs to make 40 meatballs, how many ounces of ground beef will each contain?

**Solution**:   Start by converting the pounds to ounces.

$$5 \text{ lbs} = 5 \text{ lbs} \cdot \frac{16 \text{ oz}}{1 \text{ lb}} = 80 \text{ oz}$$

$$\begin{array}{r} 2 \text{ oz} \\ 40\overline{)80} \\ -\underline{80} \\ 0 \end{array}$$

Each meatball will contain 2 ounces of ground beef.

## 9.5 EXERCISES

*Convert the following as indicated.*

1.  17 pounds to ounces

2.  6 tons to pounds

3.  11,000 pounds to tons

4.  22.25 pounds to ounces

5.  112 ounces to the nearest tenth of a pound

6.  6000 g to kilograms

7.  38 g to milligrams

8.  7.2 g to kilograms

9.  741 dg to dekagrams

10.  8025 cg to hectograms

Perform the indicated operations.

11. 13 lb 5 oz + 18 lb 14 oz

12. 1 ton 1905 lb + 5 ton 168 lb

13. 12 lb 4 oz – 2 lb 10 oz

14. 3 lb 7 oz × 9

15. 9 tons 600 lb ÷ 5

16. 89.7 g + 10.6 g

17. 7 kg – 4290 g

18. 2.9 kg × 8.6

*Solve.*

19. A Choc-o-chunk candy bar weighs 2.7 oz. How many pounds does a box of 36 of these candy bars weigh? Round to the nearest tenth.

20. Shawn is flying from New York to London and has a carry-on bag weighing 27 kg. If the weight limit for carry-on bags is 18 kg, how much weight must Shawn remove from his bag?

## 9.6 CAPACITY

**Example 1:**   Convert 17 quarts to gallons.

**Solution:**   $17 \text{ qt} = 17 \text{ qt} \cdot \dfrac{1 \text{ gal}}{4 \text{ qt}} = \dfrac{17}{4} \text{ gal} = 4\dfrac{1}{4} \text{ gal}$

**Example 2:**   Add 3 qt + 6 gal 2 qt.

**Solution:**

$$\begin{array}{r} 3 \text{ qt} \\ + \ 6 \text{ gal } 2 \text{ qt} \\ \hline 6 \text{ gai } 5 \text{ qt} \end{array}$$

= 6 gal 1 gal 1 qt

= 7 gal 1 qt

**Example 3:**   Multiply 12.4 L × 5.

**Solution:**

$$\begin{array}{r} 12.4 \text{ L} \\ \times \ \ 5 \\ \hline 62.0 \text{ L} \end{array}$$

## 9.6 EXERCISES

*Convert each measurement as indicated.*

1. 32 quarts to gallons

2. 11 quarts to pints

3. 34 cups to pints

4. 50 cups to gallons

5. $5\dfrac{3}{4}$ quarts to cups

6. $5\dfrac{7}{8}$ gallons to pints

7. 11 L to milliliters

8. 3200 ml to liters

9. 270 L to kiloliters

*Perform the indicated operations.*

10. 5 gal 3 qt + 7 gal 1 qt

11. 7 c 4 fl oz + 3 c 6 fl oz

12. 2 gal 1 pt × 5

13. 3 pt – 2pt 1 c

14. 20.2 L + 14.6 L

15. 7920 ml – 0.2 L

16. 7.2 L ÷ 0.9

17. 125 ml × 7

*Solve.*

18. A recipe calls for $2\frac{1}{4}$ cups of milk. How many fluid ounces is this?

19. Shawn wants to divide a 1-L bottle of juice equally between his 4 friends. How much will each friend get?

20. Shawn has 3 gallons of milk and Payton has 3 quarts of coffee. If Shawn and Payton combine the milk and coffee, how many cups of coffee milk will they have?

## 9.7 CONVERSIONS BETWEEN THE METRIC AND U.S. SYSTEMS

**Example 1:** Convert 2 gal to milliliters. Round to two decimal places.

**Solution:** $2 \text{ gal} \approx 2 \text{ gal} \cdot \dfrac{1 \text{ L}}{0.26 \text{ gal}} \cdot \dfrac{1000 \text{ ml}}{1 \text{ L}} = \dfrac{2000}{0.26} \text{ ml} \approx 7692.31 \text{ ml}$

**Example 2:** A football field measures 100 yards (not including the end zones). How many meters is this? Round to two decimal places.

**Solution:** $100 \text{ yds} \approx 100 \text{ yds} \cdot \dfrac{1 \text{ m}}{1.09 \text{ yd}} = \dfrac{100}{1.09} \text{ m} \approx 91.74 \text{ m}$

A football field is about 91.74 meters long.

**Example 3:** The heaviest pumpkin on record weighed in at 1385 pounds on October 4, 2003 in Pleasant Hill, Oregon. How many kilograms did the pumpkin weigh?

**Solution:** $1385 \text{ lbs} \approx 1385 \text{ lbs} \cdot \dfrac{0.45 \text{ kg}}{1 \text{ lb}} = 623.25 \text{ kg}$

The record setting pumpkin weighed 623.25 kilograms.

## 9.7 EXERCISES

*Convert each of the following as indicated. Round to two decimal places, if necessary.*

1. 400 m to feet

2. 3 mi to kilometers

3. 50 kg to lbs

4. 1.5 L to fl oz

5. 6 gal to L

6. 27 in. to cm

7. 16 fl oz to ml

8. 75 cm to yards

9. 10 km to miles

10. 2 tons to kilograms

11. 8 oz to mg

12. 2100 ml to gallons

*Solve. Round to two decimal places, if necessary.*

13. How many liters of water can be carried in a 5 gallon bucket?

14. The minimum length of a soccer field for international matches is 100 meters. How many yards is this?

15. A bottle of laundry detergent contains 200 fluid ounces. How many liters of detergent are in the bottle?

16. A recipe calls for 1 pound of butter. How many grams of butter are needed?

17. A standard sheet of typing paper is 11 inches long. How many centimeters is this?

18. Suppose the weight limit for checked baggage at an airport is 40 kg per bag. How many pounds can each bag weigh?

19. The distance from St. Louis to Chicago is about 310 miles. How many kilometers is this?

20. Nathan has a pencil that is 15 cm long. How many inches is this?

## 9.8 TEMPERATURE

**Example 1:** Convert $25°C$ to degrees Fahrenheit.

**Solution:**     $F = \dfrac{9C}{5} + 32 = \dfrac{9 \cdot 25}{5} + 32 = 45 + 32 = 77$

Thus, $25°C$ is equivalent to $77°F$.

**Example 2:** Convert $122°F$ to degrees Celsius. If necessary, round to the nearest tenth of a degree.

**Solution:**     $C = \dfrac{5(F-32)}{9} = \dfrac{5(122-32)}{9} = \dfrac{5(90)}{9} = 50$

Thus, $122°F$ is equivalent to $50°C$.

## 9.8 EXERCISES

*Convert the following as indicated. When necessary, round to the nearest tenth of a degree.*

1. $105°C$ to degrees Fahrenheit
2. $30°C$ to degrees Fahrenheit
3. $97°F$ to degrees Celsius
4. $77°F$ to degrees Celsius
5. $60°C$ to degrees Fahrenheit
6. $58°F$ to degrees Celsius
7. $81°F$ to degrees Celsius
8. $80°C$ to degrees Fahrenheit
9. $12.8°C$ to degrees Fahrenheit
10. $121.7°F$ to degrees Celsius

*Solve.*

11. Abby noticed that her outdoor thermometer was registering a temperature of $92°F$. Convert this measurement to degrees Celsius.

12. Dan's office is normally kept at a temperature of $70°F$. Convert this measurement to degrees Celsius.

13. A weather forecast in Alberta predicts a high temperature of $14°C$. Find the measurement in degrees Fahrenheit.

14. The sign at a bank indicates that the current temperature is $12°C$. Convert this measurement to degrees Fahrenheit.

15. To be safe, hamburger should generally be cooked until the center has a temperature of $160°F$. Convert this measurement to degrees Celsius.

16. Dippin' Dots, Ice Cream of the Future®, is kept at a temperature of about $-45°F$. What is the corresponding temperature in degrees Celsius?

**CHAPTER 9 PRACTICE TEST**

1. Find the complement and supplement of a 41° angle.

2. Find the measures of angles $x$, $y$, and $z$.

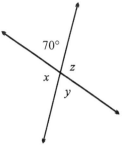

3. Find the measure of angle $\angle x$.

     (see figure: right triangle with angle $x$ at top, right angle at bottom left, 48° at bottom right)

4. Find the perimeter of a rectangle with width 19 feet and length 30 feet.

5. Shawn runs a 15 km race as part of a fundraiser for his school. How many miles is the race?

6. Find the area of a rectangle with length 11 inches and width 4.5 inches.

7. Find the volume of a cube with edges $5\frac{1}{3}$ meters.

8. How much potting soil is needed to fill a flower box that is 3 feet by $1\frac{1}{2}$ feet by $\frac{1}{2}$ foot?

*Convert as indicated.*

9. 95 in. to feet and inches.

10. 26 qt to gallons

11. 52 in. to cm

12. 4.6 tons to pounds

13. 36 pt to gallons

14. 62 mg to grams

15. 4.8 kg to grams

16. 7.2 cm to millimeters

17. 7.1 gal to L

18. 0.075 L to milliliters

*Perform the indicated operation.*

19. 7 qt 1 pt + 8 qt 1 pt

20. 10 lb 5 oz – 3 lb 7 oz

21. 5 ft 7 in × 3

22. 8 gal 1 qt ÷ 3

23. 12 cm – 18 mm

24. 2.4 km + 329 m

*Convert. Round to the nearest tenth of a degree, if necessary.*

25. Convert 63°F to degrees Celsius.

26. Convert 10.8°C to Fahrenheit.

## CHAPTER 9 HELPFUL HINTS AND INSIGHTS

- A millimeter is about the thickness of a large paper clip wire.
  A centimeter is about the width of a large paper clip.
  A meter is slightly longer than a yard.
  A kilometer is about two-thirds of a mile.

- A kilogram is slightly over 2 pounds.
  A larger paper clip weighs approximately 1 gram.

- A liter of liquid is slightly more than one quart.

- Area is almost always measured in square units. An acre is a measure of area that does not have square units.

- Volumes of solids are measured in cubic units.
  Volumes of liquids are generally not measured in cubic units.
  One cc (cubic centimeter) is equivalent to 1 ml (milliliter).

- When finding the area, perimeter, volume, etc. of figures, be sure all measures are changed to the same units before making any calculations.

## 10.1 ADDING AND SUBTRACTING POLYNOMIALS

**Example 1:** Add: $(6x+7)+(-8x+4)$

**Solution:** $(6x+7)+(-8x+4)=(6x-8x)+(7+4)$
$$=-2x+11$$

**Example 2:** Subtract $(5y^2-3y+11)$ from $(7y^2-6)$.

**Solution:** $(7y^2-6)-(5y^2-3y+11)=(7y^2-6)+(-5y^2+3y-11)$
$$=7y^2-5y^2+3y-6-11$$
$$=2y^2+3y-17$$

**Example 3:** Find the value of $-4z^2-z+16$ for $z=-3$.

**Solution:** Replace $z$ with –3 and simplify.
$$-4z^2-z+16=-4(-3)^2-(-3)+16$$
$$=-4(9)+3+16$$
$$=-36+3+16$$
$$=-17$$

## 10.1 EXERCISES

*Add of subtract the polynomials as indicated.*

1. $(5t-3)+(-9t+21)$

2. $(18y+6)+(10y-22)$

3. $(2x+8)+(6x^2-7x+3)$

4. $(30x+5)-(25x-2)$

5. $(-13a^2+6a-3)-(-5a+12)$

6. $(10y^3+15y^2-y-2)-(8y^3+6y-12)$

7. $(5.6b^3+15)+(-8.1b^2-4.9b+12.1)$

8. Subtract $(16t-7)$ from $(-9t-7)$.

9. Subtract $(4x^2-9x+17)$ from $(17x^2+4x-10)$.

10. Subtract $\left(4x^2-\dfrac{3}{8}x\right)$ from $\left(-3x^2+\dfrac{5}{8}x\right)$.

*Find the value of each polynomial for $x=3$.*

11. $-11x-6$

12. $4x+13$

13. $x^2-4x+8$

14. $-x^2-x-1$

15. $\dfrac{8x^2}{6}-12$

16. $\dfrac{x^3}{9}-x-11$

*Find the value of each polynomial for $x=-4$.*

17. $6x+5$

18. $x^2$

19. $2x^3$

20. $x^3-x^2+x+1$

## 10.2 MULTIPLICATION PROPERTIES OF EXPONENTS

**Example 1:**   Multiply: $x^6 \cdot x^9$

**Solution:**     $x^6 \cdot x^9 = x^{6+9} = x^{15}$

**Example 2:**   Multiply: $\left(-3p^4q\right)\left(-8p^2q^9\right)$

**Solution:**     $\left(-3p^4q\right)\left(-8p^2q^9\right) = (-3)(-8)\left(p^4 \cdot p^2\right)\left(q^1 \cdot q^9\right)$
$$= 24p^{4+2}q^{1+9}$$
$$= 24p^6q^{10}$$

**Example 3:**   Simplify: $\left(m^6\right)^5$

**Solution:**     $\left(m^6\right)^5 = m^{6\cdot5} = m^{30}$

**Example 4:**   Simplify: $\left(-3x^4y^9\right)^2\left(5x^2y^5\right)^4$

**Solution:**     $\left(-3x^4y^9\right)^2\left(5x^2y^5\right)^4 = (-3)^2\left(x^4\right)^2\left(y^9\right)^2(5)^4\left(x^2\right)^4\left(y^5\right)^4$
$$= 9x^8y^{18} \cdot 625x^8y^{20}$$
$$= (9 \cdot 625)\left(x^8 \cdot x^8\right)\left(y^{18} \cdot y^{20}\right)$$
$$= 5625x^{16}y^{38}$$

## 10.2 EXERCISES

*Multiply and simplify.*

1.  $x^4 \cdot x^9$

2.  $a^{15} \cdot a$

3.  $2y^3 \cdot 6y^4$

4.  $-6x \cdot 13x$

5.  $\left(-10a^2b\right)\left(-2a^6b^5\right)$

6.  $\left(-x^4yz^7\right)\left(-4x^3y^3z^5\right)$

7.  $2x \cdot 6x \cdot x^2$

8.  $4t \cdot 8t^{12} \cdot 7t^6$

9.  $\left(x^{10}\right)^9$

10.  $\left(n^{12}\right)^7$

11.  $(2m)^4$

12.  $\left(r^4\right)^5 \cdot \left(r^3\right)^2$

13.  $\left(x^3y^8\right)^7$

14.  $\left(7w^4z^{13}\right)^3$

15.  $(-4z)\left(2z^9\right)^4$

16.  $\left(3x^2y^3\right)^5\left(2x^4y^2\right)^3$

17.  $\left(14y^{12}z^8\right)^2$

18.  $\left(6a^5b^7\right)^4\left(2a^{13}b\right)^5$

*Find the area of each figure.*

19.    square        $3x^5$ feet

20.    $7y^5$ meters        rectangle    $8y^2$ meters

## 10.3 MULTIPLYING POLYNOMIALS

**Example 1:** Multiply: $6x\left(5x^2 + 9\right)$

**Solution:** $6x\left(5x^2 + 9\right) = 6x \cdot 5x^2 + 6x \cdot 9$      Apply the distributive property.

$$= 30x^3 + 54x$$

**Example 2:** Multiply: $(x+8)(x+12)$

**Solution:**
$$(x+8)(x+12) = x(x+12) + 8(x+12)$$
Apply the distributive property.
$$= x \cdot x + x \cdot 12 + 8 \cdot x + 8 \cdot 12$$
Apply the distributive property.
$$= x^2 + 12x + 8x + 96$$
Multiply.
$$= x^2 + 20x + 96$$
Combine like terms

**Example 3:** Multiply: $(3m-5)^2$

**Solution:**
$$(3m-5)^2 = (3m-5)(3m-5)$$
Apply the definition of an exponent.
$$= 3m(3m-5) - 5(3m-5)$$
Apply the distributive property.
$$= 3m \cdot 3m + 3m \cdot (-5) - 5 \cdot 3m - 5 \cdot (-5)$$
Apply the distributive property.
$$= 9m^2 - 15m - 15m + 25$$
Multiply.
$$= 9m^2 - 30m + 25$$
Combine like terms

**Example 4:** Multiply: $(3a-7)\left(a^2 + 5a - 3\right)$

**Solution:**
$$(3a-7)\left(a^2 + 5a - 3\right)$$
$$= 3a\left(a^2 + 5a - 3\right) - 7\left(a^2 + 5a - 3\right)$$
Apply the distributive property.
$$= 3a \cdot a^2 + 3a \cdot 5a + 3a \cdot (-3) - 7 \cdot a^2 - 7 \cdot 5a - 7 \cdot (-3)$$
Apply the distributive property.
$$= 3a^3 + 15a^2 - 9a - 7a^2 - 35a + 21$$
Multiply.
$$= 3a^3 + 8a^2 - 44a + 21$$
Combine like terms

## 10.3 EXERCISES

*Multiply.*

1. $5x\left(9x^2 + 11\right)$      2. $3y\left(9y^4 - y\right)$      3. $-7m\left(4m^2 - m - 6\right)$

4. $8t^3\left(-2t^2 + t + 6\right)$      5. $(p-5)(p-8)$      6. $(y+10)(y+1)$

7. $(t-7)(t+7)$      8. $(3x+5)(x-11)$      9. $(3m+8)(3m+4)$

10. $(4y-5)^2$      11. $(4x+9)^2$      12. $\left(z+\dfrac{1}{4}\right)\left(z-\dfrac{3}{4}\right)$

13. $(5a+11)(5a-11)$      14. $(x+7)^2$      15. $(n-8)\left(4n^2 + 3n + 14\right)$

16. $(x+5)(x^2-5x+25)$            17. $(b^2+3)(4b^2-b+6)$            18. $(x^2+2x+3)(x^3-x^2+4)$

*Find the area of each figure.*

19.

square        $(6x+13)$ meters

20.

rectangle        $(y+5)$ inches

$(y^2+3y+7)$ inches

## 10.4 INTRODUCTION TO FACTORING POLYNOMIALS

**Example 1:**  Find the GCF of $8x^4$, $12x^2$, and $36x^3$.

**Solution:**  The GCF of 8, 12, and 36, is 4.
The GCF of $x^4$, $x^2$, and $x^3$ is $x^2$.
Thus, the GCF of $8x^4$, $12x^2$, and $36x^3$ is $4x^2$.

**Example 2:**  Factor: $7x^2+35x-56$.

**Solution:**  The GCF of the terms is 7.
$$7x^2+35x-56 = 7\cdot x^2 + 7\cdot 5x - 7\cdot 8$$
$$= 7(x^2+5x-8)$$

**Example 3:**  Factor: $-8m+10n+12$.

**Solution:**  The GCF of the terms is 2 (or –2).
$$-8m+10n+12 = 2\cdot(-4m)+2\cdot 5n+2\cdot 6$$
$$= 2(-4m+5n+6)$$

or

$$-8m+10n+12 = -2\cdot 4m+(-2)\cdot(-5n)+(-2)\cdot(-6)$$
$$= -2(4m-5n-6)$$

## 10.4 EXERCISES

*Find the GCF of each list of terms.*

1.  75 and 90

2.  72 and 180

3.  $x^9$, $x^4$, $x^7$

4.  $4y^3$, $6y^2$, $8y$

5.  $a^2b^3$, $a^3b^2$, $ab^2$

6.  $14yz$, $21y^2z$, $35y^3z^2$

7.  $24a^5b^7$, $18a^6b^4$, $42a^3b^6$

8.  $9x^2y^5z^3$, $15x^3y^2z^4$, $12x^5y^4z^2$

*Factor.*

9. $4x^3 + 8x^2$

10. $16y^2 - 40y^4$

11. $20z^4 + 10z^2$

12. $20m^2 - 15m^4$

13. $b^{12} - 2b^8$

14. $m^9 + 7m^5$

15. $13x^6 - 26x^4 + 39x^2$

16. $12y^6 - 8y^4 + 16y^3$

17. $3a^4 - 6b^2 + 9$

18. $26m^5 + 13m^4 - 39m^2$

19. $20b^{12} - 30b^8 + 50b^6$

20. $x^2y^3 + 5x^3y^4 + 7x^2y^5$

## CHAPTER 10 PRACTICE TEST

*Add or subtract as indicated.*

1. $(13x - 12) + (4x + 7)$

2. $(15x - 7) - (2x + 8)$

3. $(6.1y^2 + 8) + (2.3y^2 - 6.1y - 13.4)$

4. Subtract $(6b^2 - 5)$ from $(4b^2 - 4b - 1)$.

5. Find the value of $x^2 + 5x - 3$ when $x = -4$.

6. Find the value of $m^3 - 4m^2 + 9$ when $m = 3$.

*Multiply and simplify.*

7. $y^6 \cdot y^8$

8. $\left(m^9\right)^7$

9. $\left(3x^6\right)^3$

10. $\left(-12a^4\right)\left(-3a^{12}\right)$

11. $\left(b^{12}\right)^5\left(b^2\right)^3$

12. $\left(3x^4y\right)^3\left(4x^2y^2\right)^2$

13. $6x\left(9x^3 - 2.6\right)$

14. $-7m\left(m^4 - 11m^3 + 4\right)$

15. $(x - 6)(x - 7)$

16. $(6x + 7)^2$

17. $(y - 7)\left(y^2 + 7y + 49\right)$

18. $(4x - 9)(4x + 9)$

19. Find the area and the perimeter of a rectangle with length $(5x + 3)$ feet and width $6x$ feet.

*Find the greatest common factor of the list of terms.*

20. 75 and 90

21. $8x^7$, $20x^5$, $24x^{12}$

*Factor.*

22. $7x^2 - 35$

23. $y^9 - 7y^5$

24. $3x^2 - 6x + 30$

25. A rock is dropped from the top of a 400-foot cliff. The height of the rock at time $t$ seconds is given by the polynomial $-16t^2 + 400$. Find the height of the rock when $t = 3$ seconds.

## CHAPTER 10 HELPFUL HINTS AND INSIGHTS

- To find the opposite of a polynomial, change the signs of all the terms of the polynomial.

- Make sure you understand when to use the product property and when to use the power of a power property.

$$x^3 \cdot x^8 = x^{3+8} = x^{11} \qquad \text{product property}$$

$$\left(x^4\right)^9 = x^{4 \cdot 9} = x^{36} \qquad \text{power of a power property}$$

**PRACTICE FINAL EXAMINATION A**

*Evaluate.*

1. $62 + 57$
2. $894 - 638$
3. $127(13)$

4. $4508 \div 49$
5. $\left(3^2 - 4\right) \cdot 8$
6. $31 + 48 \div 4 \cdot 2 - 10$

7. Round 2,137,546 to the nearest thousand.

8. Evaluate $5\left(x^3 - 7\right)$ for $x = 3$.

9. Twenty-six cans of varnish cost \$312. What is the cost of each can?

*Simplify each expression.*

10. $19 - 53$
11. $-22 + 17$
12. $(-5)(-71)$

13. $\dfrac{-57}{3}$
14. $(-6)^2 - 30 \div (-5)$
15. $\dfrac{|39 - 57|}{6}$

16. $\dfrac{7(-12) + 16}{-2(9 - 26)}$
17. $\dfrac{25}{-5} - \dfrac{4^3}{8}$

18. Evaluate $4x - y$ for $x = -6$ and $y = -7$.

19. $|x - y| + |x|$ for $x = -8$ and $y = 10$.

20. Simplify $8x - 14 - 15x + 29$ by combining like terms.

21. Multiply: $-10(2x + 9)$

22. Find the perimeter of a square with a side length of 29 feet.

*Solve each equation.*

23. $8x + x = 81$
24. $24 = 5x - 17x$
25. $19x + 12 - 18x - 30 = 20$

26. $7(x - 3) = 0$
27. $10 + 6(2y - 1) = 28$
28. $6(5x - 7) = 8(4x + 1)$

*Solve.*

29. The sum of three times a number and seven times the same number is ninety. Find the number.

30 Find the length of the side of a square porch with a 152-foot perimeter.

*Perform the indicated operations and write the answers in lowest terms.*

31. $\dfrac{4}{5} \cdot \dfrac{35}{8}$
32. $\dfrac{6x}{7} - \dfrac{4x}{7}$
33. $\dfrac{xy^3}{z^2} \cdot \dfrac{z^3}{x^4 y}$

34. $\dfrac{6y}{17} + \dfrac{5}{34}$

35. $4\dfrac{1}{5} \div \dfrac{7}{25}$

36. $5\dfrac{2}{3} + 4\dfrac{1}{6} + 8\dfrac{7}{9}$

37. $18 \div 3\dfrac{4}{9}$

38. $40y^2 \div \dfrac{y}{8}$

39. $-\dfrac{8}{7} \div \dfrac{64}{21}$

40. $\left(\dfrac{16}{7} \cdot \dfrac{42}{8}\right) \div 8$

41. Simplify: $\dfrac{6 + \dfrac{3}{5}}{4 - \dfrac{7}{10}}$

*Solve.*

42. $\dfrac{x}{4} + x = -\dfrac{15}{8}$

43. $\dfrac{5}{9} + \dfrac{x}{6} = \dfrac{2}{3} - \dfrac{x}{12}$

44. Evaluate $xy$ for $x = 3\dfrac{3}{4}$ and $y = 2\dfrac{2}{9}$.

*Perform the indicated operation. Round the result to the nearest thousandth if necessary.*

45. $11.654 + 3.71 + 9.827$

46. $-48.7 - 8.36$

47. $(14.6)(3.25)$

48. $(-1.4)^2 + 3.9$

49. $\dfrac{0.11 - 3.75}{0.2}$

50. Round 1358.6359 to the nearest hundredth.

51. Write 0.72 as a fraction in simplest form.

52. Write $\dfrac{15}{400}$ as a decimal.

53. Simplify: $-2\sqrt{36} + \sqrt{25}$

54. Find the volume of a cube with edges $3\dfrac{5}{8}$ centimeters.

55. Find the area of a rectangle with length 9 feet and width 2.7 feet.

*Complete and graph the ordered-pair solutions of the given equation.*

56. $4x + 3y = 24$ ; $(0, \quad)$, $(\quad, 0)$, $(\quad, 4)$

57. $y = 5x + 1$; $(0, \quad)$, $(1, \quad)$, $(\quad, -4)$

*Graph each linear equation.*

58. $x + y = 6$

59. $x - 5 = 0$

60. $y + 6 = 0$

61. $4x - 5y = 20$

62. Find the mean of the following list of numbers:  57, 42, 69, 74, 47, 56, 61

63. Find the median of the following list of numbers:  75, 16, 83, 92, 47, 16, 21, 28, 37

64. Find the mode of the following list of numbers:  35, 20, 94, 85, 20, 84, 21, 20, 35, 34, 49

65. Find the grade point average.  If necessary, round to the nearest hundredth.

| Grade | Credit Hours |
|-------|--------------|
| A | 3 |
| A | 4 |
| B | 5 |
| C | 3 |

66. Write the ratio as a fraction in simplest form: 270 bushes to 432 bushes.

67. Write 972 miles in 18 hours as a unit rate.

*Solve the proportion for the variable.*

68. $\dfrac{18}{x} = \dfrac{135}{210}$

69. $\dfrac{\frac{9}{5}}{\frac{3}{4}} = \dfrac{x}{25}$  $18$

*Convert as indicated.*

70. 630 inches to feet and inches

71. $7\dfrac{1}{2}$ gallons to quarts

72. 38 grams to milligrams

73. 5700 milliliters to liters

74. $77°F$ to degrees Celsius

*Perform the indicated operations.*

75. 12 lb 6 oz + 10 lb 14 oz

76. 3.4 km + 346 m

77. 9 cm − 15 mm

78. Write 0.0037 as a percent.

79. Write 32.8% as a decimal.

80. Write $\dfrac{3}{40}$ as a percent.

81. What is 68% of 900?

82. 203 is 35% of what number?

83. 40.32 is what percent of 96?

84. A birdfeed mixture is 24% sunflower seeds.  How many pounds of sunflower seeds are contained in 350 pounds of this mixture?

85. If the local sales tax rate is 6.5%, find the total amount charged for a VCR priced at $375.

86. $8300 is compounded quarterly at 8%.  Find the total amount in the account after 5 years.

87. Dolores is paid a commission rate of 2.6% of her sales.  Find her commission for a week in which her sales were $18,700.

*Add or subtract as indicated.*

88. $(10y+3)+(-8y+15)$          89. $(12x-5)-(x-1)$

90. Find the value of $x^2-x+10$ when $x=-4$.

*Multiply and simplify.*

91. $y^{15}\cdot y^{16}$      92. $\left(x^6\right)^8$      93. $\left(a^3\right)^5\left(a^{10}\right)^6$

94. $-4y\left(y^2-5y+7\right)$      95. $(x+11)(x-9)$      96. $(3x+7)^2$

97. $(b-8)\left(b^2+8b+64\right)$

98. Find the greatest common factor of $16x^5$, $24x^3$, and $32x^7$.

*Factor.*

99. $8x^3-64x^5$          100. $15y^2-20y$

**PRACTICE FINAL EXAMINATION B**

*Evaluate.*

1. $57 + 98$

2. $732 - 468$

3. $315(17)$

4. $5915 \div 65$

5. $\left(2^4 - 9\right) \cdot 8$

6. $13 + 18 \div 9 \cdot 5 - 10$

7. Round 837,951 to the nearest thousand.

8. Evaluate $9\left(x^2 - 12\right)$ for $x = 7$.

9. Eighteen cases of soda cost $86.22. What is the cost of each case?

*Simplify each expression.*

10. $21 - 58$

11. $-43 + 17$

12. $(-10)(8)$

13. $\dfrac{-68}{-4}$

14. $(-9)^2 - 35 \div (-5)$

15. $\dfrac{|8 - 60|}{-13}$

16. $\dfrac{4(-12) + 8}{-1(-2 - 6)}$

17. $\dfrac{42}{-7} - \dfrac{2^3}{4}$

18. Evaluate $5x - y$ for $x = -9$ and $y = -4$.

19. $|x + y| - |y|$ for $x = -3$ and $y = 10$.

20. Simplify $14x + 21 - 8x - 49$ by combining like terms.

21. Multiply: $-12(3x + 8)$

22. Find the perimeter of a square with a side length of 19 feet.

*Solve each equation.*

23. $15x - 4x = 33$

24. $32 = 7x - 15x$

25. $17x + 41 - 15x + 5 = 14$

26. $6(x - 8) = 0$

27. $7 + 5(5y - 3) = 42$

28. $8(2x - 6) = 4(3x + 5)$

*Solve.*

29. The sum of six times a number and nine times the same number is sixty. Find the number.

30 Find the length of the side of a square porch with a 84-foot perimeter.

*Perform the indicated operations and write the answers in lowest terms.*

31. $\dfrac{5}{6} \cdot \dfrac{27}{45}$

32. $\dfrac{7x}{5} - \dfrac{2x}{5}$

33. $\dfrac{xy^3}{z^2} \cdot \dfrac{z}{x^3 y}$

34. $\dfrac{5y}{13} + \dfrac{7}{52}$

35. $3\dfrac{3}{8} \div \dfrac{6}{7}$

36. $7\dfrac{1}{2} + 4\dfrac{3}{8} + 9\dfrac{5}{6}$

37. $24 \div 6\dfrac{3}{7}$

38. $10y^3 \div \dfrac{y}{4}$

39. $-\dfrac{5}{9} \div \left(-\dfrac{20}{27}\right)$

40. $4 \div \left(\dfrac{2}{3} \cdot \dfrac{9}{16}\right)$

41. Simplify: $\dfrac{\dfrac{1}{4} + \dfrac{5}{6}}{\dfrac{7}{8} - \dfrac{2}{3}}$

*Solve.*

42. $\dfrac{x}{6} + x = -\dfrac{5}{12}$

43. $\dfrac{5}{6} + \dfrac{x}{12} = \dfrac{1}{3} - \dfrac{x}{2}$

44. Evaluate $\dfrac{x}{y}$ for $x = -\dfrac{3}{7}$ and $y = 1\dfrac{1}{9}$.

*Perform the indicated operation. Round the result to the nearest thousandth if necessary.*

45. $6.91 + 3.805 + 2.8$

46. $-18.6 - 31.5$

47. $(3.4)(10.46)$

48. $(-2.3)^2 + 4.1$

49. $\dfrac{0.9 - 2.58}{-0.3}$

50. Round 29.0572 to the nearest thousandth.

51. Write 0.86 as a fraction in simplest form.

52. Write $\dfrac{107}{500}$ as a decimal.

53. Simplify: $-4\sqrt{121} - \sqrt{64}$

54. Find the volume of a cube with edges $1\dfrac{3}{7}$ inches.

55. Find the area of a rectangle with length 5.6 feet and width 2.5 feet.

*Complete and graph the ordered-pair solutions of the given equation.*

56. $4x - 7y = 28$; $(0, \ )$, $(\ , 0)$, $(-1, \ )$

57. $y = 3x - 5$; $(0, \ )$, $(\ , 0)$, $(2, \ )$

*Graph each linear equation.*

58. $x + 2y = 4$

59. $x - 3 = 0$

60. $2y - 3 = 0$

61. $4x + 5y = 20$

62. Find the mean of the following list of numbers: 108, 112, 137, 142, 98, 156, 110, 118

63. Find the median of the following list of numbers: 10, 59, 57, 30, 12, 14, 78, 55, 47, 34, 15, 23

64. Find the mode of the following list of numbers: 37, 10, 91, 52, 10, 37, 52, 28, 51, 29, 10, 52, 49, 52

65. Find the grade point average. If necessary, round to the nearest hundredth.

| Grade | Credit Hours |
|-------|--------------|
| B | 3 |
| A | 3 |
| C | 4 |
| B | 5 |

66. Write the ratio as a fraction in simplest form: 62 marbles to 248 marbles.

67. Write 624 miles in 24 gallons as a unit rate.

*Solve the proportion for the variable.*

68. $\dfrac{9}{60} = \dfrac{x}{20}$

69. $\dfrac{4.8}{x} = \dfrac{30}{115}$

*Convert as indicated.*

70. 1092 inches to feet

71. 78 quarts to gallons

72. 12,000 milligrams to grams

73. 13 liters to milliliters

74. $20°C$ to degrees Fahrenheit

*Perform the indicated operations.*

75. 10 ft 6 in $-$ 4 ft 9 in

76. 3.8 kg + 160 g

77. $(9 \text{ lb } 3 \text{ oz}) \times 6$

78. Write 0.126 as a percent.

79. Write 0.37% as a decimal.

80. Write $\dfrac{6}{75}$ as a percent.

81. What is 4.2% 0f 950?

82. 172.2 is what percent of 820?

83. 39.8 is 40% of what number?

84. Find the simple interest earned on $1600 saved for 2½ years at an interest rate of 8.75%.

85. $8500 is borrowed for 5 years. If the interest on the loan is $1275, find the monthly payment.

86. Suzanna is paid a commission of 4.5% of her sales. Find her commission for a week in which her sales were $283,000.

*Add or subtract as indicated.*

87. $\left(6x^2 - 8x + 5\right) + \left(3x^2 - 4x - 9\right)$

88. $\left(9x^3 - x + 5\right) - \left(4x^2 - 7x + 6\right)$

89. Find the value of $3x^2 - 2x + 7$ when $x = 2$.

*Multiply and simplify.*

90. $y^{16} \cdot y^{21}$

91. $\left(m^5\right)^{13}$

92. $\left(b^7\right)^3 \left(b^3\right)^7$

93. $6x\left(x^2 - 5x - 12\right)$

94. $(x+8)(x+3)$

95. $(x-5)(x+5)$

96. $(3y-1)^2$

97. $(b-6)\left(b^2 + 6b + 36\right)$

98. Find the greatest common factor of $21y^5$, $49y^4$, and $98y^{10}$.

*Factor.*

99. $12x^5 - 36x^3$

100. $10a^4 - 30a^3 - 20a^2$

## 1.1 SOLUTIONS TO EXERCISES

1. instructor

2. positive

3. phone numbers

4. all

5. front

6. homework

7. correct

8. learn

9. patient

10. help

11. organize

12. before

13. write down

14. ask questions

15. on time

16. directions

17. answer

18. pace

19. work; answers

20. early

## 1.2 SOLUTIONS TO EXERCISES

1. 32<u>6</u>7  hundreds place

2. 7<u>6</u>9,532  ten-thousands place

3. 1<u>6</u>,005,278,129  billions place

4. <u>6</u>72,958,010  hundred-millions place

5. nine thousand, three hundred seventy-one

6. eighty thousand, twenty-nine

7. one hundred forty-eight, five hundred fifty-two

8. eight thousand, seventy

9. 6,078

10. 15,631,890

11. 80,702

12. 7,000,004,021

13. $800 + 90 + 1$

14. $70,000 + 8000 + 90 + 4$

15. $80,000,000 + 2,000,000 + 300,000 + 40,000 + 8000 + 900 + 70 + 5$

16. $8,000,000,000 + 2,000,000 + 500,000 + 7000 + 400 + 6$

17. $8 < 14$

18. $240 > 204$

19. $121 > 97$

20. $1268 < 1286$

## 1.3 SOLUTIONS TO EXERCISES

1.
$$\begin{array}{r} \overset{1}{2}3 \\ +48 \\ \hline 71 \end{array}$$

2.
$$\begin{array}{r} \overset{1}{7}6 \\ +89 \\ \hline 165 \end{array}$$

3.
$$\begin{array}{r} \overset{1}{5}27 \\ +917 \\ \hline 1444 \end{array}$$

4.
$$\begin{array}{r} \overset{1}{3}7 \\ +49 \\ \hline 86 \end{array}$$

5.
$$\begin{array}{r} {\scriptstyle 1} \\ 354 \\ +538 \\ \hline 892 \end{array}$$

6.
$$\begin{array}{r} {\scriptstyle 1\ 1} \\ 1485 \\ +\ 347 \\ \hline 1832 \end{array}$$

7.
$$\begin{array}{r} {\scriptstyle 1} \\ 4238 \\ +\ 427 \\ \hline 4665 \end{array}$$

8.
$$\begin{array}{r} {\scriptstyle 1\ 1} \\ 3472 \\ +2541 \\ \hline 6013 \end{array}$$

9.
$$\begin{array}{r} {\scriptstyle 1} \\ 27 \\ 60 \\ +58 \\ \hline 145 \end{array}$$

10.
$$\begin{array}{r} {\scriptstyle 1} \\ 51,243 \\ +32,548 \\ \hline 83,791 \end{array}$$

11.
$$\begin{array}{r} {\scriptstyle 1\ 1\ 1} \\ 43 \\ 632 \\ +2726 \\ \hline 3401 \end{array}$$

12.
$$\begin{array}{r} {\scriptstyle 1\ 1} \\ 3074 \\ 305 \\ +2043 \\ \hline 5422 \end{array}$$

13. Use the commutative and associative properties of addition to reorder and regroup the addends in such a way as to obtain sums of 10, 20, 30, etc.
$$\begin{aligned} 12+15+8 &= 12+8+15 \\ &= (12+8)+15 \\ &= 20+15 \\ &= 35 \end{aligned}$$

14. Use the commutative and associative properties of addition to reorder and regroup the addends in such a way as to obtain sums of 10, 20, 30, etc.
$$\begin{aligned} &16+23+12+17+8 \\ &=16+23+17+12+8 \\ &=16+(23+17)+(12+8) \\ &=16+40+20 \\ &=76 \end{aligned}$$

15. Add the lengths of the four sides:
    4 in. + 11 in. + 12 in. + 11 in. = 38 in.

16. Add the lengths of the four sides:
    8 feet + 5 feet + 8 feet + 5 feet = 26 feet

17. Add the numbers of acres for the two parcels:
    537 acres + 264 acres = 801 acres total

18. Add the numbers of tickets sold by the three attendants:
    378 tickets + 543 tickets + 488 tickets = 1419 tickets altogether

19. Add up the three prices:
    $89 + $16 + $24 = $129 total

20. Add Benjamin's and Ethan's money together: $32 + $29 = $61.
    Since $61 > $59, the brothers do have enough money to buy the game.

**1.4 SOLUTIONS TO EXERCISES**

1.
$$\begin{array}{r} 67 \\ -52 \\ \hline 15 \end{array} \qquad \begin{array}{r} Check: \\ 15 \\ +52 \\ \hline 67 \end{array}$$

2.
$$\begin{array}{r} 86 \\ -56 \\ \hline 30 \end{array} \qquad \begin{array}{r} Check: \\ 30 \\ +56 \\ \hline 86 \end{array}$$

3.
$$\begin{array}{r} 947 \\ -532 \\ \hline 415 \end{array} \qquad \begin{array}{r} Check: \\ 415 \\ +532 \\ \hline 947 \end{array}$$

4.
$$
\begin{array}{r}
\overset{7\ 13}{\cancel{8}\cancel{3}} \\
-2\,9 \\
\hline
5\,4
\end{array}
$$
Check:
$$
\begin{array}{r}
\overset{1}{\phantom{0}}5\,4 \\
+2\,9 \\
\hline
8\,3
\end{array}
$$

5.
$$
\begin{array}{r}
\overset{5\ 10}{\cancel{6}\cancel{0}} \\
-3\,4 \\
\hline
2\,6
\end{array}
$$
Check:
$$
\begin{array}{r}
\overset{1}{\phantom{0}}2\,6 \\
+3\,4 \\
\hline
6\,0
\end{array}
$$

6.
$$
\begin{array}{r}
\overset{5\ 13}{\cancel{6}\cancel{3}} \\
-1\,9 \\
\hline
4\,4
\end{array}
$$
Check:
$$
\begin{array}{r}
\overset{1}{\phantom{0}}4\,4 \\
+1\,9 \\
\hline
6\,3
\end{array}
$$

7.
$$
\begin{array}{r}
\overset{\ \ \ 14}{\overset{7\ \cancel{4}}{\cancel{8}\cancel{5}\cancel{4}}} \\
-6\,5\,8 \\
\hline
1\,9\,6
\end{array}
$$
Check:
$$
\begin{array}{r}
\overset{1\ 1}{\phantom{0}}1\,9\,6 \\
+6\,5\,8 \\
\hline
8\,5\,4
\end{array}
$$

8.
$$
\begin{array}{r}
\overset{7\ 15}{4\cancel{8}\cancel{5}} \\
-3\,4\,7 \\
\hline
1\,3\,8
\end{array}
$$
Check:
$$
\begin{array}{r}
\overset{1}{\phantom{0}}1\,3\,8 \\
+3\,4\,7 \\
\hline
4\,8\,5
\end{array}
$$

9.
$$
\begin{array}{r}
\overset{\ \ 9}{\overset{6\ \cancel{10}\ 10}{\cancel{7}\cancel{0}\cancel{0}}} \\
-2\,5\,1 \\
\hline
4\,4\,9
\end{array}
$$
Check:
$$
\begin{array}{r}
\overset{1\ 1}{\phantom{0}}4\,4\,9 \\
+2\,5\,1 \\
\hline
7\,0\,0
\end{array}
$$

10.
$$
\begin{array}{r}
\overset{8\ 12}{\cancel{9}\cancel{2}8} \\
-8\,6\,3 \\
\hline
6\,5
\end{array}
$$
Check:
$$
\begin{array}{r}
\overset{1}{\phantom{0}}6\,5 \\
+8\,6\,3 \\
\hline
9\,2\,8
\end{array}
$$

11.
$$
\begin{array}{r}
\overset{\ \ \ 16}{\overset{3\ \cancel{6}\ 13}{\cancel{4}\cancel{7}\cancel{3}8}} \\
-2\,8\,5\,1 \\
\hline
1\,8\,8\,7
\end{array}
$$
Check:
$$
\begin{array}{r}
\overset{1\ 1}{\phantom{0}}1\,8\,8\,7 \\
+2\,8\,5\,1 \\
\hline
4\,7\,3\,8
\end{array}
$$

12.
$$
\begin{array}{r}
\overset{\ \ \ \ \ \ 11\ 13}{\overset{4\ 10\ \cancel{1}\ \cancel{3}\ 13}{\cancel{5}\cancel{1},\cancel{2}\cancel{4}\cancel{3}}} \\
-3\,2{,}5\,4\,8 \\
\hline
1\,8{,}6\,9\,5
\end{array}
$$
Check:
$$
\begin{array}{r}
\overset{1\ 1\ \ 1\ 1}{\phantom{0}}1\,8{,}6\,9\,5 \\
+3\,2{,}5\,4\,8 \\
\hline
5\,1{,}2\,4\,3
\end{array}
$$

13.
$$
\begin{array}{r}
7\,6 \\
-1\,2 \\
\hline
6\,4
\end{array}
$$
Check:
$$
\begin{array}{r}
6\,4 \\
+1\,2 \\
\hline
7\,6
\end{array}
$$

14.
$$
\begin{array}{r}
\overset{4\ 12}{\cancel{5}\cancel{2}} \\
-2\,9 \\
\hline
2\,3
\end{array}
$$
Check:
$$
\begin{array}{r}
\overset{1}{\phantom{0}}2\,3 \\
+2\,9 \\
\hline
5\,2
\end{array}
$$

15.
$$
\begin{array}{r}
\overset{\ \ 12}{\overset{0\ \cancel{2}\ 14}{\cancel{1}\cancel{3}\cancel{4}}} \\
-\ \ 7\,5 \\
\hline
5\,9
\end{array}
$$
Check:
$$
\begin{array}{r}
\overset{1\ 1}{\phantom{0}}5\,9 \\
+\ \ 7\,5 \\
\hline
1\,3\,4
\end{array}
$$

16.
$$
\begin{array}{r}
3\,8 \\
-1\,7 \\
\hline
2\,1
\end{array}
$$
Check:
$$
\begin{array}{r}
2\,1 \\
+1\,7 \\
\hline
3\,8
\end{array}
$$

17. Normal price   $\rightarrow$
$$
\begin{array}{r}
\overset{4\ 18}{\cancel{5}\cancel{8}9}
\end{array}
$$
Discount   $\rightarrow$
$$
\begin{array}{r}
-\ \ 9\,7 \\
\hline
4\,9\,2
\end{array}
$$

The sale price is \$492.

18. Total credit hours needed   $\rightarrow$
$$
\begin{array}{r}
\overset{5\ 10}{\cancel{6}\cancel{0}}
\end{array}
$$
Current number completed   $\rightarrow$
$$
\begin{array}{r}
-4\,2 \\
\hline
1\,8
\end{array}
$$

Julie needs 18 more credit hours.

19. Final odometer reading   $\rightarrow$
$$
\begin{array}{r}
\overset{\ \ \ \ \ \ 15}{\overset{5\ 7\ \cancel{8}\ 14}{4\cancel{8},\cancel{6}\cancel{4}3}}
\end{array}
$$
Initial odometer reading   $\rightarrow$
$$
\begin{array}{r}
-4\,3,7\,6\,1 \\
\hline
4,8\,8\,2
\end{array}
$$

Karen drove 4882 miles on her trip.

20. California   $\rightarrow$
$$
\begin{array}{r}
\overset{\ \ \ \ \ 10}{\overset{6\ \cancel{0}\ \ 16}{3\,3,8\cancel{7}\cancel{1},\cancel{6}4\,8}}
\end{array}
$$
Texas   $\rightarrow$
$$
\begin{array}{r}
-2\,0,8\,5\,1,8\,2\,0 \\
\hline
1\,3,0\,1\,9,8\,2\,8
\end{array}
$$

California has 13,019,828 more people than Texas.

## 1.5 SOLUTIONS TO EXERCISES

1. $8\underline{7}3$ :   Since $7 \geq 5$, add 1 to the 8 in the hundreds place and replace each digit to the right with 0.

   900

2. 156$\underline{4}$:  Since $4 < 5$, do not add 1 to the 6 in the tens place, but replace each digit to the right with 0.

   1560

3. 4$\underline{3}$8:  Since $3 < 5$, do not add 1 to the 4 in the hundreds place, but replace each digit to the right with 0.

   400

4. 16,$\underline{8}$25:  Since $8 \geq 5$, add 1 to the 6 in the thousands place and replace each digit to the right with 0.

   17,000

5. 9$\underline{8}$49:  Since $8 \geq 5$, add 1 to the 9 in the thousands place and replace each digit to the right with 0.

   10,000

6. 24$\underline{4}$9:  Since $4 < 5$, do not add 1 to the 4 in the hundreds place, but replace each digit to the right with 0.

   2400

7. 43,6$\underline{4}$8:  Since $4 < 5$, do not add 1 to the 6 in the hundreds place, but replace each digit to the right with 0.

   43,600

8. 134,$\underline{6}$70:  Since $6 \geq 5$, add 1 to the 4 in the thousands place and replace each digit to the right with 0.

   135,000

9. 142,049:  Since $2 < 5$, do not add 1 to the 4 in the ten-thousands place, but replace each digit to the right with 0.

   140,000

10. 69,99$\underline{9}$:  Since $9 \geq 5$, add 1 to the 9 in the tens place and replace each digit to the right with 0.

    70,000

11. 299,7$\underline{9}$2,458:  Since $9 \geq 5$, add 1 to the 7 in the hundred-thousands place and replace each digit to the right with 0.

    299,800,000

12.
$$
\begin{array}{rl}
62 & \text{rounds to} \quad 60 \\
51 & \text{rounds to} \quad 50 \\
27 & \text{rounds to} \quad 30 \\
+38 & \text{rounds to} \quad +40 \\
\hline
& \hphantom{\text{rounds to} \quad} 180
\end{array}
$$

13.
$$
\begin{array}{rl}
& \hphantom{\text{rounds to} \quad 8}2 \\
78 & \text{rounds to} \quad 80 \\
83 & \text{rounds to} \quad 80 \\
52 & \text{rounds to} \quad 50 \\
+98 & \text{rounds to} \quad +100 \\
\hline
& \hphantom{\text{rounds to} \quad} 310
\end{array}
$$

14.
$$
\begin{array}{rl}
824 & \text{rounds to} \quad 820 \\
-196 & \text{rounds to} \quad -200 \\
\hline
& \hphantom{\text{rounds to} \quad} 620
\end{array}
$$

15.
$$
\begin{array}{rl}
884 & \text{rounds to} \quad 900 \\
531 & \text{rounds to} \quad 500 \\
+378 & \text{rounds to} \quad +400 \\
\hline
& \hphantom{\text{rounds to} \quad} 1800
\end{array}
$$

16.
$$
\begin{array}{rl}
832 & \text{rounds to} \quad 800 \\
-267 & \text{rounds to} \quad -300 \\
\hline
& \hphantom{\text{rounds to} \quad} 500
\end{array}
$$

17.
$$
\begin{array}{rl}
2892 & \text{rounds to} \quad 2900 \\
-1781 & \text{rounds to} \quad -1800 \\
\hline
& \hphantom{\text{rounds to} \quad} 1100
\end{array}
$$

18.
$$
\begin{array}{rl}
& \hphantom{\text{rounds to} \quad 5}1 \\
483 & \text{rounds to} \quad 500 \\
1142 & \text{rounds to} \quad 1100 \\
+\ 687 & \text{rounds to} \quad +\ 700 \\
\hline
& \hphantom{\text{rounds to} \quad} 2300
\end{array}
$$

They have approximately $2300 in total.

19.
$$
\begin{array}{rl}
& \hphantom{\text{rounds to} \quad} {}^{5\ 11} \\
60,791 & \text{rounds to} \quad \cancel{6}\cancel{1},000 \\
-58,735 & \text{rounds to} \quad -59,000 \\
\hline
& \hphantom{\text{rounds to} \quad} 2,000
\end{array}
$$

The increase was approximately 2000 credit hours.

20.  $\begin{array}{r} 55 \\ +58 \end{array}$ rounds to $\begin{array}{r} 60 \\ +60 \\ \hline 120 \end{array}$

The distance from Springfield, MO to Rolla, MO is approximately 120 miles.

## 1.6 SOLUTIONS TO EXERCISES

1.  $4(6+1) = 4\cdot6 + 4\cdot1$

2.  $9(2+7) = 9\cdot2 + 9\cdot7$

3.  $15(30+2) = 15\cdot30 + 15\cdot2$

4.  $\begin{array}{r} 39 \\ \times\ 3 \\ \hline 117 \end{array}$

5.  $\begin{array}{r} 31 \\ \times\ 8 \\ \hline 248 \end{array}$

6.  $\begin{array}{r} 328 \\ \times\ \ 7 \\ \hline 2296 \end{array}$

7.  $\begin{array}{r} 342 \\ \times\ 31 \\ \hline \end{array}$
    $\begin{array}{rl} 342 & \leftarrow 1(342) \\ 10260 & \leftarrow 30(342) \\ \hline 10,602 & \text{Add.} \end{array}$

8.  $\begin{array}{r} 589 \\ \times\ 67 \\ \hline \end{array}$
    $\begin{array}{rl} 4123 & \leftarrow 7(589) \\ 35340 & \leftarrow 60(589) \\ \hline 39,463 & \text{Add.} \end{array}$

9.  $\begin{array}{r} 3142 \\ \times\ 82 \\ \hline \end{array}$
    $\begin{array}{rl} 6284 & \leftarrow 2(3142) \\ 251360 & \leftarrow 80(3142) \\ \hline 527,644 & \text{Add.} \end{array}$

10. $\begin{array}{r} 978 \\ \times\ 30 \\ \hline \end{array}$
    $\begin{array}{rl} 000 & \leftarrow 0(978) \\ 29340 & \leftarrow 30(978) \\ \hline 29,340 & \text{Add.} \end{array}$

11. $\begin{array}{r} 153 \\ \times 321 \\ \hline \end{array}$
    $\begin{array}{rl} 153 & \leftarrow 1(153) \\ 3060 & \leftarrow 20(153) \\ 45900 & \leftarrow 300(153) \\ \hline 49,113 & \text{Add.} \end{array}$

12. $\begin{array}{r} 2754 \\ \times\ 372 \\ \hline \end{array}$
    $\begin{array}{rl} 5508 & \leftarrow 2(2754) \\ 192780 & \leftarrow 70(2754) \\ 826200 & \leftarrow 300(2754) \\ \hline 1,024,488 & \text{Add.} \end{array}$

13. $\begin{array}{r} 70 \\ \times\ 60 \\ \hline \end{array}$
    $\begin{array}{rl} 00 & \leftarrow 0(70) \\ 4200 & \leftarrow 60(70) \\ \hline 4200 & \text{Add.} \end{array}$

14. $(23)(1) = 23$
    $\begin{array}{r} 23 \\ \times 40 \\ \hline \end{array}$
    $\begin{array}{rl} 00 & \leftarrow 0(23) \\ 920 & \leftarrow 40(23) \\ \hline 920 & \text{Add.} \end{array}$

15. $(378)(52)(0) = (378)(0)(52)$
    $= (0)(52)$
    $= 0$

16.  $\begin{array}{r} 578 \\ \times 327 \end{array}$ rounds to $\begin{array}{r} 600 \\ \times\ \ 300 \\ \hline 180,000 \end{array}$

17.  $\begin{array}{r} 324 \\ \times 478 \end{array}$ rounds to $\begin{array}{r} 300 \\ \times\ \ 500 \\ \hline 150,000 \end{array}$

18. Area = length · width
    = (15 cm)(6 cm)
    = 90 square cm

19. Area = length · width
    = (14 feet)(6 feet)
    = 84 square feet

20. The price for the four tires is $4 \cdot \$76 = \$304$.
    The price for the two seat covers is
    $2 \cdot \$49 = \$98$. The total price will be
    $\$304 + \$98 = \$402$.

## 1.7 SOLUTIONS TO EXERCISES

1.
$$
\begin{array}{r}
13 \\
8\overline{)104} \\
\underline{8} \\
24 \\
\underline{24} \\
0
\end{array}
$$
*Check*:
$$
\begin{array}{r}
13 \\
\times\ 8 \\
\hline
104
\end{array}
$$

2.
$$
\begin{array}{r}
17 \\
5\overline{)85} \\
\underline{5} \\
35 \\
\underline{35} \\
0
\end{array}
$$
*Check*:
$$
\begin{array}{r}
17 \\
\times\ 5 \\
\hline
85
\end{array}
$$

3.
$$
\begin{array}{r}
42 \\
6\overline{)252} \\
\underline{24} \\
12 \\
\underline{12} \\
0
\end{array}
$$
*Check*:
$$
\begin{array}{r}
42 \\
\times\ 6 \\
\hline
252
\end{array}
$$

4.
$$
\begin{array}{r}
65\ R\ 4 \\
5\overline{)329} \\
\underline{30} \\
29 \\
\underline{25} \\
4
\end{array}
$$
*Check*:
$$
\begin{array}{r}
65 \\
\times\ 5 \\
\hline
325 \\
+\ 4 \\
\hline
329
\end{array}
$$

5.
$$
\begin{array}{r}
79\ R\ 2 \\
3\overline{)239} \\
\underline{21} \\
29 \\
\underline{27} \\
2
\end{array}
$$
*Check*:
$$
\begin{array}{r}
79 \\
\times\ 3 \\
\hline
237 \\
+\ 2 \\
\hline
239
\end{array}
$$

6.
$$
\begin{array}{r}
43 \\
23\overline{)989} \\
\underline{92} \\
69 \\
\underline{69} \\
0
\end{array}
$$
*Check*:
$$
\begin{array}{r}
43 \\
\times\ 23 \\
\hline
129 \\
860 \\
\hline
989
\end{array}
$$

7.
$$
\begin{array}{r}
70\ R\ 5 \\
6\overline{)425} \\
\underline{42} \\
05 \\
\underline{00} \\
5
\end{array}
$$
*Check*:
$$
\begin{array}{r}
70 \\
\times\ 6 \\
\hline
420 \\
+\ 5 \\
\hline
425
\end{array}
$$

8.
$$
\begin{array}{r}
160\ R\ 1 \\
5\overline{)801} \\
\underline{5} \\
30 \\
\underline{30} \\
01 \\
\underline{00} \\
01
\end{array}
$$
*Check*:
$$
\begin{array}{r}
160 \\
\times\ 5 \\
\hline
800 \\
+\ 1 \\
\hline
801
\end{array}
$$

9.
$$
\begin{array}{r}
400\ R\ 9 \\
13\overline{)5209} \\
\underline{52} \\
00 \\
\underline{0} \\
09 \\
\underline{0} \\
9
\end{array}
$$
*Check*:
$$
\begin{array}{r}
400 \\
\times\ 13 \\
\hline
1200 \\
4000 \\
\hline
5200 \\
+\ 9 \\
\hline
5209
\end{array}
$$

10.
$$
\begin{array}{r}
328\ R\ 19 \\
21\overline{)6907} \\
\underline{63} \\
60 \\
\underline{42} \\
187 \\
\underline{168} \\
19
\end{array}
$$
*Check*:
$$
\begin{array}{r}
328 \\
\times\ 21 \\
\hline
328 \\
6560 \\
\hline
6888 \\
+\ 19 \\
\hline
6907
\end{array}
$$

11.
$$
\begin{array}{r}
101\ R\ 1 \\
38\overline{)3839} \\
\underline{38} \\
03 \\
\underline{0} \\
39 \\
\underline{38} \\
1
\end{array}
$$
*Check*:
$$
\begin{array}{r}
101 \\
\times\ 38 \\
\hline
808 \\
3030 \\
\hline
3838 \\
+\ 1 \\
\hline
3839
\end{array}
$$

12.
$$
\begin{array}{r}
54 \text{ R } 4 \\
38\overline{)2056} \\
\underline{190} \\
156 \\
\underline{152} \\
4
\end{array}
$$

Check:
$$
\begin{array}{r}
54 \\
\times\,38 \\
\hline
432 \\
1620 \\
\hline
2052 \\
+\;\;4 \\
\hline
2056
\end{array}
$$

13.
$$
\begin{array}{r}
32 \\
178\overline{)5696} \\
\underline{534} \\
356 \\
\underline{356} \\
0
\end{array}
$$

Check:
$$
\begin{array}{r}
178 \\
\times\,32 \\
\hline
356 \\
5340 \\
\hline
5696
\end{array}
$$

14.
$$
\begin{array}{r}
68 \\
257\overline{)17476} \\
\underline{1542} \\
2056 \\
\underline{2056} \\
0
\end{array}
$$

Check:
$$
\begin{array}{r}
257 \\
\times\,68 \\
\hline
2056 \\
15420 \\
\hline
17476
\end{array}
$$

15.
$$
\begin{array}{r}
111 \text{ R } 12 \\
130\overline{)14442} \\
\underline{130} \\
144 \\
\underline{130} \\
142 \\
\underline{130} \\
12
\end{array}
$$

Check:
$$
\begin{array}{r}
111 \\
\times\,130 \\
\hline
000 \\
3330 \\
11100 \\
\hline
14430 \\
+\;\;12 \\
\hline
14442
\end{array}
$$

16. Average $= \dfrac{84+79+67+92+108}{5}$

$= \dfrac{430}{5}$

$= 86$

17. Average $= \dfrac{35+28+19+31+38+41}{6}$

$= \dfrac{192}{6}$

$= 32$

18. Share = (prize money) $\div$ (no. of people)
$=$ 12,366,000 $\div$ 27
$=$ 458,000

Each person will receive $458,000.

19. No. of trips = (total tons) $\div$ (tons per trip)
$=$ 200 $\div$ 16
$=$ 12 R 8

Twelve full loads with 8 tons left over, so 13 trips must be made.

20. Cost per van = (total cost) $\div$ (no. of vans)
$=$ 224,055 $\div$ 13
$=$ 17,235

Each van costs $17,235.

**1.8 SOLUTIONS TO EXERCISES**

1. $7\cdot7\cdot7\cdot7\cdot7\cdot7 = 7^6$

2. $4\cdot4\cdot4\cdot4\cdot4\cdot4\cdot4 = 4^7$

3. $2\cdot2\cdot2\cdot2\cdot5\cdot5 = 2^4\cdot5^2$

4. $3\cdot3\cdot7\cdot8\cdot8\cdot8\cdot8\cdot8 = 3^2\cdot7\cdot8^5$

5. $9^2 = 9\cdot9 = 81$

6. $7^3 = 7\cdot7\cdot7 = 343$

7. $4^5 = 4\cdot4\cdot4\cdot4\cdot4 = 1024$

8. $2^8 = 2\cdot2\cdot2\cdot2\cdot2\cdot2\cdot2\cdot2 = 256$

9. $347^1 = 347$

10. $100\div4\cdot5 = 25\cdot5 = 125$

11. $12-3+8 = 9+8 = 17$

12. $19+3\cdot6 = 19+18 = 37$

13. $8\cdot7-23 = 56-23 = 33$

14. $24\div4+7\cdot3 = 6+7\cdot3$
$= 6+21$
$= 27$

15. $100-5\left(30-2^4\right) = 100-5\left(30-16\right)$
$= 100-5\left(14\right)$
$= 100-70$
$= 30$

16. $3 + 2\big[10 - (2 + 4)\big] = 3 + 2(10 - 6)$
$$= 3 + 2(4)$$
$$= 3 + 8$$
$$= 11$$

17. $\dfrac{27 - 3}{23 - 19} = \dfrac{24}{4} = 6$

18. $\dfrac{15 + 3 \cdot 9 - 6}{5 + 2^2} = \dfrac{15 + 27 - 6}{5 + 4}$
$$= \dfrac{42 - 6}{9}$$
$$= \dfrac{36}{9}$$
$$= 4$$

19. $7^2 - \big\{9 + 3\big[2 + 3(14 - 9)\big] - 13\big\}$
$$= 7^2 - \big\{9 + 3\big[2 + 3(5)\big] - 13\big\}$$
$$= 7^2 - \big[9 + 3(2 + 15) - 13\big]$$
$$= 7^2 - \big[9 + 3(17) - 13\big]$$
$$= 7^2 - (9 + 51 - 13)$$
$$= 7^2 - (60 - 13)$$
$$= 7^2 - 47$$
$$= 49 - 47$$
$$= 2$$

20. Area of a square $= (\text{side})^2$
$$= (25 \text{ millimeters})^2$$
$$= 625 \text{ square millimeters}$$

## 1.9 SOLUTIONS TO EXERCISES

1. $5 + 6y = 5 + 6(3)$
$$= 5 + 18$$
$$= 23$$

2. $2xz - 5y = 2(4)(7) - 5(3)$
$$= 56 - 15$$
$$= 41$$

3. $x + 2y - z = 4 + 2(3) - 7$
$$= 4 + 6 - 7$$
$$= 10 - 7$$
$$= 3$$

4. $xy^2 + 8 = 4(3)^2 + 8$
$$= 4(9) + 8$$
$$= 36 + 8$$
$$= 44$$

5. $21 - (z - x) = 21 - (7 - 4)$
$$= 21 - 3$$
$$= 18$$

6. $6z - 2(x^2 - y) = 6 \cdot 7 - 2(4^2 - 3)$
$$= 6 \cdot 7 - 2(16 - 3)$$
$$= 6 \cdot 7 - 2(13)$$
$$= 42 - 26$$
$$= 16$$

7. $\dfrac{x + 28}{z - y} = \dfrac{4 + 28}{7 - 3} = \dfrac{32}{4} = 8$

8. $\dfrac{6xz}{8y} = \dfrac{6(4)(7)}{8(3)} = \dfrac{168}{24} = 7$

9. $\dfrac{3z + x}{5} = \dfrac{3(7) + 4}{5} = \dfrac{21 + 4}{5} = \dfrac{25}{5} = 5$

10. $x^3 + y^2 - z = 4^3 + 3^2 - 7$
$$= 64 + 9 - 7$$
$$= 73 - 7$$
$$= 66$$

11. $\dfrac{5x}{2} + \dfrac{21}{y} = \dfrac{5(4)}{2} + \dfrac{21}{3}$
$$= \dfrac{20}{2} + \dfrac{21}{3}$$
$$= 10 + 7$$
$$= 17$$

12. $x^2 - (y + z) = 4^2 - (3 + 7)$
$$= 4^2 - 10$$
$$= 16 - 10$$
$$= 6$$

13. $(xy - z)^2 = (4 \cdot 3 - 7)^2$
$$= (12 - 7)^2$$
$$= (5)^2$$
$$= 25$$

14. $\dfrac{5z+3y}{z+x} = \dfrac{5(7)+3(3)}{7+4} = \dfrac{35+9}{11} = \dfrac{44}{11} = 4$

15. $y^4 - (5z+2x) = 3^4 - (5\cdot7+2\cdot4)$
$= 3^4 - (35+8)$
$= 3^4 - 43$
$= 81 - 43$
$= 38$

16. $15 - x$

17. $x \div 8$ or $\dfrac{x}{8}$

18. $x + 27$

19. $x \div 7 - 40$ or $\dfrac{x}{7} - 40$

20. $5(x+12)$

## CHAPTER 1 PRACTICE TEST SOLUTIONS

1. $\begin{array}{r} \overset{1}{3\,7} \\ +5\,6 \\ \hline 9\,3 \end{array}$

2. $\begin{array}{r} \overset{6}{\cancel{7}}\,\overset{\overset{11}{\cancel{1}}}{\cancel{2}}\,\overset{15}{\cancel{5}} \\ -2\,4\,8 \\ \hline 4\,7\,7 \end{array}$

3. $\begin{array}{r} 375 \\ \times\ 34 \\ \hline 1500 \\ 11250 \\ \hline 12,750 \end{array}$

4. $\begin{array}{r} 929\ R\ 13 \\ 56\overline{)52037} \\ \underline{504}\phantom{00} \\ 163\phantom{0} \\ \underline{112}\phantom{0} \\ 517 \\ \underline{504} \\ 13 \end{array}$

5. $5^2 \cdot 2^4 = 25 \cdot 16 = 400$

6. $7^1 \cdot 3^4 = 7 \cdot 81 = 567$

7. $237 \div 1 = 237$

8. $0 \div 12 = 0$

9. $31 \div 0$ is undefined.

10. $\dfrac{2^5 - 5}{9} = \dfrac{32 - 5}{9} = \dfrac{27}{9} = 3$

11. $17 + 20 \div 2 \cdot 5 - 15 = 17 + 10 \cdot 5 - 15$
$= 17 + 50 - 15$
$= 67 - 15$
$= 52$

12. $4\left[ (7-5)^3 + (25-22)^2 \right] + 12 \cdot$
$= 4\left[ (2)^3 + (3)^2 \right] + 12$
$= 4(8+9) + 12$
$= 4(17) + 12$
$= 68 + 12$
$= 80$

13. $1,93\underline{7},216:$ Since $7 \geq 5$, add 1 to the 3 in the ten-thousands place and replace each digit to the right with 0.

1,940,000

14. $\begin{array}{rll} 3481 & \text{rounds to} & \overset{1}{3500} \\ 6228 & \text{rounds to} & 6200 \\ +2949 & \text{rounds to} & +2900 \\ \hline && 12,600 \end{array}$

15. $\begin{array}{rll} 3827 & \text{rounds to} & 3800 \\ -1692 & \text{rounds to} & -1700 \\ \hline && 2100 \end{array}$

16. Cost per TV = (total cost) ÷ (no. of TVs)
$= \quad 14{,}094 \quad \div \quad 58$
$= \quad 243$
Each television set costs $243.

17. Total cost = (ticket price) · (no. of tickets)
$= \quad 38 \quad \cdot \quad 24$
$= \quad \$912$
The total cost of their tickets is $912.

18. Total cost = (washer price) + (dryer price)

           =      569     +     479

           =      $1048

     The total cost of the washer and dryer is $1048.

19. 
$$6\left(2x^2 - 15\right) = 6\left(2 \cdot 5^2 - 15\right)$$
$$= 6\left(2 \cdot 25 - 15\right)$$
$$= 6\left(50 - 15\right)$$
$$= 6\left(35\right)$$
$$= 210$$

20. 
$$\frac{7x - 5y}{4} = \frac{7(13) - 5(7)}{4} = \frac{91 - 35}{4} = \frac{56}{4} = 14$$

21. a.   $32 - x$

     b.   $12x - 14$

22. Perimeter $= 4 \cdot$ side

                $= 4(8 \text{ meters})$

                $= 32 \text{ meters}$

     Area $= (\text{side})^2$

            $= (8 \text{ meters})^2$

            $= 64 \text{ square meters}$

23. Perimeter = Add the lengths of the four sides

                = 16 in. + 7 in. + 16 in. + 7 in.

                = 46 inches

     Area  = length · width

             = (16 inches)(7 inches)

             = 112 square inches

24. Jupiter has the largest diameter. That diameter is 88,846 miles.

25. Earth's diameter  $\rightarrow$    7,926

     Mar's diameter   $\rightarrow$   $-4,221$

                             $\overline{\phantom{-}3,705}$

     Earth's diameter is 3,705 miles greater than Mar's diameter.

## 2.1 SOLUTIONS TO EXERCISES

1. If 0 represents the starting point of the football, then a gain of 45 yards can be expressed as $+45$.

2. If 0 represents the baseline temperature, then 16 degrees Fahrenheit below zero can be expressed as $-16$.

3.
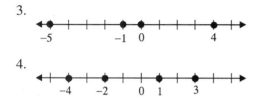

4.

5. $-15$ is to the left of $-14$ on a number line, so $-15 < -14$.

6. $-3$ is to the left of 0 on a number line, so $-3 < 0$.

7. 5 is to the right of $-5$ on a number line, so $5 > -5$.

8. 7 is to the right of $-9$ on a number line, so $7 > -9$.

9. $|35| = 35$ because 35 is 35 units from 0.

10. $|-12| = 12$ because $-12$ is 12 units from 0.

11. $|-68| = 68$ because $-68$ is 68 units from 0.

12. The opposite of 23 is $-23$.

13. The opposite of $-22$ is 22.

14. The opposite of 132 is $-132$.

15. $-|-8| = -(8) = -8$

16. $-(-6) = 6$

17. $-|34| = -(34) = -34$

18. $-|14| = -(14) = -14$ and
    $-|-14| = -(14) = -14$, so $-|14| = -|-14|$.

19. $-|-4| = -(4) = -4$ and $-|-7| = -(7) = -7$. Since $-7$ is to the left of $-4$ on a number line, we have $-|-4| > -|-7|$.

20. $-(-30) = 30$
    $-28$ is to the left of 30 on a number line, so $-28 < -(-30)$.

## 2.2 SOLUTIONS TO EXERCISES

1. $31 + 17 = 48$

2. $-5 + (-2) = -7$

3. $43 + (-43) = 0$

4. $11 + (-9) = 2$

5. $14 + (-41) = -27$

6. $-17 + (-50) = -67$

7. $-20 + 13 + (-4) = -7 + (-4) = -11$

8. $12 + (-1) + (-7) = 11 + (-7) = 4$

9. $12 + 4 + (-8) + (-30) = 16 + (-8) + (-30)$
   $= 8 + (-30)$
   $= -22$

10. $(-19) + 20 + (-12) + 8 = 1 + (-12) + 8$
    $= -11 + 8$
    $= -3$

11. $-112 + (-63) = -175$

12. $141 + (-38) = 103$

13. $-71 + 16 = -55$

14. $-7 + (-15) + 28 + (-6) = -22 + 28 + (-6)$
    $= 6 + (-6)$
    $= 0$

15. $x + y = (-3) + (12) = 9$

16. $x + y = (-40) + (-23) = -63$

17. $x + y = (18) + (-42) = -24$

18. $x + y = (-34) + (-79) = -113$

19. 
| temperature at 5:00 p.m. | + | degrees dropped | = | temperature at 11:30 p.m. |
|---|---|---|---|---|
| $-15$ | + | $(-12)$ | = | $-27$ |

The temperature at 11:30 p.m. was $-27°C$.

20. 
| depth of orig. dive | + | additional feet | = | new depth |
|---|---|---|---|---|
| $-150$ | + | $(-30)$ | = | $-180$ |

The diver would be 180 feet below the surface.

## 2.3 SOLUTIONS TO EXERCISES

1. $-37 - (-37) = -37 + 37 = 0$

2. $12 - 4 = 12 + (-4) = 8$

3. $14 - 17 = 14 + (-17) = -3$

4. $-17 - (-19) = -17 + 19 = 2$

5. $6 - 8 = 6 + (-8) = -2$

6. $-28 - 49 = -28 + (-49) = -77$

7. $-51 - 12 = -51 + (-12) = -63$

8. $-20 - (-25) = -20 + 25 = 5$

9. $40 - 25 - 15 = 40 + (-25) + (-15)$
$$= 15 + (-15)$$
$$= 0$$

10. $-7 - 11 - (-16) = -7 + (-11) + 16$
$$= -18 + 16$$
$$= -2$$

11. $5 - (-7) + 12 = 5 + 7 + 12$
$$= 12 + 12$$
$$= 24$$

12. $-(-8) - 16 + 21 = 8 + (-16) + 21$
$$= -8 + 21$$
$$= 13$$

13. $-10 - 10 - 14 = -10 + (-10) + (-14)$
$$= -20 + (-14)$$
$$= -34$$

14. $-31 - (-31) - 5 = -31 + 31 + (-5)$
$$= 0 + (-5)$$
$$= -5$$

15. $x - y = (-22) - (14) = -22 + (-14) = -36$

16. $x - y = (-42) - (-27) = -42 + 27 = -15$

17. $x - y + z = (-5) - (8) + (14)$
$$= -5 + (-8) + 14$$
$$= -13 + 14$$
$$= 1$$

18. $-x - y + z = -(60) - (-30) + (-50)$
$$= -60 + 30 + (-50)$$
$$= -30 + (-50)$$
$$= -80$$

19. 
| beg. balance | – | amt. of check 1 | + | amt. of deposit | – | amt. of check 2 | = | current balance |
|---|---|---|---|---|---|---|---|---|
| 400 | – | 132 | + | 75 | – | 212 | = | balance |

$400 - 132 + 75 - 212$
$$= 400 + (-132) + 75 + (-212)$$
$$= 268 + 75 + (-212)$$
$$= 343 + (-212)$$
$$= 131$$

Payton has \$131 left in her account.

20. boiling   &minus;   freezing   =   difference
    point         point

  $-182$   &minus;   $(-218)$   =   $36$

There is a difference of $36°C$ between the two temperatures.

## 2.4 SOLUTIONS TO EXERCISES

1. $(-6)(-2) = 12$

2. $0(-8) = 0$

3. $(-54)(3) = -162$

4. $\dfrac{-39}{-3} = 13$

5. $\dfrac{42}{-6} = -7$

6. $\dfrac{217}{0}$ is undefined

7. $(3)(-4)(-5) = -12(-5) = 60$

8. $(-8)(-10)(-2) = 80(-2) = -160$

9. $(-2)(5)(-3)(-1) = -10(-3)(-1)$
$= 30(-1)$
$= -30$

10. $(-9)^2 = (-9)(-9) = 81$

11. $(-7)^3 = (-7)(-7)(-7) = 49(-7) = -343$

12. $-45 \div 5 = -9$

13. $a \cdot b = (-7)(-7) = 49$

14. $a \cdot b = (-30)(-8) = 240$

15. $a \cdot b = (75)(-4) = -300$

16. $\dfrac{x}{y} = \dfrac{120}{-40} = -3$

17. $\dfrac{x}{y} = \dfrac{-196}{-14} = 14$

18. $\dfrac{x}{y} = \dfrac{0}{77} = 0$

19. num. of months  &middot;  amt. per  =  total loss
                 month

     $(5)$    &middot;  $(-3000)$  =  $-15,000$

Eric's total loss was $15,000.

20. num. of days  &middot;  degrees  =  total drop
               changed

     $7$    &middot;  $(-4)$  =  $-28$

The temperature will drop a total of 28 degrees over the next 7 days.

## 2.5 SOLUTIONS TO EXERCISES

1. $7 + (-18) \div 3 = 7 + (-6) = 1$

2. $11 + 5(8) = 11 + 40 = 51$

3. $9(-2) + 4 = -18 + 4 = -14$

4. $25 + 3^3 = 25 + 27 = 52$

5. $\dfrac{26 - 11}{-5} = \dfrac{15}{-5} = -3$

6. $\dfrac{92}{-9 + 32} = \dfrac{92}{23} = 4$

7. $\left[3 + (-5)\right]^4 = \left[-2\right]^4 = 16$

8. $60 - (-7)^2 = 60 - 49 = 60 + (-49) = 11$

9. $|13 - 17| \cdot (-4)^2 = |13 + (-17)| \cdot (-4)^2$
$= |-4| \cdot (-4)^2$
$= 4 \cdot (-4)^2$
$= 4 \cdot 16$
$= 64$

10. $4 \cdot 2^2 + 35 = 4 \cdot 4 + 35$
$= 16 + 35$
$= 51$

11. $8 + 4^2 - 3^3 = 8 + 16 - 27$
$= 24 - 27$
$= 24 + (-27)$
$= -3$

12. $(12 - 24) \div 4 = -12 \div 4 = -3$

13. $(64 - 36) \div (27 - 41) = 28 \div (-14) = -2$

14. $(-30 - 6) \div 12 - 11 = -36 \div 12 - 11$
$= -3 - 11$
$= -3 + (-11)$
$= -14$

15. $-8^2 - (-7)^2 = -64 - 49 = -113$

16. $4(-7) \div \left[ 2(-6) - 8(-5) \right]$
$= 4(-7) \div [-12 + 40]$
$= 4(-7) \div 28$
$= -28 \div 28$
$= -1$

17. $\dfrac{(-4)(-8) - 6(2)}{2[7 + (9 - 6)]} = \dfrac{32 - 12}{2[7 + 3]}$
$= \dfrac{20}{2(10)}$
$= \dfrac{20}{20}$
$= 1$

18. $\dfrac{40(-1) - (-4)(-5)}{3[-10 \div (-7 + 2)]} = \dfrac{-40 - 20}{3[-10 \div -5]}$
$= \dfrac{-60}{3(2)}$
$= \dfrac{-60}{6}$
$= -10$

19. $5x - y^2 = 5(2) - (-4)^2$
$= 5(2) - 16$
$= 10 - 16$
$= -6$

20. $\dfrac{6x}{z} - 3y = \dfrac{6(2)}{(-3)} - 3(-4)$
$= \dfrac{12}{-3} + 12$
$= -4 + 12$
$= 8$

## CHAPTER 2 PRACTICE TEST SOLUTIONS

1. $12 - 27 = 12 + (-27) = -15$

2. $-18 + 11 = -7$

3. $5 \cdot (-20) = -100$

4. $(-21) \div (-7) = 3$

5. $(-31) + (-11) = -42$

6. $-14 - (-38) = -14 + 38 = 24$

7. $(-30) \cdot (-5) = 150$

8. $\dfrac{-105}{-7} = 15$

9. $|-79| + (-65) = 79 + (-65) = 14$

10. $40 - |-70| = 40 - 70 = 40 + (-70) = -30$

11. $|13| \cdot |-5| = 13 \cdot 5 = 65$

12. $\dfrac{|-52|}{-|-13|} = \dfrac{52}{-13} = -4$

13. $(-15) + 70 \div (-10) = (-15) + (-7) = -22$

14. $-7 + (-81) \div (-9) = -7 + 9 = 2$

15. $(-3)^3 - 52 \div (-13) = (-27) - 52 \div (-13)$
$$= (-27) - (-4)$$
$$= -27 + 4$$
$$= -23$$

16. $(3-5)^2 \cdot (9-5)^3 = (-2)^2 \cdot (4)^3$
$$= (4) \cdot (64)$$
$$= 256$$

17. $18 \cdot (-2) - (-7)^2 = 18 \cdot (-2) - 49$
$$= -36 - 49$$
$$= -85$$

18. $48 - (24-26)^3 = 48 - (-2)^3$
$$= 48 - (-8)$$
$$= 48 + 8$$
$$= 56$$

19. $\dfrac{12}{6} - \dfrac{8^2}{16} = \dfrac{12}{6} - \dfrac{64}{16} = 2 - 4 = 2 + (-4) = -2$

20. $\dfrac{|45-50|^2}{8(-3)+19} = \dfrac{|-5|^2}{-24+19} = \dfrac{(5)^2}{-5} = \dfrac{25}{-5} = -5$

21. $\dfrac{30-8(-2)}{(-15-8)} = \dfrac{30-(-16)}{-23}$
$$= \dfrac{30+16}{-23}$$
$$= \dfrac{46}{-23}$$
$$= -2$$

22. $3x - 2y = 3(3) - 2(0) = 9 - 0 = 9$

23. $|x| - |y| - |z| = |3| - |0| - |-5|$
$$= 3 - 0 - 5$$
$$= 3 - 5$$
$$= 3 + (-5)$$
$$= -2$$

24. $\dfrac{18z}{-2x} = \dfrac{18(-5)}{-2(3)} = \dfrac{-90}{-6} = 15$

25. beginning + change in  =  final
    elevation    elevation      elevation
    $1,772$  $+ (-734)$  $=$  $1,038$
    Shawn's final elevation was 1,038 feet.

26. original + 1st + 2nd + 3rd = new
    total    carry  carry  carry  total
    $675$ + $12$ + $(-3)$ + $5$ = total

    $675 + 12 + (-3) + 5 = 687 + (-3) + 5$
    $$= 684 + 5$$
    $$= 689$$
    His total rushing yards was 689 after the three carries.

27. temperature  + degrees  =  temperature
    at noon        dropped       at 3 p.m.
    $72$  $+ (-28)$  $=$  $44$
    The temperature at 3 p.m. was 44°F.

## 3.1 SOLUTIONS TO EXERCISES

1.  The numerical coefficient of $53x$ is 53.

2.  The numerical coefficient of $-y$ is $-1$.

3.  The numerical coefficient of $-17x^2y^2z^3$ is $-17$.

4.  $13x - 4x = (13 - 4)x$
    $= 9x$

5.  $2c - 4c + 7c = (2 - 4 + 7)c$
    $= (-2 + 7)c$
    $= 5c$

6.  $12y + 9y - 2y + 7 = (12 + 9 - 2)y + 7$
    $= (21 - 2)y + 7$
    $= 19y + 7$

7.  $-2(21x) = -42x$

8.  $2(3x - 1) = 2 \cdot 3x - 2 \cdot 1$
    $= 6x - 2$

9.  $5(3x - 10) = 5 \cdot 3x - 5 \cdot 10$
    $= 15x - 50$

10. $4(x - 11) + 16 = 4 \cdot x - 4 \cdot 11 + 16$
    $= 4x - 44 + 16$
    $= 4x - 28$

11. $3(8 - 5b) - 12b = 3 \cdot 8 - 3 \cdot 5b - 12b$
    $= 24 - 15b - 12b$
    $= 24 - 27b$

12. $-5(2x + 7) + 4(x - 6) = -10x - 35 + 4x - 24$
    $= -10x + 4x - 35 - 24$
    $= -6x - 59$

13. $-2y - 12y + 8y + 3y = -14y + 8y + 3y$
    $= -6y + 3y$
    $= -3y$

14. $-12(1 + 2v) + 4v = -12 - 24v + 4v$
    $= -12 - 20v$
    $= -20v - 12$

15. $2(k + 3) - 7(2k - 1) = 2k + 6 - 14k + 7$
    $= 2k - 14k + 6 + 7$
    $= -12k + 13$

16. $22x + 6(2x - 5) = 22x + 12x - 30$
    $= 34x - 30$

17. $2(5xy - 4) + (8xy - 3) = 10xy - 8 + 8xy - 3$
    $= 10xy + 8xy - 8 - 3$
    $= 18xy - 11$

18. Find the perimeter by adding up the lengths of all the sides.
    $(x + 3) + 5x + (3x + 2) + 2x + 4x + x$
    $= x + 3 + 5x + 3x + 2 + 2x + 4x + x$
    $= x + 5x + 3x + 2x + 4x + x + 3 + 2$
    $= 16x + 5$
    The perimeter of the figure is $(16x + 5)$ cm.

19. Since there are six sides and each has the same length, the perimeter can be found by multiplying the length by 6.
    $6(2x + 1) = 12x + 6$
    The perimeter of the figure is $12x + 6$ in.

20. Total = Area of 1st + Area of 2nd
    Area   Rectangle   Rectangle
    Area of 1st rectangle = length · width
    $= 9 \cdot (8x - 3)$
    $= 72x - 27$
    Area of 2nd rectangle = length · width
    $= 20 \cdot (2x + 1)$
    $= 40x + 20$
    So, we have
    Total area $= (72x - 27) + (40x + 20)$
    $= 72x - 27 + 40x + 20$
    $= 72x + 40x - 27 + 20$
    $= 112x - 7$
    The total area is $(112x - 7)$ square feet.

**3.2 SOLUTIONS TO EXERCISES**

1. $x + 3 = 8$

   $5 + 3 = 8$ ?

   $8 = 8$ True

   5 is a solution.

2. $x - 7 = -10$

   $-3 - 7 = -10$ ?

   $-10 = -10$ True

   $-3$ is a solution.

3. $4(m - 2) = 8$

   $4(0 - 2) = 8$ ?

   $4(-2) = 8$ ?

   $-8 = 8$ False

   0 is not a solution.

4. $4h + 2 = 23 - h$

   $4(-2) + 2 = 23 - (-2)$ ?

   $-8 + 2 = 23 + 2$ ?

   $-6 = 25$ False

   $-2$ is not a solution.

5. $x - 3 = 19$

   $x - 3 + 3 = 19 + 3$

   $x = 22$

6. $t - 14 = 21$

   $t - 14 + 14 = 21 + 14$

   $t = 35$

7. $x - 4 = 7 + 9$

   $x - 4 = 16$

   $x - 4 + 4 = 16 + 4$

   $x = 20$

8. $-9 - 2 = -5 + y$

   $-11 = -5 + y$

   $-11 + 5 = -5 + y + 5$

   $-11 + 5 = -5 + 5 + y$

   $-6 = y$

9. $2x + 3 - x = -4 - 7$

   $2x - x + 3 = -4 - 7$

   $x + 3 = -11$

   $x + 3 - 3 = -11 - 3$

   $x = -14$

10. $11 - 11 = 9x - 8x$

    $0 = x$

11. $34 + (-12) = 5x + 6 - 4x$

    $34 + (-12) = 5x - 4x + 6$

    $22 = x + 6$

    $22 - 6 = x + 6 - 6$

    $16 = x$

12. $78 = w + 78$

    $78 - 78 = w + 78 - 78$

    $0 = w$

13. $z - 3 = -16$

    $z - 3 + 3 = -16 + 3$

    $z = -13$

14. $m + 20 = 22$

    $m + 20 - 20 = 22 - 20$

    $m = 2$

15. $-14 + x = -29$

    $-14 + x + 14 = -29 + 14$

    $-14 + 14 + x = -29 + 14$

    $x = -15$

16. $-17n - 10 + 18n = -6$

    $-17n + 18n - 10 = -6$

    $n - 10 = -6$

    $n - 10 + 10 = -6 + 10$

    $n = 4$

17. $7w + 8 - 6w = 37 - 18$

    $7w - 6w + 8 = 37 - 18$

    $w + 8 = 19$

    $w + 8 - 8 = 19 - 8$

    $w = 11$

18. $-19x + 13 + 20x = -1 - 5$
$-19x + 20x + 13 = -1 - 5$
$x + 13 = -6$
$x + 13 - 13 = -6 - 13$
$x = -19$

19. $x + 32 = -17$
$x + 32 - 32 = -17 - 32$
$x = -49$

20. $15x + 20 - 14x = -51$
$15x - 14x + 20 = -51$
$x + 20 = -51$
$x + 20 - 20 = -51 - 20$
$x = -71$

## 3.3 SOLUTIONS TO EXERCISES

1. $4x = 72$
$\dfrac{4x}{4} = \dfrac{72}{4}$
$x = 18$

2. $-9z = 99$
$\dfrac{-9z}{-9} = \dfrac{99}{-9}$
$z = -11$

3. $-7y = -35$
$\dfrac{-7y}{-7} = \dfrac{-35}{-7}$
$y = 5$

4. $2m = 24$
$\dfrac{2m}{2} = \dfrac{24}{2}$
$m = 12$

5. $6b - 9b = -42$
$-3b = -42$
$\dfrac{-3b}{-3} = \dfrac{-42}{-3}$
$b = 14$

6. $18 = -6t - 3t$
$18 = -9t$
$\dfrac{18}{-9} = \dfrac{-9t}{-9}$
$-2 = t$  or  $t = -2$

7. $9x - 4x = -15 + (-10)$
$5x = -25$
$\dfrac{5x}{5} = \dfrac{-25}{5}$
$x = -5$

8. $-13y = 13$
$\dfrac{-13y}{-13} = \dfrac{13}{-13}$
$y = -1$

9. $11n - 5n = 54$
$6n = 54$
$\dfrac{6n}{6} = \dfrac{54}{6}$
$n = 9$

10. $-8x = -8$
$\dfrac{-8x}{-8} = \dfrac{-8}{-8}$
$x = 1$

11. $y - 3y = 18$
$-2y = 18$
$\dfrac{-2y}{-2} = \dfrac{18}{-2}$
$y = -9$

12. $21a - 4a = 34$
$17a = 34$
$\dfrac{17a}{17} = \dfrac{34}{17}$
$a = 2$

13. $28x - 17x = -17 - 27$
$11x = -44$
$\dfrac{11x}{11} = \dfrac{-44}{11}$
$x = -4$

14. $7v + 11v = 36$
$$18v = 36$$
$$\frac{18v}{18} = \frac{36}{18}$$
$$v = 2$$

15. $48y - 8y = -70 - 10$
$$40y = -80$$
$$\frac{40y}{40} = \frac{-80}{40}$$
$$y = -2$$

16. Let $x$ = a number

Six   more than   three times a number
↓         ↓              ↓
6        +             3x

17. Let $x$ = a number

Eight   added to   the product of 9 and a number
↓          ↓                  ↓
8         +                  9x

18. Let $x$ = a number

Four times a number   decreased by   18
↓                              ↓          ↓
4x                            –          18

19. Let $x$ = a number
quotient → divide
sum → add

$x$  ← a number
quotient →  $\dfrac{\phantom{x}}{x+4}$  ← the sum of the
number and 4

20. Let $x$ = a number

Twice   the difference   all decreased by   8
of a number
and 4
↓            ↓                    ↓          ↓
2  ·   $(x-4)$                 –          8

**3.4 SOLUTIONS TO EXERCISES**

1. $7x - 56 = 0$
$$7x - 56 + 56 = 0 + 56$$
$$7x = 56$$
$$\frac{7x}{7} = \frac{56}{7}$$
$$x = 8$$

2. $2b - 6 = 8$
$$2b - 6 + 6 = 8 + 6$$
$$2b = 14$$
$$\frac{2b}{2} = \frac{14}{2}$$
$$b = 7$$

3. $2y + 11 = -5y - 17$
$$2y + 11 - 11 = -5y - 17 - 11$$
$$2y = -5y - 28$$
$$2y + 5y = -5y - 28 + 5y$$
$$7y = -28$$
$$\frac{7y}{7} = \frac{-28}{7}$$
$$y = -4$$

4. $9 - a = 11$
$$9 - a - 9 = 11 - 9$$
$$-a = 2$$
$$\frac{-a}{-1} = \frac{2}{-1}$$
$$a = -2$$

5. $12m + 19 = 79$
$$12m + 19 - 19 = 79 - 19$$
$$12m = 60$$
$$\frac{12m}{12} = \frac{60}{12}$$
$$m = 5$$

6. $8y - 3 = -19$
$$8y - 3 + 3 = -19 + 3$$
$$8y = -16$$
$$\frac{8y}{8} = \frac{-16}{8}$$
$$y = -2$$

7.
$$6m - 24 = 0$$
$$6m - 24 + 24 = 0 + 24$$
$$6m = 24$$
$$\frac{6m}{6} = \frac{24}{6}$$
$$m = 4$$

8.
$$5t + 2 = 37$$
$$5t + 2 - 2 = 37 - 2$$
$$5t = 35$$
$$\frac{5t}{5} = \frac{35}{5}$$
$$t = 7$$

9.
$$10z + 9 = 5z - 6$$
$$10z + 9 - 9 = 5z - 6 - 9$$
$$10z = 5z - 15$$
$$10z - 5z = 5z - 15 - 5z$$
$$5z = -15$$
$$\frac{5z}{5} = \frac{-15}{5}$$
$$z = -3$$

10.
$$-y - 11 = 5y - 17$$
$$-y - 11 + 11 = 5y - 17 + 11$$
$$-y = 5y - 6$$
$$-y - 5y = 5y - 6 - 5y$$
$$-6y = -6$$
$$\frac{-6y}{-6} = \frac{-6}{-6}$$
$$y = 1$$

11.
$$-4m + 2 = -5m + 3$$
$$-4m + 2 - 2 = -5m + 3 - 2$$
$$-4m = -5m + 1$$
$$-4m + 5m = -5m + 1 + 5m$$
$$m = 1$$

12.
$$14 - 5y = 14 + 2y$$
$$14 - 5y - 14 = 14 + 2y - 14$$
$$-5y = 2y$$
$$-5y - 2y = 2y - 2y$$
$$-7y = 0$$
$$\frac{-7y}{-7} = \frac{0}{-7}$$
$$y = 0$$

13.
$$2(x - 7) = 4x + 8$$
$$2x - 14 = 4x + 8$$
$$2x - 14 + 14 = 4x + 8 + 14$$
$$2x = 4x + 22$$
$$2x - 4x = 4x + 22 - 4x$$
$$-2x = 22$$
$$\frac{-2x}{-2} = \frac{22}{-2}$$
$$x = -11$$

14.
$$7(4c + 2) - 1 = 26c + 5$$
$$28c + 14 - 1 = 26c + 5$$
$$28c + 13 = 26c + 5$$
$$28c + 13 - 13 = 26c + 5 - 13$$
$$28c = 26c - 8$$
$$28c - 26c = 26c - 8 - 26c$$
$$2c = -8$$
$$\frac{2c}{2} = \frac{-8}{2}$$
$$c = -4$$

15.
$$-6(2 - x) = 3(x - 3)$$
$$-12 + 6x = 3x - 9$$
$$-12 + 6x + 12 = 3x - 9 + 12$$
$$6x = 3x + 3$$
$$6x - 3x = 3x + 3 - 3x$$
$$3x = 3$$
$$\frac{3x}{3} = \frac{3}{3}$$
$$x = 1$$

16. $20 + 8(y - 1) = 6y + 32$

$20 + 8y - 8 = 6y + 32$

$8y + 12 = 6y + 32$

$8y + 12 - 12 = 6y + 32 - 12$

$8y = 6y + 20$

$8y - 6y = 6y + 20 - 6y$

$2y = 20$

$\dfrac{2y}{2} = \dfrac{20}{2}$

$y = 10$

17. The sum of      is      $-13$
    $-18$ and 5
    
    $\downarrow$          $\downarrow$      $\downarrow$
    
    $-18 + 5$      $=$      $-13$

18. Four   times   the difference   amounts   $-52$
                   of $-10$ and 3      to
    
    $\downarrow$      $\downarrow$      $\downarrow$      $\downarrow$      $\downarrow$
    
    $4$    $\cdot$    $(-10 - 3)$    $=$    $-52$

19. Forty subtracted      equals      $-58$
       from $-18$
    
    $\downarrow$          $\downarrow$      $\downarrow$
    
    $-18 - 40$      $=$      $-58$

20. The quotient of      is equal to      15
    150 and twice 5
    
    $\downarrow$          $\downarrow$      $\downarrow$
    
    $\dfrac{150}{2(5)}$      $=$      15

## 3.5 SOLUTIONS TO EXERCISES

1. A number   added to   $-4$   is   $-19$
   
   $\downarrow$          $\downarrow$      $\downarrow$   $\downarrow$   $\downarrow$
   
   $x$      $+$      $-4$   $=$   $-19$

2. Four   times   a number   yields   44
   
   $\downarrow$   $\downarrow$   $\downarrow$      $\downarrow$   $\downarrow$
   
   $4$   $\cdot$   $x$      $=$   44

3. Six   added to   twice a number   gives   10
   
   $\downarrow$   $\downarrow$      $\downarrow$      $\downarrow$   $\downarrow$
   
   $6$   $+$      $2x$      $=$   10

4. Seven   times   the difference   amounts   $-14$
                    of 6 and a        to
                    number
   
   $\downarrow$   $\downarrow$      $\downarrow$      $\downarrow$   $\downarrow$
   
   $7$   $\cdot$      $(6 - x)$      $=$   $-14$

5. Four times   added to   fifteen   is   forty-three
   a number
   
   $\downarrow$      $\downarrow$      $\downarrow$   $\downarrow$   $\downarrow$
   
   $4x$      $+$      15   $=$   43
   
   $4x + 15 = 43$
   
   $4x + 15 - 15 = 43 - 15$
   
   $4x = 28$
   
   $\dfrac{4x}{4} = \dfrac{28}{4}$
   
   $x = 7$
   
   The unknown number is 7.

6. The product of   gives   56
   8 and a number
   
   $\downarrow$      $\downarrow$   $\downarrow$
   
   $8x$      $=$   56
   
   $8x = 56$
   
   $\dfrac{8x}{8} = \dfrac{56}{8}$
   
   $x = 7$
   
   The unknown number is 7.

7. Seven less than   is   twenty-three
   three times a
   number
   
   $\downarrow$      $\downarrow$   $\downarrow$
   
   $3x - 7$      $=$   23

$$3x - 7 = 23$$
$$3x - 7 + 7 = 23 + 7$$
$$3x = 30$$
$$\frac{3x}{3} = \frac{30}{3}$$
$$x = 10$$
The unknown number is 10.

8. 

| Fourteen | decreased by | some number | equals | the quotient of twenty and four |
|:---:|:---:|:---:|:---:|:---:|
| ↓ | ↓ | ↓ | ↓ | ↓ |
| 14 | − | $x$ | = | $\frac{20}{4}$ |

$$14 - x = \frac{20}{4}$$
$$14 - x = 5$$
$$14 - x - 14 = 5 - 14$$
$$-x = -9$$
$$\frac{-x}{-1} = \frac{-9}{-1}$$
$$x = 9$$
The unknown number is 9.

9. The sum of four, five, and a number    is 10

| | | | |
|:---:|:---:|:---:|:---:|
| ↓ | | ↓ | ↓ |
| $4 + 5 + x$ | | = | 10 |

$$4 + 5 + x = 10$$
$$9 + x = 10$$
$$9 + x - 9 = 10 - 9$$
$$x = 1$$
The unknown number is 1.

10. The product of eight and a number    is    one hundred twenty-eight

| | | |
|:---:|:---:|:---:|
| ↓ | ↓ | ↓ |
| $8x$ | = | 128 |

$$8x = 128$$
$$\frac{8x}{8} = \frac{128}{8}$$
$$x = 16$$
The unknown number is 16.

11. 

| Seventeen | added to | the product of five and some number | amounts to | the product of seven and the same number | added to | twenty-five |
|:---:|:---:|:---:|:---:|:---:|:---:|:---:|
| ↓ | ↓ | ↓ | ↓ | ↓ | ↓ | ↓ |
| 17 | + | $5x$ | = | $7x$ | + | 25 |

$$17 + 5x = 7x + 25$$
$$17 + 5x - 17 = 7x + 25 - 17$$
$$5x = 7x + 8$$
$$5x - 7x = 7x + 8 - 7x$$
$$-2x = 8$$
$$\frac{-2x}{-2} = \frac{8}{-2}$$
$$x = -4$$
The unknown number is $-4$.

12.  Seventy-one | less | a number | is equal to | the product of three and | the difference of the number and three

$$\downarrow \qquad \downarrow \qquad \downarrow \qquad \downarrow \qquad \downarrow \qquad \downarrow$$
$$71 \qquad - \qquad x \qquad = \qquad 3\cdot \qquad (x-3)$$

$$71-x=3(x-3)$$
$$71-x=3x-9$$
$$71-x-71=3x-9-71$$
$$-x=3x-80$$
$$-x-3x=3x-80-3x$$
$$-4x=-80$$
$$\frac{-4x}{-4}=\frac{-80}{-4}$$
$$x=20$$

The unknown number is $20$.

13.  If the sum of three times a number | and two times the same number | is increased by | 1 | the result is | 16

$$\downarrow \qquad\qquad \downarrow \qquad\qquad \downarrow \qquad \downarrow \qquad \downarrow \qquad \downarrow$$
$$(3x \qquad + \qquad 2x) \qquad + \qquad 1 \qquad = \qquad 16$$

$$(3x+2x)+1=16$$
$$5x+1=16$$
$$5x+1-1=16-1$$
$$5x=15$$
$$\frac{5x}{5}=\frac{15}{5}$$
$$x=3$$

The unknown number is 3.

14.  Four times | the sum of twice a number | and 6 | is | $-8$

$$\downarrow \qquad\qquad \downarrow \qquad\qquad \downarrow \quad \downarrow \quad \downarrow$$
$$4\cdot \qquad (2x \quad + \qquad 6) \quad = \quad -8$$

$$4(2x+6)=-8$$
$$8x+24=-8$$
$$8x+24-24=-8-24$$
$$8x=-32$$
$$\frac{8x}{8}=\frac{-32}{8}$$
$$x=-4$$

The unknown number is $-4$.

15. 

| If 5 | is added | the sum of twice | and three times | the result | 25 |
|------|----------|------------------|-----------------|------------|-----|
|      | to       | a number         | the number      | is         |     |
|      | ↓        | ↓                | ↓               | ↓          | ↓   |
| 5    | +        | (2x +            | 3x)             | =          | 25  |

$$5 + (2x + 3x) = 25$$
$$5 + 5x = 25$$
$$5 + 5x - 5 = 25 - 5$$
$$5x = 20$$
$$\frac{5x}{5} = \frac{20}{5}$$
$$x = 4$$

The unknown number is 4.

16. Let $x =$ Payton's age now

Then $x + 4 =$ Shawn's age now

Five years ago, the sum of their ages was 64.
$$(x - 5) + (x + 4 - 5) = 64$$
$$x - 5 + x + 4 - 5 = 64$$
$$2x - 6 = 64$$
$$2x - 6 + 6 = 64 + 6$$
$$2x = 70$$
$$\frac{2x}{2} = \frac{70}{2}$$
$$x = 35$$

Payton is 35 years old and Shawn is 39 years old.

17. Let $x =$ number of cards that Bobby has

Then $3x =$ number of cards that Josh has

Together they have 960 cards.

| Josh's cards | + | Bobby's cards | = | Total cards |
|--------------|---|---------------|---|-------------|
| 3x           | + | x             | = | 960         |

$$3x + x = 960$$
$$4x = 960$$
$$\frac{4x}{4} = \frac{960}{4}$$
$$x = 240$$

Bobby has 240 cards and Josh has 720 cards.

18. Let $x$ = value of trailer
Then $5x$ = value of boat

Total value is \$7800

Value of trailer + value of boat = \$7800
$$x \quad + \quad 5x \quad = 7800$$
$$6x = 7800$$
$$\frac{6x}{6} = \frac{7800}{6}$$
$$x = 1300$$
The trailer is worth \$1300 and the boat is worth \$6500.

19. Let $x$ = price of accessories
Then $6x$ = price of dolls

Total price is \$560.

price of accesories + price of dolls = 560
$$x \quad + \quad 6x \quad = 560$$
$$7x = 560$$
$$\frac{7x}{7} = \frac{560}{7}$$
$$x = 80$$
The accessories cost \$80 and the dolls cost \$480.

20. Let $x$ = Chad's speed
Then $2x$ = Nathan's speed

Total speed is 60 miles per hour.
Chad's speed + Nathan's speed = total speed
$$x \quad + \quad 2x \quad = \quad 60$$
$$3x = 60$$
$$\frac{3x}{3} = \frac{60}{3}$$
$$x = 20$$
Chad is traveling at 20 miles per hour and Nathan is traveling at 40 miles per hour.

**CHAPTER 3 PRACTICE TEST SOLUTIONS**

1. $12x - 4 - 3x + 13 = 12x - 3x - 4 + 13$
$$= (12 - 3)x + (-4) + 13$$
$$= 9x + 9$$

2. $-5(4y - 5) = -5 \cdot 4y - 5(-5)$
$$= -20y + 25$$

3. $5(3z + 5) - 4z + 16 = 15z + 25 - 4z + 16$
$$= 15z - 4z + 25 + 16$$
$$= 11z + 41$$

4. $P = 4(side)$
$$= 4(5x + 8)$$
$$= 20x + 32$$
The perimeter of the square is $(20x + 32)$ meters.

5. Area of 1st rectangle = width · length
$$= (3x)(4)$$
$$= 12x$$

    Area of 2nd rectangle = width · length
$$= (4x - 2)(9)$$
$$= 36x - 18$$

    Total area = 1st area + 2nd area
$$= 12x + (36x - 18)$$
$$= 12x + 36x - 18$$
$$= 48x - 18$$

The total area is $(48x - 18)$ square feet.

6. $11x + 5x = -48$
$$16x = -48$$
$$\frac{16x}{16} = \frac{-48}{16}$$
$$x = -3$$

7. $29 = 2x - 31x$
$$29 = -29x$$
$$\frac{29}{-29} = \frac{-29x}{-29}$$
$$-1 = x \text{ or } x = -1$$

8. $3z - 8 = 31$
$$3z - 8 + 8 = 31 + 8$$
$$3z = 39$$
$$\frac{3z}{3} = \frac{39}{3}$$
$$z = 13$$

9. $42 + 5z = 12$
$$42 + 5z - 42 = 12 - 42$$
$$5z = -30$$
$$\frac{5z}{5} = \frac{-30}{5}$$
$$z = -6$$

10. $11x + 21 - 10x - 18 = 30$
$$x + 3 = 30$$
$$x + 3 - 3 = 30 - 3$$
$$x = 27$$

11. $3 - 2d + 3d = 25$
$$3 + d = 25$$
$$3 + d - 3 = 25 - 3$$
$$d = 22$$

12. $6x - 9 = -57$
$$6x - 9 + 9 = -57 + 9$$
$$6x = -48$$
$$\frac{6x}{6} = \frac{-48}{6}$$
$$x = -8$$

13. $-5y + 10 = -10$

$-5y + 10 - 10 = -10 - 10$

$-5y = -20$

$\dfrac{-5y}{-5} = \dfrac{-20}{-5}$

$y = 4$

14. $4(x - 3) = 0$

$4x - 12 = 0$

$4x - 12 + 12 = 0 + 12$

$4x = 12$

$\dfrac{4x}{4} = \dfrac{12}{4}$

$x = 3$

15. $7(1 + 3y) = 112$

$7 + 21y = 112$

$7 + 21y - 7 = 112 - 7$

$21y = 105$

$\dfrac{21y}{21} = \dfrac{105}{21}$

$y = 5$

16. $11x - 5 = x + 25$

$11x - 5 + 5 = x + 25 + 5$

$11x = x + 30$

$11x - x = x + 30 - x$

$10x = 30$

$\dfrac{10x}{10} = \dfrac{30}{10}$

$x = 3$

17. $9a - 7 = 7a + 19$

$9a - 7 + 7 = 7a + 19 + 7$

$9a = 7a + 26$

$9a - 7a = 7a + 26 - 7a$

$2a = 26$

$\dfrac{2a}{2} = \dfrac{26}{2}$

$a = 13$

18. $4 + 5(2m - 3) = 9$

$4 + 10m - 15 = 9$

$10m - 11 = 9$

$10m - 11 + 11 = 9 + 11$

$10m = 20$

$\dfrac{10m}{10} = \dfrac{20}{10}$

$m = 2$

19. $6(3x + 8) = 10(2x - 3)$

$18x + 48 = 20x - 30$

$18x + 48 - 48 = 20x - 30 - 48$

$18x = 20x - 78$

$18x - 20x = 20x - 78 - 20x$

$-2x = -78$

$\dfrac{-2x}{-2} = \dfrac{-78}{-2}$

$x = 39$

20. The product of  yields  $-54$

$-18$ and 3

$\quad\downarrow\qquad\qquad\downarrow\qquad\downarrow$

$-18 \cdot 3 \qquad = \qquad -54$

21. Twice  the sum of  amounts  6

$-8$ and 11       to

$\;\downarrow\qquad\quad\downarrow\qquad\qquad\downarrow\qquad\downarrow$

$2 \cdot \qquad (-8 + 11) \qquad = \qquad 6$

22. The sum of four  and six times  is  30

times a number   the number

$\quad\downarrow\qquad\qquad\qquad\downarrow\qquad\quad\downarrow\;\;\downarrow$

$4x \quad + \qquad\qquad 6x \qquad = \quad 30$

$4x + 6x = 30$

$10x = 30$

$\dfrac{10x}{10} = \dfrac{30}{10}$

$x = 3$

The unknown number is 3.

23.

| Three | times | the sum of a number and 1 | is | 18 |
|-------|-------|---------------------------|-----|-----|
| ↓ | ↓ | ↓ | ↓ | ↓ |
| 3 | · | $(x+1)$ | = | 18 |

$$3(x+1)=18$$
$$3x+3=18$$
$$3x+3-3=18-3$$
$$3x=15$$
$$\frac{3x}{3}=\frac{15}{3}$$
$$x=5$$

The unknown number is 5.

24. Let $x=$ num. of free throws made by Jeff

Then $3x=$ free throws made by Brian

Total number of free throws $=24$

Brian's free throws + Jeff's free throws $=24$

| $3x$ | $+$ | $x$ | $=24$ |
|------|-----|-----|-------|

$$3x+x=24$$
$$4x=24$$
$$\frac{4x}{4}=\frac{24}{4}$$
$$x=6$$

Brian made $3x=3(6)=18$ free throws.

25. Let $x=$ number of women in league

Then $x+18=$ number of men in league

Total number of members $=120$

num. of men + num. of women $=120$

| $(x+18)$ | $+$ | $x$ | $=120$ |
|----------|-----|-----|--------|

$$x+18+x=120$$
$$2x+18=120$$
$$2x+18-18=120-18$$
$$2x=102$$
$$\frac{2x}{2}=\frac{102}{2}$$
$$x=51$$

There are 51 women in the bowling league.

**4.1 SOLUTIONS TO EXERCISES**

1. $\dfrac{9 \text{ shaded}}{16 \text{ total}} = \dfrac{9}{16}$

2. $\dfrac{2 \text{ shaded}}{9 \text{ total}} = \dfrac{2}{9}$

3. $\dfrac{7 \text{ shaded}}{6 \text{ total per figure}} = \dfrac{7}{6}$

4. $\dfrac{7 \text{ shaded}}{4 \text{ total per figure}} = \dfrac{7}{4}$

5.

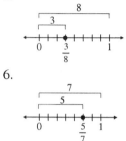

6.

7.

8. $\dfrac{7}{9} = \dfrac{7 \cdot 5}{9 \cdot 5} = \dfrac{35}{45}$

9. $\dfrac{3}{5} = \dfrac{3 \cdot 15}{5 \cdot 15} = \dfrac{45}{75}$

10. $\dfrac{6a}{11} = \dfrac{6a \cdot 3}{11 \cdot 3} = \dfrac{18a}{33}$

11. $\dfrac{9x}{17} = \dfrac{9x \cdot 3}{17 \cdot 3} = \dfrac{27x}{51}$

12. $\dfrac{4}{9b} = \dfrac{4 \cdot 4}{9b \cdot 4} = \dfrac{16}{36b}$

13. $8 = \dfrac{8}{1} = \dfrac{8 \cdot 7}{1 \cdot 7} = \dfrac{56}{7}$

14. $2 = \dfrac{2}{1} = \dfrac{2 \cdot 15}{1 \cdot 15} = \dfrac{30}{15}$

15. $\dfrac{12}{12} = 1$

16. $\dfrac{-9}{-9} = 1$

17. $\dfrac{24}{6} = 4$

18. $\dfrac{-36}{12} = -3$

19. $\dfrac{14}{-14} = -1$

20. $\dfrac{30}{1} = 30$

**4.2 SOLUTIONS TO EXERCISES**

1.

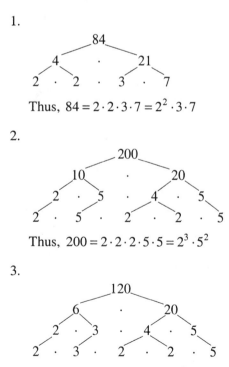

Thus, $84 = 2 \cdot 2 \cdot 3 \cdot 7 = 2^2 \cdot 3 \cdot 7$

2.

Thus, $200 = 2 \cdot 2 \cdot 2 \cdot 5 \cdot 5 = 2^3 \cdot 5^2$

3.

Thus, $120 = 2 \cdot 2 \cdot 2 \cdot 3 \cdot 5 = 2^3 \cdot 3 \cdot 5$

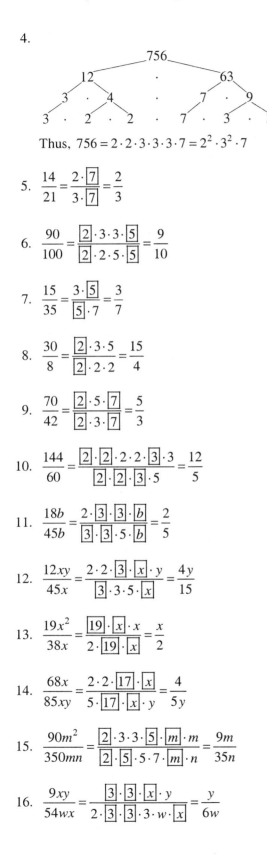

4.

$$756$$

Thus, $756 = 2 \cdot 2 \cdot 3 \cdot 3 \cdot 3 \cdot 7 = 2^2 \cdot 3^2 \cdot 7$

5. $\dfrac{14}{21} = \dfrac{2 \cdot \boxed{7}}{3 \cdot \boxed{7}} = \dfrac{2}{3}$

6. $\dfrac{90}{100} = \dfrac{\boxed{2} \cdot 3 \cdot 3 \cdot \boxed{5}}{\boxed{2} \cdot 2 \cdot 5 \cdot \boxed{5}} = \dfrac{9}{10}$

7. $\dfrac{15}{35} = \dfrac{3 \cdot \boxed{5}}{\boxed{5} \cdot 7} = \dfrac{3}{7}$

8. $\dfrac{30}{8} = \dfrac{\boxed{2} \cdot 3 \cdot 5}{\boxed{2} \cdot 2 \cdot 2} = \dfrac{15}{4}$

9. $\dfrac{70}{42} = \dfrac{\boxed{2} \cdot 5 \cdot \boxed{7}}{\boxed{2} \cdot 3 \cdot \boxed{7}} = \dfrac{5}{3}$

10. $\dfrac{144}{60} = \dfrac{\boxed{2} \cdot \boxed{2} \cdot 2 \cdot 2 \cdot \boxed{3} \cdot 3}{\boxed{2} \cdot \boxed{2} \cdot \boxed{3} \cdot 5} = \dfrac{12}{5}$

11. $\dfrac{18b}{45b} = \dfrac{2 \cdot \boxed{3} \cdot \boxed{3} \cdot \boxed{b}}{\boxed{3} \cdot \boxed{3} \cdot 5 \cdot \boxed{b}} = \dfrac{2}{5}$

12. $\dfrac{12xy}{45x} = \dfrac{2 \cdot 2 \cdot \boxed{3} \cdot \boxed{x} \cdot y}{\boxed{3} \cdot 3 \cdot 5 \cdot \boxed{x}} = \dfrac{4y}{15}$

13. $\dfrac{19x^2}{38x} = \dfrac{\boxed{19} \cdot \boxed{x} \cdot x}{2 \cdot \boxed{19} \cdot \boxed{x}} = \dfrac{x}{2}$

14. $\dfrac{68x}{85xy} = \dfrac{2 \cdot 2 \cdot \boxed{17} \cdot \boxed{x}}{5 \cdot \boxed{17} \cdot \boxed{x} \cdot y} = \dfrac{4}{5y}$

15. $\dfrac{90m^2}{350mn} = \dfrac{\boxed{2} \cdot 3 \cdot 3 \cdot \boxed{5} \cdot \boxed{m} \cdot m}{\boxed{2} \cdot \boxed{5} \cdot 5 \cdot 7 \cdot \boxed{m} \cdot n} = \dfrac{9m}{35n}$

16. $\dfrac{9xy}{54wx} = \dfrac{\boxed{3} \cdot \boxed{3} \cdot \boxed{x} \cdot y}{2 \cdot \boxed{3} \cdot \boxed{3} \cdot 3 \cdot w \cdot \boxed{x}} = \dfrac{y}{6w}$

17. $\dfrac{144ab}{84b^2} = \dfrac{\boxed{2} \cdot \boxed{2} \cdot 2 \cdot 2 \cdot \boxed{3} \cdot 3 \cdot a \cdot \boxed{b}}{\boxed{2} \cdot \boxed{2} \cdot \boxed{3} \cdot 7 \cdot \boxed{b} \cdot b} = \dfrac{12a}{7b}$

18. $\dfrac{432x}{120x^2} = \dfrac{\boxed{2} \cdot \boxed{2} \cdot \boxed{2} \cdot 2 \cdot \boxed{3} \cdot 3 \cdot 3 \cdot \boxed{x}}{\boxed{2} \cdot \boxed{2} \cdot \boxed{2} \cdot \boxed{3} \cdot 5 \cdot \boxed{x} \cdot x} = \dfrac{18}{5x}$

19. $\dfrac{220 \text{ yards}}{1760 \text{ yards}} = \dfrac{\boxed{2} \cdot \boxed{2} \cdot \boxed{5} \cdot \boxed{11}}{\boxed{2} \cdot \boxed{2} \cdot 2 \cdot 2 \cdot 2 \cdot \boxed{5} \cdot \boxed{11}} = \dfrac{1}{8}$

20. $\dfrac{12 \text{ hours}}{45 \text{ hours}} = \dfrac{2 \cdot 2 \cdot \boxed{3}}{\boxed{3} \cdot 3 \cdot 5} = \dfrac{4}{15}$

## 4.3 SOLUTIONS TO EXERCISES

1. $\dfrac{7}{10} \cdot \dfrac{4}{21} = \dfrac{7 \cdot 4}{10 \cdot 21} = \dfrac{\boxed{7} \cdot \boxed{2} \cdot 2}{\boxed{2} \cdot 5 \cdot 3 \cdot \boxed{7}} = \dfrac{2}{15}$

2. $-\dfrac{5}{6} \cdot \dfrac{4}{7} = -\dfrac{5 \cdot 4}{6 \cdot 7} = -\dfrac{5 \cdot \boxed{2} \cdot 2}{\boxed{2} \cdot 3 \cdot 7} = -\dfrac{10}{21}$

3. $\dfrac{9x}{11} \cdot \dfrac{22}{15} = \dfrac{9x \cdot 22}{11 \cdot 15} = \dfrac{3 \cdot \boxed{3} \cdot x \cdot 2 \cdot \boxed{11}}{\boxed{11} \cdot \boxed{3} \cdot 5} = \dfrac{6x}{5}$

4. $9 \cdot \dfrac{1}{2} = \dfrac{9}{1} \cdot \dfrac{1}{2} = \dfrac{9 \cdot 1}{1 \cdot 2} = \dfrac{9}{2}$

5. $-\dfrac{3}{8} \cdot 16 = -\dfrac{3}{8} \cdot \dfrac{16}{1}$

$\qquad = -\dfrac{3 \cdot 16}{8 \cdot 1}$

$\qquad = -\dfrac{3 \cdot \boxed{2} \cdot \boxed{2} \cdot \boxed{2} \cdot 2}{\boxed{2} \cdot \boxed{2} \cdot \boxed{2} \cdot 1}$

$\qquad = -\dfrac{6}{1}$

$\qquad = -6$

6. $\dfrac{5}{3} \div \dfrac{1}{6} = \dfrac{5}{3} \cdot \dfrac{6}{1}$

$\qquad = \dfrac{5 \cdot 6}{3 \cdot 1}$

$\qquad = \dfrac{5 \cdot 2 \cdot \boxed{3}}{\boxed{3} \cdot 1}$

$\qquad = \dfrac{10}{1}$

$\qquad = 10$

7. 
$$\frac{22}{35} \div -\frac{55}{14} = \frac{22}{35} \cdot -\frac{14}{55}$$
$$= -\frac{22 \cdot 14}{35 \cdot 55}$$
$$= -\frac{2 \cdot \boxed{11} \cdot 2 \cdot \boxed{7}}{5 \cdot \boxed{7} \cdot 5 \cdot \boxed{11}}$$
$$= -\frac{4}{25}$$

8. 
$$\frac{12y}{13} \div \frac{3}{26} = \frac{12y}{13} \cdot \frac{26}{3}$$
$$= \frac{12y \cdot 26}{13 \cdot 3}$$
$$= \frac{2 \cdot 2 \cdot \boxed{3} \cdot y \cdot 2 \cdot \boxed{13}}{\boxed{13} \cdot \boxed{3}}$$
$$= \frac{8y}{1}$$
$$= 8y$$

9. 
$$-\frac{3}{4} \div 12 = -\frac{3}{4} \cdot \frac{1}{12}$$
$$= -\frac{3 \cdot 1}{4 \cdot 12}$$
$$= -\frac{\boxed{3} \cdot 1}{2 \cdot 2 \cdot 2 \cdot 2 \cdot \boxed{3}}$$
$$= -\frac{1}{16}$$

10. 
$$\left(-\frac{7}{8}\right)^2 = \left(-\frac{7}{8}\right)\left(-\frac{7}{8}\right) = \frac{7 \cdot 7}{8 \cdot 8} = \frac{49}{64}$$

11. 
$$\left(\frac{2}{5}\right)^3 = \left(\frac{2}{5}\right)\left(\frac{2}{5}\right)\left(\frac{2}{5}\right) = \frac{2 \cdot 2 \cdot 2}{5 \cdot 5 \cdot 5} = \frac{8}{125}$$

12. 
$$\frac{1}{4} \cdot \frac{2}{5} \div \frac{3}{10} = \frac{1}{4} \cdot \frac{2}{5} \cdot \frac{10}{3}$$
$$= \frac{1 \cdot 2 \cdot 10}{4 \cdot 5 \cdot 3}$$
$$= \frac{1 \cdot \boxed{2} \cdot \boxed{2} \cdot \boxed{5}}{\boxed{2} \cdot \boxed{2} \cdot \boxed{5} \cdot 3}$$
$$= \frac{1}{3}$$

13. 
$$\frac{3}{4} \div \frac{2}{9} \cdot -\frac{16}{3} = \frac{3}{4} \cdot \frac{9}{2} \cdot -\frac{16}{3}$$
$$= -\frac{3 \cdot 9 \cdot 16}{4 \cdot 2 \cdot 3}$$
$$= -\frac{\boxed{3} \cdot 3 \cdot 3 \cdot \boxed{2} \cdot \boxed{2} \cdot \boxed{2} \cdot 2}{\boxed{2} \cdot \boxed{2} \cdot \boxed{2} \cdot \boxed{3}}$$
$$= -\frac{18}{1}$$
$$= -18$$

14. 
$$12x \div \frac{24x}{5} = \frac{12x}{1} \div \frac{24x}{5}$$
$$= \frac{12x}{1} \cdot \frac{5}{24x}$$
$$= \frac{12x \cdot 5}{1 \cdot 24x}$$
$$= \frac{\boxed{2} \cdot \boxed{2} \cdot \boxed{3} \cdot \boxed{x} \cdot 5}{1 \cdot \boxed{2} \cdot \boxed{2} \cdot 2 \cdot \boxed{3} \cdot \boxed{x}}$$
$$= \frac{5}{2}$$

15. 
$$\frac{3}{16} \cdot \left(35 \div \frac{5}{8}\right) = \frac{3}{16} \cdot \left(\frac{35}{1} \cdot \frac{8}{5}\right)$$
$$= \frac{3}{16} \cdot \left(\frac{\boxed{5} \cdot 7 \cdot 8}{1 \cdot \boxed{5}}\right)$$
$$= \frac{3}{16} \cdot \left(\frac{7 \cdot 8}{1}\right)$$
$$= \frac{3 \cdot 7 \cdot 8}{16 \cdot 1}$$
$$= \frac{3 \cdot 7 \cdot \boxed{8}}{2 \cdot \boxed{8} \cdot 1}$$
$$= \frac{21}{2}$$

16. a. 
$$xy = \frac{3}{7} \cdot \frac{7}{9} = \frac{3 \cdot 7}{7 \cdot 9} = \frac{\boxed{3} \cdot \boxed{7}}{\boxed{7} \cdot \boxed{3} \cdot 3} = \frac{1}{3}$$

   b. 
$$x \div y = \frac{3}{7} \div \frac{7}{9} = \frac{3}{7} \cdot \frac{9}{7} = \frac{3 \cdot 9}{7 \cdot 7} = \frac{27}{49}$$

**4.4 SOLUTIONS TO EXERCISES**

17.　　　　$2x = -\dfrac{5}{8}$

$$2\left(-\dfrac{5}{16}\right) = -\dfrac{5}{8}$$

$$-\dfrac{2}{1}\cdot\dfrac{5}{16} = -\dfrac{5}{8}$$

$$-\dfrac{\boxed{2}\cdot 5}{\boxed{2}\cdot 2\cdot 2\cdot 2} = -\dfrac{5}{8}$$

$$-\dfrac{5}{8} = -\dfrac{5}{8} \quad \leftarrow \text{True}$$

Thus, $x = -\dfrac{5}{16}$ is a solution.

18. Area $=$ length $\cdot$ width

$$= \left(\dfrac{15}{16}\text{ inch}\right)\left(\dfrac{4}{5}\text{ inch}\right)$$

$$= \dfrac{15\cdot 4}{16\cdot 5}\text{ square inches}$$

$$= \dfrac{3\cdot\boxed{5}\cdot\boxed{4}}{\boxed{4}\cdot 4\cdot\boxed{5}}\text{ square inches}$$

$$= \dfrac{3}{4}\text{ square inches}$$

19. $\begin{array}{l}\text{number} \\ \text{of books}\end{array} = \begin{array}{l}\text{total} \\ \text{weight}\end{array} \div \begin{array}{l}\text{weight} \\ \text{per book}\end{array}$

$$= \quad 12 \quad \div \quad \dfrac{3}{4}$$

$$= \quad \dfrac{12}{1} \quad \cdot \quad \dfrac{4}{3}$$

$$= \quad \dfrac{2\cdot 2\cdot\boxed{3}\cdot 2\cdot 2}{1\cdot\boxed{3}}$$

$$= \quad 16$$

There are 16 books in the box.

20. $\begin{array}{l}\text{number} \\ \text{of apple} \\ \text{trees}\end{array} = \begin{array}{l}\text{fraction of} \\ \text{apple trees} \\ \text{in orchard}\end{array} \cdot \begin{array}{l}\text{total} \\ \text{number} \\ \text{of trees}\end{array}$

$$= \quad \dfrac{5}{8} \quad \cdot \quad 64$$

$$= \quad \dfrac{5\cdot\boxed{2}\cdot\boxed{2}\cdot\boxed{2}\cdot 2\cdot 2\cdot 2}{\boxed{2}\cdot\boxed{2}\cdot\boxed{2}}$$

$$= \quad 40$$

There are 40 apple trees in the orchard.

1. $\dfrac{1}{8}+\dfrac{5}{8}=\dfrac{1+5}{8}=\dfrac{6}{8}=\dfrac{\boxed{2}\cdot 3}{\boxed{2}\cdot 2\cdot 2}=\dfrac{3}{4}$

2. $\dfrac{11}{16}+\dfrac{5}{16}=\dfrac{11+5}{16}=\dfrac{16}{16}=1$

3. $-\dfrac{1}{3}+\dfrac{1}{3}=\dfrac{-1+1}{3}=\dfrac{0}{3}=0$

4. $-\dfrac{7}{x}+\dfrac{9}{x}=\dfrac{-7+9}{x}=\dfrac{2}{x}$

5. $\dfrac{7}{10y}+\dfrac{1}{10y}=\dfrac{7+1}{10y}=\dfrac{8}{10y}=\dfrac{\boxed{2}\cdot 2\cdot 2}{\boxed{2}\cdot 5\cdot y}=\dfrac{4}{5y}$

6. $\dfrac{4}{21}+\dfrac{8}{21}+\dfrac{5}{21}=\dfrac{4+8+5}{21}=\dfrac{17}{21}$

7. $\dfrac{9}{13}-\dfrac{5}{13}=\dfrac{9-5}{13}=\dfrac{4}{13}$

8. $\dfrac{6}{y}-\dfrac{10}{y}=\dfrac{6-10}{y}=\dfrac{-4}{y}$ or $-\dfrac{4}{y}$

9. $\dfrac{5}{22}-\dfrac{3}{22}=\dfrac{5-3}{22}=\dfrac{2}{22}=\dfrac{\boxed{2}}{\boxed{2}\cdot 11}=\dfrac{1}{11}$

10. $\dfrac{13}{15a}+\dfrac{7}{15a}=\dfrac{13+7}{15a}=\dfrac{20}{15a}=\dfrac{2\cdot 2\cdot\boxed{5}}{3\cdot\boxed{5}\cdot a}=\dfrac{4}{3a}$

11. $-\dfrac{5}{14}+\dfrac{3}{14}=\dfrac{-5+3}{14}=\dfrac{-2}{14}=-\dfrac{\boxed{2}}{\boxed{2}\cdot 7}=-\dfrac{1}{7}$

12. $\dfrac{11x}{12}-\dfrac{17x}{12}=\dfrac{11x-17x}{12}$

$$=\dfrac{-6x}{12}$$

$$=-\dfrac{\boxed{2}\cdot\boxed{3}\cdot x}{\boxed{2}\cdot 2\cdot\boxed{3}}$$

$$=-\dfrac{x}{2}$$

13. $x+y=-\dfrac{1}{8}+\dfrac{5}{8}=\dfrac{-1+5}{8}=\dfrac{4}{8}=\dfrac{\boxed{2}\cdot\boxed{2}}{\boxed{2}\cdot\boxed{2}\cdot 2}=\dfrac{1}{2}$

14. $x - y = -\dfrac{2}{9} - \left(-\dfrac{5}{9}\right)$

$= -\dfrac{2}{9} + \dfrac{5}{9}$

$= \dfrac{-2+5}{9}$

$= \dfrac{3}{9}$

$= \dfrac{\boxed{3}}{\boxed{3} \cdot 3}$

$= \dfrac{1}{3}$

15. $6 = 2 \cdot 3$

$27 = 3 \cdot 3 \cdot 3$

$\text{LCD} = 2 \cdot 3 \cdot 3 \cdot 3 = 54$

16. $18 = 2 \cdot 3 \cdot 3$

$30 = 2 \cdot 3 \cdot 5$

$\text{LCD} = 2 \cdot 3 \cdot 3 \cdot 5 = 90$

17. $x + \dfrac{1}{10} = -\dfrac{7}{10}$

$x + \dfrac{1}{10} - \dfrac{1}{10} = -\dfrac{7}{10} - \dfrac{1}{10}$

$x = \dfrac{-7-1}{10}$

$x = \dfrac{-8}{10}$

$x = -\dfrac{4}{5}$

18. $5x + \dfrac{1}{7} - 4x = \dfrac{2}{7} - \dfrac{4}{7}$

$x + \dfrac{1}{7} = \dfrac{2-4}{7}$

$x + \dfrac{1}{7} = \dfrac{-2}{7}$

$x + \dfrac{1}{7} - \dfrac{1}{7} = \dfrac{-2}{7} - \dfrac{1}{7}$

$x = \dfrac{-2-1}{7}$

$x = \dfrac{-3}{7} \ \text{ or } \ -\dfrac{3}{7}$

19. $\begin{array}{lcccc} \text{total} & = & \text{1st amount} & + & \text{2nd amount} \\ \text{flour} & & \text{of flour} & & \text{of flour} \end{array}$

$= \dfrac{4}{3} + \dfrac{2}{3}$

$= \dfrac{4+2}{3}$

$= \dfrac{6}{3}$

$= 2$

The recipe requires 2 cups of flour.

20. $\begin{array}{lcccc} \text{length} & = & \text{original} & - & \text{length} \\ \text{remaining} & & \text{length} & & \text{removed} \end{array}$

$= \dfrac{25}{36} - \dfrac{15}{36}$

$= \dfrac{25-15}{36}$

$= \dfrac{10}{36}$

$= \dfrac{5}{18}$

Judy has $\dfrac{5}{18}$ of a yard of material left.

## 4.5 SOLUTIONS TO EXERCISES

1. $\dfrac{1}{8} + \dfrac{7}{16} = \dfrac{1 \cdot 2}{8 \cdot 2} + \dfrac{7}{16} = \dfrac{2}{16} + \dfrac{7}{16} = \dfrac{9}{16}$

2. $\dfrac{4}{5} - \dfrac{7}{10} = \dfrac{4 \cdot 2}{5 \cdot 2} - \dfrac{7}{10} = \dfrac{8}{10} - \dfrac{7}{10} = \dfrac{1}{10}$

3. $-\dfrac{4}{9} + \dfrac{7}{3} = -\dfrac{4}{9} + \dfrac{7 \cdot 3}{3 \cdot 3} = -\dfrac{4}{9} + \dfrac{21}{9} = \dfrac{17}{9}$

4. $\dfrac{7x}{13} - \dfrac{5}{26} = \dfrac{7x \cdot 2}{13 \cdot 2} - \dfrac{5}{26} = \dfrac{14x}{26} - \dfrac{5}{26} = \dfrac{14x-5}{26}$

5. $\dfrac{4x}{9} - \dfrac{7}{18} = \dfrac{4x \cdot 2}{9 \cdot 2} - \dfrac{7}{18} = \dfrac{8x}{18} - \dfrac{7}{18} = \dfrac{8x-7}{18}$

6. $9x - \dfrac{3}{10} = \dfrac{9x}{1} - \dfrac{3}{10}$

$\qquad = \dfrac{9x \cdot 10}{1 \cdot 10} - \dfrac{3}{10}$

$\qquad = \dfrac{90x}{10} - \dfrac{3}{10}$

$\qquad = \dfrac{90x - 3}{10}$

7. $\dfrac{2}{5} + \dfrac{1}{4} + \dfrac{3}{10} = \dfrac{2 \cdot 4}{5 \cdot 4} + \dfrac{1 \cdot 5}{4 \cdot 5} + \dfrac{3 \cdot 2}{10 \cdot 2}$

$\qquad = \dfrac{8}{20} + \dfrac{5}{20} + \dfrac{6}{20}$

$\qquad = \dfrac{19}{20}$

8. $\dfrac{8}{23} + \dfrac{31}{23} - \dfrac{16}{23} = \dfrac{8 + 31 - 16}{23}$

$\qquad = \dfrac{23}{23}$

$\qquad = 1$

9. $-\dfrac{4}{7} + \dfrac{11}{14} - \dfrac{2}{21} = -\dfrac{4 \cdot 6}{7 \cdot 6} + \dfrac{11 \cdot 3}{14 \cdot 3} - \dfrac{2 \cdot 2}{21 \cdot 2}$

$\qquad = -\dfrac{24}{42} + \dfrac{33}{42} - \dfrac{4}{42}$

$\qquad = \dfrac{-24 + 33 - 4}{42}$

$\qquad = \dfrac{5}{42}$

10. $\dfrac{y}{2} + \dfrac{y}{6} + \dfrac{5y}{12} = \dfrac{y \cdot 6}{2 \cdot 6} + \dfrac{y \cdot 2}{6 \cdot 2} + \dfrac{5y}{12}$

$\qquad = \dfrac{6y}{12} + \dfrac{2y}{12} + \dfrac{5y}{12}$

$\qquad = \dfrac{13y}{12}$

11. $\dfrac{3}{8} + \dfrac{5}{7x} = \dfrac{3 \cdot 7x}{8 \cdot 7x} + \dfrac{5 \cdot 8}{7x \cdot 8}$

$\qquad = \dfrac{21x}{56x} + \dfrac{40}{56x}$

$\qquad = \dfrac{21x + 40}{56x}$

12. $\dfrac{4}{15x} + \dfrac{3}{4} = \dfrac{4 \cdot 4}{15x \cdot 4} + \dfrac{3 \cdot 15x}{4 \cdot 15x}$

$\qquad = \dfrac{16}{60x} + \dfrac{45x}{60x}$

$\qquad = \dfrac{16 + 45x}{60x}$

13. $\dfrac{7}{15} + \dfrac{11m}{20} - \dfrac{3}{10} = \dfrac{7 \cdot 4}{15 \cdot 4} + \dfrac{11m \cdot 3}{20 \cdot 3} - \dfrac{3 \cdot 6}{10 \cdot 6}$

$\qquad = \dfrac{28}{60} + \dfrac{33m}{60} - \dfrac{18}{60}$

$\qquad = \dfrac{28 + 33m - 18}{60}$

$\qquad = \dfrac{33m + 10}{60}$

14. $\dfrac{4x}{13} - \dfrac{3x}{26} - \dfrac{5}{2} = \dfrac{4x \cdot 2}{13 \cdot 2} - \dfrac{3x}{26} - \dfrac{5 \cdot 13}{2 \cdot 13}$

$\qquad = \dfrac{8x}{26} - \dfrac{3x}{26} - \dfrac{65}{26}$

$\qquad = \dfrac{8x - 3x - 65}{26}$

$\qquad = \dfrac{5x - 65}{26}$

15. $2y - x = 2\left(\dfrac{2}{5}\right) - \dfrac{1}{4}$

$\qquad = \dfrac{2}{1} \cdot \dfrac{2}{5} - \dfrac{1}{4}$

$\qquad = \dfrac{4}{5} - \dfrac{1}{4}$

$\qquad = \dfrac{4 \cdot 4}{5 \cdot 4} - \dfrac{1 \cdot 5}{4 \cdot 5}$

$\qquad = \dfrac{16}{20} - \dfrac{5}{20}$

$\qquad = \dfrac{11}{20}$

16. $x - y = \dfrac{1}{4} - \dfrac{2}{5}$

$\qquad = \dfrac{1 \cdot 5}{4 \cdot 5} - \dfrac{2 \cdot 4}{5 \cdot 4}$

$\qquad = \dfrac{5}{20} - \dfrac{8}{20}$

$\qquad = \dfrac{-3}{20} \ \text{ or } \ -\dfrac{3}{20}$

17.
$$x + \frac{11}{15} = \frac{2}{3}$$
$$x + \frac{11}{15} - \frac{11}{15} = \frac{2}{3} - \frac{11}{15}$$
$$x = \frac{2 \cdot 5}{3 \cdot 5} - \frac{11}{15}$$
$$x = \frac{10}{15} - \frac{11}{15}$$
$$x = \frac{-1}{15} \quad \text{or} \quad -\frac{1}{15}$$

18.
$$15y - \frac{3}{7} - 14y = \frac{13}{14}$$
$$y - \frac{3}{7} = \frac{13}{14}$$
$$y - \frac{3}{7} + \frac{3}{7} = \frac{13}{14} + \frac{3}{7}$$
$$y = \frac{13}{14} + \frac{3 \cdot 2}{7 \cdot 2}$$
$$y = \frac{13}{14} + \frac{6}{14}$$
$$y = \frac{19}{14}$$

19.
$$\text{Perimeter} = \frac{4}{15} + \frac{2}{9} + \frac{4}{15} + \frac{2}{9}$$
$$= \frac{4 \cdot 3}{15 \cdot 3} + \frac{2 \cdot 5}{9 \cdot 5} + \frac{4 \cdot 3}{15 \cdot 3} + \frac{2 \cdot 5}{9 \cdot 5}$$
$$= \frac{12}{45} + \frac{10}{45} + \frac{12}{45} + \frac{10}{45}$$
$$= \frac{44}{45}$$

The perimeter of the rectangle is $\frac{44}{45}$ inches.

20.
$$\begin{aligned}
\text{difference} \ &= \ \text{1st length} \ - \ \text{2nd length} \\
&= \quad \frac{5}{6} \qquad - \qquad \frac{3}{4} \\
&= \quad \frac{5 \cdot 2}{6 \cdot 2} \qquad - \qquad \frac{3 \cdot 3}{4 \cdot 3} \\
&= \quad \frac{10}{12} \qquad - \qquad \frac{9}{12} \\
&= \quad \frac{1}{12}
\end{aligned}$$

The difference is $\frac{1}{12}$ of a foot.

**4.6 SOLUTIONS TO EXERCISES**

1. $\dfrac{\dfrac{8}{27}}{\dfrac{1}{9}} = \dfrac{8}{27} \div \dfrac{1}{9} = \dfrac{8}{27} \cdot \dfrac{9}{1} = \dfrac{8 \cdot \boxed{9}}{\boxed{9} \cdot 3 \cdot 1} = \dfrac{8}{3}$

2. $\dfrac{\dfrac{6x}{13}}{\dfrac{9}{4}} = \dfrac{6x}{13} \div \dfrac{9}{4} = \dfrac{6x}{13} \cdot \dfrac{4}{9} = \dfrac{2 \cdot \boxed{3} \cdot x \cdot 4}{13 \cdot \boxed{3} \cdot 3} = \dfrac{8x}{39}$

3. $\dfrac{\dfrac{3}{8} + \dfrac{1}{4}}{\dfrac{2}{5} + \dfrac{7}{10}} = \dfrac{40\left(\dfrac{3}{8} + \dfrac{1}{4}\right)}{40\left(\dfrac{2}{5} + \dfrac{7}{10}\right)}$

$= \dfrac{40\left(\dfrac{3}{8}\right) + 40\left(\dfrac{1}{4}\right)}{40\left(\dfrac{2}{5}\right) + 40\left(\dfrac{7}{10}\right)}$

$= \dfrac{15 + 10}{16 + 28}$

$= \dfrac{25}{44}$

4. $\dfrac{\dfrac{2x}{5}}{5 - \dfrac{3}{10}} = \dfrac{10\left(\dfrac{2x}{5}\right)}{10\left(5 - \dfrac{3}{10}\right)}$

$= \dfrac{10\left(\dfrac{2x}{5}\right)}{10(5) - 10\left(\dfrac{3}{10}\right)}$

$= \dfrac{4x}{50 - 3}$

$= \dfrac{4x}{47}$

5. $\dfrac{\dfrac{6}{11} + 1}{\dfrac{3}{8a}} = \dfrac{88a\left(\dfrac{6}{11} + 1\right)}{88a\left(\dfrac{3}{8a}\right)}$

$= \dfrac{88a\left(\dfrac{6}{11}\right) + 88a(1)}{88a\left(\dfrac{3}{8a}\right)}$

$= \dfrac{48a + 88a}{33}$

$= \dfrac{136a}{33}$

6. $\dfrac{8-\dfrac{1}{3}}{6+\dfrac{3}{5}} = \dfrac{15\left(8-\dfrac{1}{3}\right)}{15\left(6+\dfrac{3}{5}\right)}$

$= \dfrac{15(8)-15\left(\dfrac{1}{3}\right)}{15(6)+15\left(\dfrac{3}{5}\right)}$

$= \dfrac{120-5}{90+9}$

$= \dfrac{115}{99}$

7. $\left(-\dfrac{3}{8}-\dfrac{9}{8}\right)\div\dfrac{5}{16} = -\dfrac{12}{8}\div\dfrac{5}{16}$

$= -\dfrac{3}{2}\cdot\dfrac{16}{5}$

$= -\dfrac{3\cdot\boxed{2}\cdot8}{\boxed{2}\cdot5}$

$= -\dfrac{24}{5}$

8. $3^2-\left(\dfrac{2}{3}\right)^2 = 9-\dfrac{4}{9} = \dfrac{81}{9}-\dfrac{4}{9} = \dfrac{77}{9}$

9. $\left(3-\dfrac{5}{2}\right)^2 = \left(\dfrac{6}{2}-\dfrac{5}{2}\right)^2 = \left(\dfrac{1}{2}\right)^2 = \dfrac{1}{4}$

10. $\left(\dfrac{4}{5}-\dfrac{9}{10}\right)\left(\dfrac{3}{4}+\dfrac{5}{8}\right) = \left(\dfrac{8}{10}-\dfrac{9}{10}\right)\left(\dfrac{6}{8}+\dfrac{5}{8}\right)$

$= \left(-\dfrac{1}{10}\right)\left(\dfrac{11}{8}\right)$

$= -\dfrac{11}{80}$

11. $\dfrac{4}{5}\cdot\dfrac{5}{9}-\dfrac{2}{3}\div\dfrac{3}{7} = \dfrac{4\cdot\boxed{5}}{\boxed{5}\cdot9}-\dfrac{2}{3}\cdot\dfrac{7}{3}$

$= \dfrac{4}{9}-\dfrac{14}{9}$

$= \dfrac{-10}{9}$ or $-\dfrac{10}{9}$

12. $\left(\dfrac{1}{6}-\dfrac{5}{2}\right)^3 = \left(\dfrac{1}{6}-\dfrac{15}{6}\right)^3$

$= \left(\dfrac{-14}{6}\right)^3$

$= \left(-\dfrac{7}{3}\right)^3$

$= -\dfrac{343}{27}$

13. $\dfrac{\dfrac{x}{4}+5}{2+\dfrac{2}{3}} = \dfrac{12\left(\dfrac{x}{4}+5\right)}{12\left(2+\dfrac{2}{3}\right)}$

$= \dfrac{12\left(\dfrac{x}{4}\right)+12(5)}{12(2)+12\left(\dfrac{2}{3}\right)}$

$= \dfrac{3x+60}{24+8}$

$= \dfrac{3x+60}{32}$

14. $\dfrac{\dfrac{5}{8}-\dfrac{x}{6}}{3-\dfrac{5}{12}} = \dfrac{24\left(\dfrac{5}{8}-\dfrac{x}{6}\right)}{24\left(3-\dfrac{5}{12}\right)}$

$= \dfrac{24\left(\dfrac{5}{8}\right)-24\left(\dfrac{x}{6}\right)}{24(3)-24\left(\dfrac{5}{12}\right)}$

$= \dfrac{15-4x}{72-10}$

$= \dfrac{15-4x}{62}$

15. $\dfrac{1+x}{y} = \dfrac{1+\dfrac{2}{5}}{-\dfrac{5}{6}}$

$= \dfrac{30\left(1+\dfrac{2}{5}\right)}{30\left(-\dfrac{5}{6}\right)}$

$= \dfrac{30+12}{-25}$

$= -\dfrac{42}{25}$

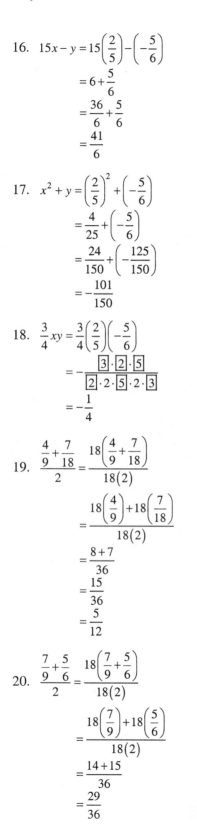

16. $15x - y = 15\left(\frac{2}{5}\right) - \left(-\frac{5}{6}\right)$

$= 6 + \frac{5}{6}$

$= \frac{36}{6} + \frac{5}{6}$

$= \frac{41}{6}$

17. $x^2 + y = \left(\frac{2}{5}\right)^2 + \left(-\frac{5}{6}\right)$

$= \frac{4}{25} + \left(-\frac{5}{6}\right)$

$= \frac{24}{150} + \left(-\frac{125}{150}\right)$

$= -\frac{101}{150}$

18. $\frac{3}{4}xy = \frac{3}{4}\left(\frac{2}{5}\right)\left(-\frac{5}{6}\right)$

$= -\frac{\boxed{3} \cdot \boxed{2} \cdot \boxed{5}}{\boxed{2} \cdot 2 \cdot \boxed{5} \cdot 2 \cdot \boxed{3}}$

$= -\frac{1}{4}$

19. $\frac{\frac{4}{9} + \frac{7}{18}}{2} = \frac{18\left(\frac{4}{9} + \frac{7}{18}\right)}{18(2)}$

$= \frac{18\left(\frac{4}{9}\right) + 18\left(\frac{7}{18}\right)}{18(2)}$

$= \frac{8 + 7}{36}$

$= \frac{15}{36}$

$= \frac{5}{12}$

20. $\frac{\frac{7}{9} + \frac{5}{6}}{2} = \frac{18\left(\frac{7}{9} + \frac{5}{6}\right)}{18(2)}$

$= \frac{18\left(\frac{7}{9}\right) + 18\left(\frac{5}{6}\right)}{18(2)}$

$= \frac{14 + 15}{36}$

$= \frac{29}{36}$

## 4.7 SOLUTIONS TO EXERCISES

1. $12x = 7$

$\frac{12x}{12} = \frac{7}{12}$

$x = \frac{7}{12}$

2. $-6y = 5$

$\frac{-6y}{-6} = \frac{5}{-6}$

$y = -\frac{5}{6}$

3. $\frac{3}{5}a = 15$

$\frac{5}{3}\left(\frac{3}{5}a\right) = \frac{5}{3}(15)$

$a = 25$

4. $-\frac{5}{6}m = -\frac{7}{12}$

$-\frac{6}{5}\left(-\frac{5}{6}m\right) = -\frac{6}{5}\left(-\frac{7}{12}\right)$

$m = \frac{7}{10}$

5. $\frac{4}{5}x + \frac{1}{3} = \frac{7}{15}$

$15\left(\frac{4}{5}x + \frac{1}{3}\right) = 15\left(\frac{7}{15}\right)$

$15\left(\frac{4}{5}x\right) + 15\left(\frac{1}{3}\right) = 15\left(\frac{7}{15}\right)$

$12x + 5 = 7$

$12x + 5 - 5 = 7 - 5$

$12x = 2$

$\frac{12x}{12} = \frac{2}{12}$

$x = \frac{1}{6}$

6. 
$$\frac{y}{8} - \frac{8}{16} = 1$$
$$16\left(\frac{y}{8} - \frac{8}{16}\right) = 16(1)$$
$$16\left(\frac{y}{8}\right) - 16\left(\frac{8}{16}\right) = 16(1)$$
$$2y - 8 = 16$$
$$2y - 8 + 8 = 16 + 8$$
$$2y = 24$$
$$\frac{2y}{2} = \frac{24}{2}$$
$$y = 12$$

7. 
$$\frac{7}{8}n - n = -3$$
$$8\left(\frac{7}{8}n - n\right) = 8(-3)$$
$$8\left(\frac{7}{8}n\right) - 8(n) = 8(-3)$$
$$7n - 8n = -24$$
$$-1n = -24$$
$$\frac{-1n}{-1} = \frac{-24}{-1}$$
$$n = 24$$

8. 
$$\frac{3}{10} - \frac{1}{3} = \frac{x}{20}$$
$$60\left(\frac{3}{10} - \frac{1}{3}\right) = 60\left(\frac{x}{20}\right)$$
$$60\left(\frac{3}{10}\right) - 60\left(\frac{1}{3}\right) = 60\left(\frac{x}{20}\right)$$
$$18 - 20 = 3x$$
$$-2 = 3x$$
$$\frac{-2}{3} = \frac{3x}{3}$$
$$-\frac{2}{3} = x$$

9. 
$$\frac{5}{2}b + \frac{2}{3}b = \frac{13}{6}$$
$$6\left(\frac{5}{2}b + \frac{2}{3}b\right) = 6\left(\frac{13}{6}\right)$$
$$6\left(\frac{5}{2}b\right) + 6\left(\frac{2}{3}b\right) = 6\left(\frac{13}{6}\right)$$
$$15b + 4b = 13$$
$$19b = 13$$
$$\frac{19b}{19} = \frac{13}{19}$$
$$b = \frac{13}{19}$$

10. 
$$-\frac{4}{11} + \frac{y}{6} = -\frac{4\cdot 6}{11\cdot 6} + \frac{y\cdot 11}{6\cdot 11}$$
$$= -\frac{24}{66} + \frac{11y}{66}$$
$$= \frac{-24 + 11y}{66}$$

11. 
$$\frac{5m}{12} - \frac{4m}{9} = \frac{5m\cdot 3}{12\cdot 3} - \frac{4m\cdot 4}{9\cdot 4}$$
$$= \frac{15m}{36} - \frac{16m}{36}$$
$$= -\frac{m}{36}$$

12. 
$$\frac{8a}{5} - \frac{7a}{10} = \frac{8a\cdot 2}{5\cdot 2} - \frac{7a}{10}$$
$$= \frac{16a}{10} - \frac{7a}{10}$$
$$= \frac{9a}{10}$$

13. 
$$\frac{5}{6}p = \frac{10}{21}$$
$$\frac{6}{5}\left(\frac{5}{6}p\right) = \frac{6}{5}\left(\frac{10}{21}\right)$$
$$p = \frac{4}{7}$$

14.
$$\frac{5}{4} + \frac{4}{x} = \frac{1}{8}$$
$$8x\left(\frac{5}{4} + \frac{4}{x}\right) = 8x\left(\frac{1}{8}\right)$$
$$8x\left(\frac{5}{4}\right) + 8x\left(\frac{4}{x}\right) = 8x\left(\frac{1}{8}\right)$$
$$10x + 32 = x$$
$$10x + 32 - 10x = x - 10x$$
$$32 = -9x$$
$$\frac{32}{-9} = \frac{-9x}{-9}$$
$$-\frac{32}{9} = x$$

15.
$$\frac{11}{14} - \frac{6}{7} = \frac{11}{14} - \frac{6 \cdot 2}{7 \cdot 2}$$
$$= \frac{11}{14} - \frac{12}{14}$$
$$= -\frac{1}{14}$$

16.
$$-\frac{5}{9}x = \frac{5}{18} - \frac{7}{18}$$
$$18\left(-\frac{5}{9}x\right) = 18\left(\frac{5}{18} - \frac{7}{18}\right)$$
$$18\left(-\frac{5}{9}x\right) = 18\left(\frac{5}{18}\right) - 18\left(\frac{7}{18}\right)$$
$$-10x = 5 - 7$$
$$-10x = -2$$
$$\frac{-10x}{-10} = \frac{-2}{-10}$$
$$x = \frac{1}{5}$$

17.  $16 - \dfrac{11}{4} = \dfrac{16 \cdot 4}{1 \cdot 4} - \dfrac{11}{4}$
$$= \frac{64}{4} - \frac{11}{4}$$
$$= \frac{53}{4}$$

18.
$$\frac{y}{4} = -3 + y$$
$$4\left(\frac{y}{4}\right) = 4(-3 + y)$$
$$4\left(\frac{y}{4}\right) = 4(-3) + 4(y)$$
$$y = -12 + 4y$$
$$y - 4y = -12 + 4y - 4y$$
$$-3y = -12$$
$$\frac{-3y}{-3} = \frac{-12}{-3}$$
$$y = 4$$

19.
$$\frac{7}{9}x = \frac{4}{5} - \frac{1}{2}$$
$$90\left(\frac{7}{9}x\right) = 90\left(\frac{4}{5} - \frac{1}{2}\right)$$
$$90\left(\frac{7}{9}x\right) = 90\left(\frac{4}{5}\right) - 90\left(\frac{1}{2}\right)$$
$$70x = 72 - 45$$
$$70x = 27$$
$$\frac{70x}{70} = \frac{27}{70}$$
$$x = \frac{27}{70}$$

20.
$$\frac{8}{15}b = -\frac{4}{5} + \frac{1}{3}$$
$$15\left(\frac{8}{15}b\right) = 15\left(-\frac{4}{5} + \frac{1}{3}\right)$$
$$15\left(\frac{8}{15}b\right) = 15\left(-\frac{4}{5}\right) + 15\left(\frac{1}{3}\right)$$
$$8b = -12 + 5$$
$$8b = -7$$
$$\frac{8b}{8} = \frac{-7}{8}$$
$$b = -\frac{7}{8}$$

## 4.8 SOLUTIONS TO EXERCISES

1. $9\dfrac{1}{4} = \dfrac{9 \cdot 4 + 1}{4} = \dfrac{36 + 1}{4} = \dfrac{37}{4}$

2. $3\dfrac{5}{13} = \dfrac{3 \cdot 13 + 5}{13} = \dfrac{39 + 5}{13} = \dfrac{44}{13}$

3. $12\dfrac{4}{5} = \dfrac{12 \cdot 5 + 4}{5} = \dfrac{60 + 4}{5} = \dfrac{64}{5}$

4.
$$\begin{array}{r} 2 \\ 6\overline{)17} \\ \underline{12} \\ 5 \end{array}$$

   Thus, $\dfrac{17}{6} = 2\dfrac{5}{6}$.

5.
$$\begin{array}{r} 19 \\ 3\overline{)57} \\ \underline{3} \\ 27 \\ \underline{27} \\ 0 \end{array}$$

   Thus, $\dfrac{57}{3} = 19$.

6.
$$\begin{array}{r} 8 \\ 10\overline{)87} \\ \underline{80} \\ 7 \end{array}$$

   Thus, $\dfrac{87}{10} = 8\dfrac{7}{10}$.

7. $3\dfrac{4}{5} \cdot \dfrac{1}{8} = \dfrac{19}{5} \cdot \dfrac{1}{8} = \dfrac{19 \cdot 1}{5 \cdot 8} = \dfrac{19}{40}$

8. $6\dfrac{1}{4} \cdot 3\dfrac{3}{5} = \dfrac{25}{4} \cdot \dfrac{18}{5}$
$$= \dfrac{\boxed{5} \cdot 5 \cdot \boxed{2} \cdot 3 \cdot 3}{\boxed{2} \cdot 2 \cdot \boxed{5}}$$
$$= \dfrac{45}{2} \text{ or } 22\dfrac{1}{2}$$

9. $\dfrac{4}{9} \div 6\dfrac{3}{4} = \dfrac{4}{9} \div \dfrac{27}{4} = \dfrac{4}{9} \cdot \dfrac{4}{27} = \dfrac{4 \cdot 4}{9 \cdot 27} = \dfrac{16}{243}$

10. $10\dfrac{3}{8} \cdot 5 = \dfrac{83}{8} \cdot \dfrac{5}{1} = \dfrac{83 \cdot 5}{8 \cdot 1} = \dfrac{415}{8} \text{ or } 51\dfrac{7}{8}$

11. $15\dfrac{2}{7} \div \dfrac{9}{14} = \dfrac{107}{7} \div \dfrac{9}{14}$
$$= \dfrac{107}{7} \cdot \dfrac{14}{9}$$
$$= \dfrac{107 \cdot 2 \cdot \boxed{7}}{\boxed{7} \cdot 3 \cdot 3}$$
$$= \dfrac{214}{9} \text{ or } 23\dfrac{7}{9}$$

12. $12 \div 6\dfrac{3}{7} = \dfrac{12}{1} \div \dfrac{45}{7}$
$$= \dfrac{12}{1} \cdot \dfrac{7}{45}$$
$$= \dfrac{2 \cdot 2 \cdot \boxed{3} \cdot 7}{1 \cdot \boxed{3} \cdot 3 \cdot 5}$$
$$= \dfrac{28}{15} \text{ or } 1\dfrac{13}{15}$$

13.
$$\begin{array}{r} 4\dfrac{3}{14} = \quad 4\dfrac{3}{14} \\ + 2\dfrac{5}{7} = + 2\dfrac{10}{14} \\ \hline 6\dfrac{13}{14} \end{array}$$

14.
$$\begin{array}{r} 25\dfrac{7}{10} = \quad 25\dfrac{7}{10} \\ + 12\dfrac{4}{5} = + 12\dfrac{8}{10} \\ \hline 37\dfrac{15}{10} \end{array}$$
$$= 37 + 1\dfrac{5}{10}$$
$$= 38\dfrac{1}{2}$$

15.
$$\begin{array}{r} 9\dfrac{7}{8} = \quad 9\dfrac{7}{8} \\ - 2\dfrac{1}{4} = - 2\dfrac{2}{8} \\ \hline 7\dfrac{5}{8} \end{array}$$

16.

$$17\frac{3}{8} = \quad 17\frac{9}{24} = 16+1\frac{9}{24} = \quad 16\frac{33}{24}$$
$$-11\frac{7}{12} = -\ 11\frac{14}{24} = \ -11\frac{14}{24} = -\ 11\frac{14}{24}$$
$$\phantom{-11\frac{7}{12} = -\ 11\frac{14}{24} = \ -11\frac{14}{24} =}\ \ 5\frac{19}{24}$$

17.

$$19 \quad = \quad 18\frac{10}{10}$$
$$-18\frac{9}{10} = -\ 18\frac{9}{10}$$
$$\phantom{-18\frac{9}{10} = -\ 18}\ \ \frac{1}{10}$$

18.

$$21\frac{1}{6} = \quad 21\frac{12}{72}$$
$$17\frac{5}{8} = \quad 17\frac{45}{72}$$
$$+11\frac{7}{9} = +\ 11\frac{56}{72}$$
$$\phantom{+11\frac{7}{9} =}\ \ 49\frac{113}{72}$$
$$= 49+1\frac{41}{72}$$
$$= 50\frac{41}{72}$$

19.

$$\begin{array}{ccccc} \text{total} \\ \text{weight} \end{array} = \begin{array}{c} \text{1st} \\ \text{weight} \end{array} + \begin{array}{c} \text{2nd} \\ \text{weight} \end{array}$$

$$= \quad 2\frac{3}{5} \quad + \quad 3\frac{1}{4}$$

$$2\frac{3}{5} = \quad 2\frac{12}{20}$$
$$+3\frac{1}{4} = +3\frac{5}{20}$$
$$\phantom{+3\frac{1}{4} =}\ \ 5\frac{17}{20}$$

The total weight is $5\frac{17}{20}$ pounds.

20. Area = length · width

$$= \left(3\frac{2}{3}\ \text{inch}\right)\left(5\frac{1}{4}\ \text{inch}\right)$$

$$= \left(\frac{11}{3}\ \text{inch}\right)\left(\frac{21}{4}\ \text{inch}\right)$$

$$= \frac{11\cdot\boxed{3}\cdot 7}{\boxed{3}\cdot 2\cdot 2}\ \text{square inches}$$

$$= \frac{77}{4}\ \text{square inches}$$

$$\text{or}\ \ 19\frac{1}{4}\ \text{square inches}$$

$$\text{Perimeter} = 3\frac{2}{3}+5\frac{1}{4}+3\frac{2}{3}+5\frac{1}{4}$$

$$3\frac{2}{3} = \quad 3\frac{8}{12}$$
$$5\frac{1}{4} = \quad 5\frac{3}{12}$$
$$3\frac{2}{3} = \quad 3\frac{8}{12}$$
$$+5\frac{1}{4} = +5\frac{3}{12}$$
$$\phantom{+5\frac{1}{4} =}\ \ 16\frac{22}{12}$$
$$= 16+1\frac{10}{12}$$
$$= 17\frac{5}{6}$$

The perimeter is $17\frac{5}{6}$ inches.

## CHAPTER 4 PRACTICE TEST SOLUTIONS

1. $\dfrac{13}{15} \div \dfrac{5}{3} = \dfrac{13}{15} \cdot \dfrac{3}{5} = \dfrac{13\cdot\boxed{3}}{\boxed{3}\cdot 5\cdot 5} = \dfrac{13}{25}$

2. $-\dfrac{5}{7} \cdot \dfrac{9}{5} = -\dfrac{\boxed{5}\cdot 9}{7\cdot\boxed{5}} = -\dfrac{9}{7}$

3. $\dfrac{3x}{8} + \dfrac{x}{4} = \dfrac{3x}{8} + \dfrac{x\cdot 4}{2\cdot 4} = \dfrac{3x}{8} + \dfrac{2x}{8} = \dfrac{5x}{8}$

4. $\dfrac{1}{10} - \dfrac{2}{x} = \dfrac{1 \cdot x}{10 \cdot x} - \dfrac{2 \cdot 10}{x \cdot 10} = \dfrac{x}{10x} - \dfrac{20}{10x} = \dfrac{x-20}{10x}$

5. $\dfrac{xy^2}{z} \cdot \dfrac{z^3}{x^2 y} = \dfrac{\boxed{x} \cdot \boxed{y} \cdot y \cdot \boxed{z} \cdot z \cdot z}{\boxed{z} \cdot \boxed{x} \cdot x \cdot \boxed{y}} = \dfrac{yz^2}{x}$

6. $-\dfrac{4}{9} \cdot -\dfrac{16}{30} = \dfrac{\boxed{2} \cdot 2 \cdot 2 \cdot 2 \cdot 2 \cdot 2}{3 \cdot 3 \cdot \boxed{2} \cdot 3 \cdot 5} = \dfrac{32}{135}$

7. $\dfrac{4m}{7} + \dfrac{5}{14} = \dfrac{4m \cdot 2}{7 \cdot 2} + \dfrac{5}{14} = \dfrac{8m}{14} + \dfrac{5}{14} = \dfrac{8m+5}{14}$

8. $-\dfrac{4}{13m} - \dfrac{6}{13m} = \dfrac{-4-6}{13m} = \dfrac{-10}{13m}$ or $-\dfrac{10}{13m}$

9. $12xy \div \dfrac{y}{8} = \dfrac{12xy}{1} \cdot \dfrac{8}{y}$

$= \dfrac{12 \cdot x \cdot \boxed{y} \cdot 8}{1 \cdot \boxed{y}}$

$= \dfrac{96x}{1}$

$= 96x$

10. $3\dfrac{1}{8} \div \dfrac{5}{24} = \dfrac{25}{8} \div \dfrac{5}{24}$

$= \dfrac{25}{8} \cdot \dfrac{24}{5}$

$= \dfrac{\boxed{5} \cdot 5 \cdot 3 \cdot \boxed{8}}{\boxed{8} \cdot \boxed{5}}$

$= \dfrac{15}{1}$

$= 15$

11. $\begin{array}{r} 4\dfrac{5}{6} = \quad 4\dfrac{5}{6} \\[2mm] 2\dfrac{1}{2} = \quad 2\dfrac{3}{6} \\[2mm] + 8\dfrac{1}{3} = + 8\dfrac{2}{6} \\ \hline 14\dfrac{10}{6} \end{array}$

$= 14 + 1\dfrac{4}{6}$

$= 15\dfrac{2}{3}$

12. $\dfrac{4x}{7} \cdot \dfrac{14}{8x^4} = \dfrac{\boxed{4} \cdot \boxed{x} \cdot \boxed{2} \cdot \boxed{7}}{\boxed{7} \cdot \boxed{2} \cdot \boxed{4} \cdot \boxed{x} \cdot x \cdot x \cdot x} = \dfrac{1}{x^3}$

13. $-\dfrac{21}{2} \div -\dfrac{15}{8} = -\dfrac{21}{2} \cdot -\dfrac{8}{15}$

$= \dfrac{\boxed{3} \cdot 7 \cdot \boxed{2} \cdot 4}{\boxed{2} \cdot \boxed{3} \cdot 5}$

$= \dfrac{28}{5}$ or $5\dfrac{3}{5}$

14. $9\dfrac{1}{5} \cdot 4\dfrac{3}{10} = \dfrac{46}{5} \cdot \dfrac{43}{10}$

$= \dfrac{\boxed{2} \cdot 23 \cdot 43}{5 \cdot \boxed{2} \cdot 5}$

$= \dfrac{989}{25}$ or $39\dfrac{14}{25}$

15. $30 \div 6\dfrac{1}{4} = \dfrac{30}{1} \div \dfrac{25}{4}$

$= \dfrac{30}{1} \cdot \dfrac{4}{25}$

$= \dfrac{2 \cdot 3 \cdot \boxed{5} \cdot 2 \cdot 2}{1 \cdot \boxed{5} \cdot 5}$

$= \dfrac{24}{5}$ or $4\dfrac{4}{5}$

16. $\left(\dfrac{12}{7} \cdot \dfrac{21}{6}\right) \div 8 = \left(\dfrac{\boxed{2} \cdot 2 \cdot \boxed{3} \cdot 3 \cdot \boxed{7}}{\boxed{7} \cdot \boxed{2} \cdot \boxed{3}}\right) \cdot \dfrac{1}{8}$

$= \dfrac{6}{1} \cdot \dfrac{1}{8}$

$= \dfrac{\boxed{2} \cdot 3 \cdot 1}{1 \cdot \boxed{2} \cdot 2 \cdot 2}$

$= \dfrac{3}{4}$

17. $\dfrac{7}{8} - \dfrac{2}{3} + \dfrac{5}{12} = \dfrac{7 \cdot 3}{8 \cdot 3} - \dfrac{2 \cdot 8}{3 \cdot 8} + \dfrac{5 \cdot 2}{12 \cdot 2}$

$= \dfrac{21}{24} - \dfrac{16}{24} + \dfrac{10}{24}$

$= \dfrac{21 - 16 + 10}{24}$

$= \dfrac{15}{24}$

$= \dfrac{5}{8}$

18. $\dfrac{\dfrac{4x}{15}}{\dfrac{16x^2}{60}} = \dfrac{4x}{15} \div \dfrac{16x^2}{60}$

$= \dfrac{4x}{15} \cdot \dfrac{60}{16x^2}$

$= \dfrac{\boxed{4} \cdot \boxed{x} \cdot \boxed{4} \cdot \boxed{15}}{\boxed{15} \cdot \boxed{4} \cdot \boxed{4} \cdot \boxed{x} \cdot x}$

$= \dfrac{1}{x}$

19. $\dfrac{\dfrac{5}{6} - \dfrac{1}{8}}{1 + \dfrac{3}{4}} = \dfrac{24\left(\dfrac{5}{6} - \dfrac{1}{8}\right)}{24\left(1 + \dfrac{3}{4}\right)}$

$= \dfrac{24\left(\dfrac{5}{6}\right) - 24\left(\dfrac{1}{8}\right)}{24(1) + 24\left(\dfrac{3}{4}\right)}$

$= \dfrac{20 - 3}{24 + 18}$

$= \dfrac{17}{42}$

20. $-\dfrac{7}{8}x = \dfrac{5}{16}$

$-\dfrac{8}{7}\left(-\dfrac{7}{8}x\right) = -\dfrac{8}{7}\left(\dfrac{5}{16}\right)$

$x = -\dfrac{5}{14}$

21. $\dfrac{3}{7}x + \dfrac{1}{2}x = -\dfrac{15}{14}$

$14\left(\dfrac{3}{7}x + \dfrac{1}{2}x\right) = 14\left(-\dfrac{15}{14}\right)$

$14\left(\dfrac{3}{7}x\right) + 14\left(\dfrac{1}{2}x\right) = 14\left(-\dfrac{15}{14}\right)$

$6x + 7x = -15$

$13x = -15$

$\dfrac{13x}{13} = \dfrac{-15}{13}$

$x = -\dfrac{15}{13}$

22. $\dfrac{1}{4} + \dfrac{x}{3} = \dfrac{5}{6} + \dfrac{x}{2}$

$12\left(\dfrac{1}{4} + \dfrac{x}{3}\right) = 12\left(\dfrac{5}{6} + \dfrac{x}{2}\right)$

$12\left(\dfrac{1}{4}\right) + 12\left(\dfrac{x}{3}\right) = 12\left(\dfrac{5}{6}\right) + 12\left(\dfrac{x}{2}\right)$

$3 + 4x = 10 + 6x$

$3 + 4x - 4x = 10 + 6x - 4x$

$3 = 10 + 2x$

$3 - 10 = 10 + 2x - 10$

$-7 = 2x$

$\dfrac{-7}{2} = \dfrac{2x}{x}$

$-\dfrac{7}{2} = x$

23. $-8x = -8\left(-\dfrac{5}{12}\right) = \dfrac{8}{1} \cdot \dfrac{5}{12} = \dfrac{2 \cdot \boxed{4} \cdot 5}{1 \cdot 3 \cdot \boxed{4}} = \dfrac{10}{3}$

24. $xy = \dfrac{2}{3} \cdot 4\dfrac{5}{6} = \dfrac{2}{3} \cdot \dfrac{29}{6} = \dfrac{\boxed{2} \cdot 29}{3 \cdot \boxed{2} \cdot 3} = \dfrac{29}{9}$ or $3\dfrac{2}{9}$

25. $\begin{array}{ccc} \text{length} \\ \text{remaining} \end{array} = \begin{array}{c} \text{original} \\ \text{length} \end{array} - \begin{array}{c} \text{length} \\ \text{removed} \end{array}$

$= \quad 14\dfrac{3}{5} \quad - \quad 8\dfrac{9}{10}$

$14\dfrac{3}{5} = \ 14\dfrac{6}{10} = 13 + 1\dfrac{6}{10} = \ 13\dfrac{16}{10}$

$-\ 8\dfrac{9}{10} = -\ 8\dfrac{9}{10} = \ -\ 8\dfrac{9}{10} = -\ 8\dfrac{9}{10}$

$\overline{\qquad\qquad\qquad\qquad\qquad 5\dfrac{7}{10}}$

Cedric has $5\dfrac{7}{10}$ feet of rope remaining.

## 5.1 SOLUTIONS TO EXERCISES

1. 3.002
   three and two thousandths

2. 17.13
   seventeen and thirteen hundredths

3. 100.25
   one hundred and twenty-five hundredths

4. 10.12

5. 0.0465

6. 96.3

7. $0.05 = \dfrac{5}{100} = \dfrac{1}{20}$

8. $3.72 = 3\dfrac{72}{100} = 3\dfrac{18}{25}$

9. $0.45 = \dfrac{45}{100} = \dfrac{9}{20}$

10. $14.606 = 14\dfrac{606}{1000} = 14\dfrac{303}{500}$

11. $200.237 = 200\dfrac{237}{1000}$

12. $0.3005 = \dfrac{3005}{10000} = \dfrac{601}{2000}$

13. $0.129 \ < \ 0.131$

14. $321.874 \ > \ 321.868$

15. $10,000 \ > \ 0.0001$

16. $0.67000 \ = 0.67$

17. 2.4<u>6</u>7 is 2.47 rounded to the nearest hundredth

18. 0.<u>5</u>3 is 0.5 rounded to the nearest tenth

19. 0.56<u>8</u>6 is 0.569 rounded to the nearest thousandth

20. 1<u>4</u>5.827 is 150 rounded to nearest ten

## 5.2 SOLUTIONS TO EXERCISES

1. 
$$\begin{array}{r} \overset{1\ \ \ 1}{17.030} \\ +\ 5.682 \\ \hline 22.712 \end{array}$$

2. 
$$\begin{array}{r} \overset{1}{7.6} \\ +9.5 \\ \hline 17.1 \end{array}$$

3. Subtract the absolute values.
$$\begin{array}{r} \overset{9\ \ 10}{1\!\!\not{0}.\not{0}} \\ -\ 4.5 \\ \hline 5.5 \end{array}$$
   The sign of the answer is the sign of the number with the larger absolute value, so the answer is −5.5.

4. Add the absolute values.
$$\begin{array}{r} 14.00 \\ +\ 2.37 \\ \hline 16.37 \end{array}$$
   The sign is the same sign as both numbers, so the answer is −16.37.

5. 
$$\begin{array}{r} \overset{3\ \ \not{1}0\ \not{1}0\ \not{1}0\ \not{1}0}{\not{4}.\not{0}\,\not{0}\,\not{0}\,\not{0}} \\ -\ 0.0932 \\ \hline 3.9068 \end{array}$$

6. $-3.2 - 55.7 = -3.2 + -55.7$
   Add the absolute values.
$$\begin{array}{r} 55.7 \\ +\ 3.2 \\ \hline 58.9 \end{array}$$
   The sign is the same as both numbers, so the answer is −58.9.

7. $23.9 - 50 = 23.9 + -50$
   Subtract the absolute values.

   $$\begin{array}{r} {}^{4}\cancel{5}\,{}^{9}\cancel{0}\,{}^{10}0 \\ \cancel{5}\,\cancel{0}.\cancel{0} \\ -\ 2\,3.\ 9 \\ \hline 2\,6.\ 1 \end{array}$$

   The sign of the answer is the sign of the number with larger absolute value, so the answer is $-26.1$.

8. $$\begin{array}{r} {}^{5}\cancel{6}\,{}^{9}\cancel{0}\,{}^{12}\cancel{3}\,{}^{10}0 \\ \cancel{6}\,\cancel{0}.\cancel{3}\,\cancel{0} \\ -\ 3\,3.\ 8\ 1 \\ \hline 2\,6.\ 4\ 9 \end{array}$$

9. $$\begin{array}{r} {}^{6}\cancel{7}\,{}^{10}0 \\ 1\,\cancel{7}.\cancel{0} \\ -\ \ \ 4.\ 9 \\ \hline 1\,2.\ 1 \end{array}$$

10. Subtract the absolute values.

    $$\begin{array}{r} {}^{6}\cancel{7}.\,{}^{12}\cancel{3}\,{}^{2}\cancel{0}\,{}^{10}0 \\ \cancel{7}.\cancel{3}\,\cancel{0} \\ -\ 2.3\ 5 \\ \hline 4.\ 9\ 5 \end{array}$$

    The answer has the same sign as the number with the larger absolute value, so the answer is 4.95.

11. $y - x = 2.1 - 14$
    $= 2.1 + -14$
    $= -11.9$

12. $x - y + z = 14 - 2.1 + 0.412$
    $= 11.9 + 0.412$
    $= 12.312$

13. $z + x + y = 0.412 + 14 + 2.1$
    $= 14.412 + 2.1$
    $= 16.512$

14. $x + 7.3 = 9.8$
    $2.6 + 7.3 = 9.8$
    $9.9 = 9.8$
    False
    $x = 2.6$ is not a solution.

15. $51.7 - y = 92$
    $51.7 - (-40.3) = 92$
    $51.7 + 40.3 = 92$
    $92 = 92$
    True
    $x = -40.3$ is a solution.

16. $a + 9.3 = 7.2 - a$
    $(-1.8) + 9.3 = 7.2 - (-1.8)$
    $7.5 = 7.2 + 1.8$
    $7.5 = 9$
    False
    $a = -1.8$ is not a solution.

17. $12.3y - 3 - 6.13y + 7.2$
    $= 12.3y - 6.13y - 3 + 7.2$
    $= 6.17y + 4.2$

18. $4x - 0.45 - 8.3x - 2$
    $= 4x - 8.3x - 0.45 - 2$
    $= -4.3x - 2.45$

19. $\begin{array}{ccccc} \text{pizza} & + & \text{tip} & = & \text{total cost} \\ \$12.99 & + & \$3.00 & = & \$15.99 \end{array}$

    $\$20 - \$15.99 = \$4.01$

20. $P = a + b + c$
    $P = 14.2 \text{ cm} + 8.95 \text{ cm} + 10 \text{ cm} = 33.15 \text{ cm}$

## 5.3 SOLUTIONS TO EXERCISES

1. $$\begin{array}{r} 3.76 \\ \times\ 0.52 \\ \hline 752 \\ 18800 \\ \hline 1.9552 \end{array}$$

2. $$\begin{array}{r} 2.19 \\ \times\ 0.31 \\ \hline 219 \\ 6570 \\ \hline 0.6789 \end{array}$$

3. $$\begin{array}{r} 1.0004 \\ \times\ \ \ 6.1 \\ \hline 10004 \\ 600240 \\ \hline 6.10244 \end{array}$$

   $(1.0004)(-6.1) = -6.10244$

4.  $(-24.039)(100) = -2403.9$
    There are two zeros in 100, so move decimal point to the right two places.

5.  $\begin{array}{r} 32.17 \\ \times\ 2.9 \\ \hline 28953 \\ 64340 \\ \hline 93.293 \end{array}$

    $(-32.17)(-2.9) = 93.293$

6.  $(452.33)(0.01) = 4.5233$
    There are two decimal places in 0.01, so move decimal point to the left two places.

7.  $\begin{array}{r} 4.75 \\ \times\ 12 \\ \hline 950 \\ 4750 \\ \hline 57.00 \end{array}$

8.  $(8.32)(1000) = 8320$
    There are three zeros in 1000, so move the decimal point three places to the right.

9.  $\begin{array}{r} 3.33 \\ \times 3.33 \\ \hline 999 \\ 9990 \\ 99900 \\ \hline 11.0889 \end{array}$

    $(-3.33)(3.33) = -11.0889$

10. $\begin{array}{r} 5.29 \\ \times 13.7 \\ \hline 3703 \\ 15870 \\ 52900 \\ \hline 72.473 \end{array}$

    $5.29 \times -13.7 = -72.473$

11. $xy = (-9)(0.12)$
    $\quad = -1.08$

12. $xy = (4.7)(0.001)$
    $\quad = 0.0047$

13. $xy = (-2.5)(-0.3)$
    $\quad = 0.75$

14. $\quad -2.9x = 9.57$
    $-2.9(-3.3) = 9.57$
    $\quad\quad 9.57 = 9.57$
    $\quad\quad\quad\text{True}$
    $x = -3.3$ is a solution.

15. $\quad\quad 7x = 14.28$
    $7(2.04) = 14.28$
    $\quad 14.28 = 14.28$
    $\quad\quad\quad\text{True}$
    $x = 2.04$ is a solution.

16. $C = 2\pi r$
    $\quad = 2\pi(4 \text{ meters})$
    $\quad = 8\pi \text{ meters}$

    $8\pi \text{ meters} \approx 8(3.14) \text{ meters} = 25.12 \text{ meters}$

17. $C = 2\pi r$
    $\quad = 2\pi(8.25 \text{ feet})$
    $\quad = 16.5\pi \text{ feet}$

    $16.5\pi \text{ feet} \approx 16.5(3.14) \text{ feet} = 51.81 \text{ feet}$

18. Since diameter is 12.1 yards,
    the radius is $12.1 \div 2 = 6.05$ yards.
    $C = 2\pi r$
    $\quad = 2\pi(6.05 \text{ yards})$
    $\quad = 12.1\pi \text{ yards}$

    $12.1\pi \text{ yards} \approx 12.1(3.14) = 37.994 \text{ yards}$

19. cost per gallon × number of gallons
    $\quad \$1.69 \quad\quad \times \quad 12.5 \ \approx\ \$21.13$

20. $A = L \times W$
    $\quad = 14.75 \text{ feet} \times 13 \text{ feet}$
    $\quad = 191.75 \text{ square feet}$

## 5.4 SOLUTIONS TO EXERCISES

1.
$$
\begin{array}{r}
0.842 \\
5{\overline{\smash{\big)}\,4.210}} \\
\underline{40} \\
21 \\
\underline{20} \\
10 \\
\underline{10}
\end{array}
$$

2. $0.02{\overline{\smash{\big)}\,231.045}}$

becomes

$$
\begin{array}{r}
11552.25 \\
2{\overline{\smash{\big)}\,23104.50}} \\
\underline{2} \\
3 \\
\underline{2} \\
11 \\
\underline{10} \\
10 \\
\underline{10} \\
4 \\
\underline{4} \\
5 \\
\underline{4} \\
10 \\
\underline{10}
\end{array}
$$

$-231.045 \div (-0.02) = 11552.25$

3. $0.78{\overline{\smash{\big)}\,7.488}}$

becomes

$$
\begin{array}{r}
9.6 \\
78{\overline{\smash{\big)}\,748.8}} \\
\underline{702} \\
468 \\
\underline{468}
\end{array}
$$

4.
$$
\begin{array}{r}
.031 \\
3{\overline{\smash{\big)}\,0.093}} \\
\underline{9} \\
3 \\
\underline{3}
\end{array}
$$

5. $2.7{\overline{\smash{\big)}\,9.438}}$

becomes

$$
\begin{array}{r}
3.4955 \\
27{\overline{\smash{\big)}\,94.3800}} \\
\underline{81} \\
133 \\
\underline{108} \\
258 \\
\underline{243} \\
150 \\
\underline{135} \\
150 \\
\underline{135}
\end{array}
$$

$-9.438 \div 2.7 \approx -3.496$

6. $0.04{\overline{\smash{\big)}\,36}}$

becomes

$$
\begin{array}{r}
900 \\
4{\overline{\smash{\big)}\,3600}} \\
\underline{36} \\
0
\end{array}
$$

7. $(-237.14) \div (1000) = -0.23714$

Since 1000 has three zeros move the decimal point three places to the left.

8. $0.011{\overline{\smash{\big)}\,32.45}}$

becomes

$$
\begin{array}{r}
2950 \\
11{\overline{\smash{\big)}\,32450}} \\
\underline{22} \\
104 \\
\underline{99} \\
55 \\
\underline{55}
\end{array}
$$

$\dfrac{32.45}{-0.011} = -2950$

9. $\dfrac{2.004}{-100,000} = -0.00002004$

10. $0.02\overline{)10}$

becomes

$$\begin{array}{r} 500 \\ 2\overline{)1000} \end{array}$$

$-10 \div 0.02 = -500$

11. $\dfrac{81.29}{0.06}$ becomes

$$\begin{array}{r} 1354.8333 \\ 6\overline{)8129.0000} \\ \underline{6}\phantom{000000} \\ 21\phantom{00000} \\ \underline{18}\phantom{0000} \\ 32\phantom{000} \\ \underline{30}\phantom{00} \\ 29\phantom{00} \\ \underline{24}\phantom{0} \\ 50 \\ \underline{48} \\ 20 \\ \underline{18} \\ 20 \\ \underline{18} \\ 20 \end{array}$$

$\dfrac{81.29}{0.06} \approx 1354.833$

12. $\dfrac{115.2}{0.25}$ becomes

$$\begin{array}{r} 460.8 \\ 25\overline{)11520.0} \\ \underline{100}\phantom{0000} \\ 152\phantom{000} \\ \underline{150}\phantom{00} \\ 200 \\ \underline{200} \end{array}$$

$\dfrac{115.2}{0.25} = 460.8$

13. $x \div y = 8.92 \div -0.4 = -22.3$

14. $z \div -0.005 = -2.7 \div -0.005 = 540$

15. $\dfrac{x}{6} = 4.02$

$\dfrac{24.12}{6} = 4.02$

$4.02 = 4.02$

True

$x = 24.12$ is the solution.

16. $\dfrac{y}{1000} = 0.204$

$\dfrac{2040}{1000} = 0.204$

$2.04 = 0.204$

False

$x = 2040$ is not the solution.

17. Since $A = L \times W$, divide the area 40.85 by the width 4.3 to get the length.

40.85 square inches $\div$ 4.3 inches $= 9.5$ inches

9.5 inches is the length of the rectangle.

18. $400 \div 2.54 \approx 157.48$

There are approximately 157.48 inches in 400 centimeters.

## 5.5 SOLUTIONS TO EXERCISES

1. 
| Actual | Estimate |
|---|---|
| 14.9 | 15 |
| 7.2 | 7 |
| +19.5 | +20 |
| 41.6 | 42 |

2. 
| Actual | Estimate |
|---|---|
| 48.2 | 48 |
| −37.8 | − 38 |
| 10.4 | 10 |

3. 
| Actual | Estimate |
|---|---|
| 32.1 | 30 |
| × 6.8 | × 7 |
| 2568 | 210 |
| 19260 | |
| 218.28 | |

4. Actual

$$9.6\overline{)238.42} \quad \text{becomes} \quad 96\overline{)2384.2000}$$

$$\begin{array}{r} 24.8354 \\ \underline{192} \\ 464 \\ \underline{384} \\ 802 \\ \underline{768} \\ 340 \\ \underline{288} \\ 520 \\ \underline{480} \\ 400 \\ \underline{384} \end{array}$$

$238.42 \div 9.6 \approx 24.835$

Estimate   $200 \div 10 = 20$

5.   Actual
     $(-3.3)(-3.3) = 10.89$
     Estimate
     $(3)(3) = 9$

6.   Actual       Estimate
     $-44.44$        $-40$
     $\underline{\times \quad 7}$        $\underline{\times 7}$
     $-311.08$        $-280$

7.   $x^2 - z = (-5.6)^2 - 2.6$
     $= 31.36 - 2.6$
     $= 28.76$

8.   $-4x + 2y = -4(-5.6) + 2(0.4)$
     $= 22.4 + 0.8$
     $= 23.2$

9.   $\dfrac{xz}{y} = \dfrac{(-5.6)(2.6)}{0.4} = \dfrac{-14.56}{0.4} = -36.4$

10.    $4.6x + 9 = -6.64$
       $4.6(-3) + 9 = -6.64$
       $-13.8 + 9 = -6.64$
       $-4.8 = -6.64$
       False
     $x = -3$ is not a solution.

11.    $7.1x + 0.3 = 2.5x - 4.3$
       $7.1(-1) + 0.3 = 2.5(-1) - 4.3$
       $-7.1 + 0.3 = -2.5 - 4.3$
       $-6.8 = -6.8$
       True
     $x = -1$ is a solution.

12.  $-3.2(4 - 8.3)$
     $= -3.2(4 + -8.3)$
     $= -3.2(-4.3) = 13.76$

13.  $\dfrac{-4.49 - 1.2}{-0.5} = \dfrac{-5.69}{-0.5} = 11.38$

14.  $(-3.7)^2 = (-3.7)(-3.7) = 13.69$

15.  $(1 - 0.34)(1 + 0.34) = (0.66)(1.34) = 0.8844$

16.  $\dfrac{2(-3.4) - 6}{5} = \dfrac{-6.8 - 6}{5} = \dfrac{-12.8}{5} = -2.56$

17.  $(-2.4 + 3)^2 = (0.6)^2 = 0.36$

18.  $40 \times 11 = \$440$

19.  $C = 2\pi r = 2(3.14)(10.3) \approx 64.684$ inches

20.  $A = L \times W = 20 \times 20 = 400$ square feet

**5.6 SOLUTIONS TO EXERCISES**

1.   $$\begin{array}{r} 1.4 \\ 5\overline{)7.0} \\ \underline{5} \\ 20 \\ \underline{20} \end{array}$$

2.   $$\begin{array}{r} 2.25 \\ 4\overline{)9.00} \\ \underline{8} \\ 10 \\ \underline{8} \\ 20 \\ \underline{20} \end{array}$$

3. $25\overline{)3.00}$ with quotient $0.12$

$$\begin{array}{r} 0.12 \\ 25\overline{)3.00} \\ \underline{25} \\ 50 \\ \underline{50} \end{array}$$

4. $$\begin{array}{r} 0.571 \\ 7\overline{)4.000} \\ \underline{35} \\ 50 \\ \underline{49} \\ 10 \\ \underline{7} \\ 3 \end{array}$$

$\dfrac{4}{7} \approx 0.57$

5. $$\begin{array}{r} 0.111 \\ 9\overline{)1.0000} \\ \underline{9} \\ 10 \\ \underline{9} \\ 10 \\ \underline{9} \\ 1 \end{array}$$

$\dfrac{1}{9} \approx 0.11$

6. $$\begin{array}{r} 0.666... \\ 3\overline{)2.0000} \\ \underline{18} \\ 20 \\ \underline{18} \\ 20 \\ \underline{18} \end{array}$$

$\dfrac{2}{3} \approx 0.67$

7. $0.33 = \dfrac{33}{100}$

8. $0.002 = \dfrac{2}{1000} = \dfrac{1}{500}$

9. $0.125 = \dfrac{125}{1000} = \dfrac{1}{8}$

10. $13.5 = 13\dfrac{5}{10} = 13\dfrac{1}{2}$

11. $9.25 = 9\dfrac{25}{100} = 9\dfrac{1}{4}$

12. $5.063 = 5\dfrac{63}{1000}$

13. $\dfrac{8}{9} > \dfrac{7}{8}$

$0.889 > 0.875$

14. $\dfrac{25}{27} < \dfrac{65}{67}$

$0.926 < 0.970$

15. $\dfrac{71}{12} < 5.92$

$0.591 < 5.92$

16. Original numbers     0.814    0.836    0.83
Compare in order      1st       3rd      2nd

0.814, 0.83, 0.836

17. Original numbers    $\dfrac{11}{9}$    1.22    $\dfrac{13}{8}$
Decimals           1.222   1.22   1.625
Compare in order    2nd    1st     3rd

$1.22, \dfrac{11}{9}, \dfrac{13}{8}$

18. Original numbers    0.2    0.20    $\dfrac{1}{6}$
Decimals           0.2    0.20    0.167
Compare in order   2nd    2nd    1st

0.167, 0.2 = 0.20

19. $-4\left(2.5-\dfrac{1}{4}\right)=-4(2.5-0.25)$

$\quad\ =-4(2.25)=-9$

20. $-4(2.5)-\dfrac{1}{4}=-4(2.5)-0.25$

$\quad\ =-10-0.25=-10.25$

## 5.7 SOLUTIONS TO EXERCISES

1. $\quad x-4.1=5$

$\quad x-4.1+4.1=5+4.1$

$\quad\quad\quad x=9.1$

2. $\quad y+3.9=21.7$

$\quad y+3.9-3.9=21.7-3.9$

$\quad\quad\quad y=17.8$

3. $5x=-7.25$

$\quad \dfrac{5x}{5}=\dfrac{-7.25}{5}$

$\quad\quad x=-1.45$

4. $0.2a=10.8$

$\quad \dfrac{0.2a}{0.2}=\dfrac{10.8}{0.2}$

$\quad\quad a=54$

5. $\quad 3x-8=2x+6.5$

$\quad 3x-2x-8=2x-2x+6.5$

$\quad\quad x-8=6.5$

$\quad x-8+8=6.5+8$

$\quad\quad\quad x=14.5$

6. $\quad 5y+7.2=7y-7.2$

$\quad 5y+7.2-7.2=7y-7.2-7.2$

$\quad\quad\quad 5y=7y-14.4$

$\quad 5y-7y=7y-7y-14.4$

$\quad\quad\quad -2y=-14.4$

$\quad\quad \dfrac{-2y}{-2}=\dfrac{-14.4}{-2}$

$\quad\quad\quad y=7.2$

7. $\quad 2(x-3.4)=-10$

$\quad\quad 2x-6.8=-10$

$\quad 2x-6.8+6.8=-10+6.8$

$\quad\quad\quad 2x=-3.2$

$\quad\quad\quad x=-1.6$

8. $\quad 7(n+3.3)=87.5$

$\quad\quad 7n+23.1=87.5$

$\quad 7n+23.1-23.1=87.5-23.1$

$\quad\quad\quad 7n=64.4$

$\quad\quad \dfrac{7n}{7}=\dfrac{64.4}{7}$

$\quad\quad\quad n=9.2$

9. $\quad 0.6x+0.12=-0.24$

$\quad 100(0.6x+0.12)=(-0.24)\cdot100$

$\quad\quad 60x+12=-24$

$\quad 60x+12-12=-24-12$

$\quad\quad\quad 60x=-36$

$\quad\quad \dfrac{60x}{60}=\dfrac{-36}{60}$

$\quad\quad\quad x=-0.6$

10. $\quad 6x-12.5=x$

$\quad 10(6x-12.5)=x\cdot10$

$\quad\quad 60x-125=10x$

$\quad 60x-10x-125=10x-10x$

$\quad\quad 50x-125=0$

$\quad 50x-125+125=0+125$

$\quad\quad\quad 50x=125$

$\quad\quad \dfrac{50x}{50}=\dfrac{125}{50}$

$\quad\quad\quad x=2.5$

11. $\quad 3.8a+7-1.2a=22.6$

$\quad 10(3.8a+7-1.2a)=22.6\cdot10$

$\quad\quad 38a+70-12a=226$

$\quad\quad 26a+70=226$

$\quad 26a+70-70=226-70$

$\quad\quad\quad 26a=156$

$\quad\quad \dfrac{26a}{26}=\dfrac{156}{26}$

$\quad\quad\quad a=6$

12. $$-0.005x = 29.65$$
$$1000(-0.005x) = 29.65(1000)$$
$$-5x = 29650$$
$$\frac{-5x}{-5} = \frac{29650}{-5}$$
$$x = -5930$$

13. $$y + 15.04 = 11.2$$
$$100(y + 15.04) = 11.2(100)$$
$$100y + 1504 = 1120$$
$$100y = -384$$
$$\frac{100y}{100} = \frac{-384}{100}$$
$$y = -3.84$$

14. $$300x - 0.74 = 200x + 0.9$$
$$100(300x - 0.74) = (200x + 0.9)100$$
$$30000x - 74 = 20000x + 90$$
$$30000x - 20000x - 74 = 20000x - 20000x + 90$$
$$10000x - 74 = 90$$
$$10000x - 74 + 74 = 90 + 74$$
$$10000x = 164$$
$$\frac{10000x}{10000} = \frac{164}{10000}$$
$$x = 0.0164$$

15. $$3.2(x - 4) = 5.2x$$
$$3.2x - 12.8 = 5.2x$$
$$3.2x - 5.2x - 12.8 = 5.2x - 5.2x$$
$$-2x - 12.8 = 0$$
$$-2x - 12.8 + 12.8 = 0 + 12.8$$
$$-2x = 12.8$$
$$\frac{-2x}{-2} = \frac{12.8}{-2}$$
$$x = -6.4$$

16. $$15x + 14 = 2(5.4x - 7.2)$$
$$15x + 14 = 10.8x - 14.4$$
$$15x - 10.8x + 14 = 10.8x - 10.8x - 14.4$$
$$4.2x + 14 = -14.4$$
$$4.2x + 14 - 14 = -14.4 - 14$$
$$4.2x = -28.4$$
$$\frac{4.2x}{4.2} = \frac{-28.4}{4.2}$$
$$x \approx -6.76$$

17. $$0.9x + 42.1 = x - 57.09$$
$$0.9x - x + 42.1 = x - x - 57.09$$
$$-0.1x + 42.1 = -57.09$$
$$-0.1x + 42.1 - 42.1 = -57.09 - 42.1$$
$$-0.1x = -99.19$$
$$\frac{-0.1x}{-0.1} = \frac{-99.19}{-0.1}$$
$$x = 991.9$$

18. $$0.004x - 12 = 0.008$$
$$1000(0.004x - 12) = 0.008(1000)$$
$$4x - 12000 = 8$$
$$4x - 12000 + 12000 = 8 + 12000$$
$$4x = 12008$$
$$\frac{4x}{4} = \frac{12008}{4}$$
$$x = 3002$$

## 5.8 SOLUTIONS TO EXERCISES

1. $\sqrt{100} = 10$ since $10 \cdot 10 = 100$

2. $\sqrt{1} = 1$ since $1 \cdot 1 = 1$

3. $\sqrt{625} = 25$ since $25 \cdot 25 = 625$

4. $\sqrt{\dfrac{4}{25}} = \dfrac{2}{5}$ since $\dfrac{2}{5} \cdot \dfrac{2}{5} = \dfrac{4}{25}$

5. $\sqrt{\dfrac{81}{49}} = \dfrac{9}{7}$ since $\dfrac{9}{7} \cdot \dfrac{9}{7} = \dfrac{81}{49}$

6. $\sqrt{\dfrac{1}{64}} = \dfrac{1}{8}$ since $\dfrac{1}{8} \cdot \dfrac{1}{8} = \dfrac{1}{64}$

7. $\sqrt{19} \approx 4.359$

8. $\sqrt{99} \approx 9.95$

9. $\sqrt{40} \approx 6.325$

10. $\sqrt{300} \approx 17.321$

11. $\sqrt{2} \approx 1.414$

12. $\sqrt{82} \approx 9.055$

13. $a^2 + b^2 = c^2$
$18^2 + 24^2 = c^2$
$324 + 576 = c^2$
$900 = c^2$
$30 = c$

14. $a^2 + b^2 = c^2$
$7^2 + 9^2 = c^2$
$49 + 81 = c^2$
$130 = c^2$
$\sqrt{130} = c \approx 11.402$

15. $a^2 + b^2 = c^2$
$20^2 + 20^2 = c^2$
$400 + 400 = c^2$
$800 = c^2$
$\sqrt{800} = c \approx 28.284$

16. $a^2 + b^2 = c^2$
$15^2 + 20^2 = c^2$
$225 + 400 = c^2$
$625 = c^2$
$25 = c$

17. $a^2 + b^2 = c^2$
$40^2 + 19^2 = c^2$
$1600 + 361 = c^2$
$1961 = c^2$
$\sqrt{1961} = c \approx 44.28$ feet

18. $a^2 + b^2 = c^2$
$90^2 + 90^2 = c^2$
$8100 + 8100 = c^2$
$16200 = c^2$
$\sqrt{16200} = c \approx 127.28$ feet

**CHAPTER 5 PRACTICE TEST SOLUTIONS**

1. 13.013 – thirteen and thirteen thousandths

2. 35.012

3. $\overset{2}{2}3.912$
$\phantom{2}4.770$
$+\phantom{2}0.800$
$\overline{\phantom{2}29.482}$

4. $\overset{7\phantom{.}\overset{10}{\cancel{8}}\phantom{.}12}{\cancel{8}\cancel{1}.\cancel{2}}$
$-\phantom{0}1\phantom{.}2.8$
$\overline{\phantom{00}6\phantom{.}8.4}$

$-12.8 + 81.2 = 68.4$

5. $-6 - 3.81 = -6 + -3.81$
$\phantom{+}6.00$
$+3.81$
$\overline{\phantom{+}9.81}$
$-6 - 3.81 = -9.81$

6. $(14.3)(-0.001) = -0.0143$

7. $0.04\overline{)80}$  becomes

$\phantom{4)}2000$
$4\overline{)8000}$

$-80 \div -0.04 = 2000$

8. 47.4747 rounded to the nearest hundredth is 47.47

9. 2.0399 rounded to the nearest thousandth is 2.04

10. $2.099 < 2.1$

11.     $\dfrac{5}{7} \approx 0.714$

       $0.71\underline{4} > 0.71\underline{0}$

       $\dfrac{5}{7} > 0.71$

12.   $0.225 = \dfrac{225}{1000} = \dfrac{9}{40}$

13.   $9.48 = 9\dfrac{48}{100} = 9\dfrac{12}{25}$

14.
$$\begin{array}{r} 0.3625 \\ 80\overline{)29.0000} \\ \underline{240}\phantom{0000} \\ 500\phantom{00} \\ \underline{480}\phantom{00} \\ 200\phantom{0} \\ \underline{160}\phantom{0} \\ 400 \\ \underline{400} \end{array}$$

     $\dfrac{29}{80} = 0.3625$

15.
$$\begin{array}{r} 0.16 \\ 25\overline{)4.00} \\ \underline{25}\phantom{0} \\ 150 \\ \underline{150} \end{array}$$

     $\dfrac{4}{25} = 0.16$

16.   $(-0.4)^2 + 2.68$

     $= (-0.4)(-0.4) + 2.68$

     $= 0.16 + 2.68$

     $= 2.84$

17.   $\dfrac{0.56 + 2.34}{-0.2} = \dfrac{2.9}{-0.2} = -14.5$

18.   $12.1x - 6.4 - 9.8x - 7.6$

     $= 12.1x - 9.8x - 6.4 - 7.6$

     $= 2.3x - 14$

19.   $\sqrt{36} = 6$ since $6 \cdot 6 = 36$

20.   $\sqrt{22} \approx 4.69$

21.   $\sqrt{\dfrac{1}{121}} = \dfrac{1}{11}$ since $\dfrac{1}{11} \cdot \dfrac{1}{11} = \dfrac{1}{121}$

22.   $a^2 + b^2 = c^2$

     $7^2 + 7^2 = c^2$

     $49 + 49 = c^2$

        $98 = c^2$

     $\sqrt{98} = c \approx 9.9$ inches

23.   $a^2 + b^2 = c^2$

     $9^2 + 11^2 = c^2$

     $81 + 121 = c^2$

       $202 = c^2$

     $\sqrt{202} = c \approx 14.21$ meters

24.     $0.6x + 5.7 = 0.3$

    $10(0.6x + 5.7) = 0.3(10)$

      $6x + 57 = 3$

    $6x + 57 - 57 = 3 - 57$

         $6x = -54$

        $\dfrac{6x}{6} = \dfrac{-54}{6}$

          $x = -9$

25.      $12(x + 1.6) = 10x - 8.4$

      $12x + 19.2 = 10x - 8.4$

   $12x - 10x + 19.2 = 10x - 10x - 8.4$

        $2x + 19.2 = -8.4$

    $2x + 19.2 - 19.2 = -8.4 - 19.2$

           $2x = -27.6$

          $\dfrac{2x}{2} = \dfrac{-27.6}{2}$

            $x = -13.8$

## 6.1 SOLUTIONS TO EXERCISES

1. $\dfrac{17}{29}$

2. $\dfrac{48}{7}$

3. $\dfrac{\frac{3}{5}}{9}$

4. $\dfrac{6\frac{1}{7}}{3\frac{8}{11}}$

5. $\dfrac{14}{35} = \dfrac{2}{5}$

6. $\dfrac{40}{70} = \dfrac{4}{7}$

7. $\dfrac{42 \text{ miles}}{160 \text{ miles}} = \dfrac{21}{80}$

8. $\dfrac{33 \text{ feet}}{15 \text{ feet}} = \dfrac{11}{5}$

9. $\dfrac{\$100}{\$125} = \dfrac{4}{5}$

10. $\dfrac{99 \text{ cm}}{102 \text{ cm}} = \dfrac{33}{34}$

11. $\dfrac{4.6}{9} = \dfrac{4.6}{9} \cdot \dfrac{10}{10} = \dfrac{46}{90} = \dfrac{23}{45}$

12. $\dfrac{5.82}{9.1} = \dfrac{5.82}{9.1} \cdot \dfrac{100}{100} = \dfrac{582}{910} = \dfrac{291}{455}$

13. $\dfrac{10 \text{ men}}{15 \text{ women}} = \dfrac{2 \text{ men}}{3 \text{ women}}$

14. $\dfrac{15 \text{ women}}{25 \text{ people}} = \dfrac{3 \text{ women}}{5 \text{ people}}$

15. $\dfrac{40 \text{ feet}}{22 \text{ feet}} = \dfrac{20}{11}$

16. Perimeter is $2 \cdot 22 + 2 \cdot 40 = 124$ feet

$\dfrac{22 \text{ feet}}{124 \text{ feet}} = \dfrac{11}{62}$

## 6.2 SOLUTIONS TO EXERCISES

1. $\dfrac{\$400}{12 \text{ people}} = \dfrac{\$100}{3 \text{ people}}$

2. $\dfrac{25 \text{ pecan trees}}{3 \text{ acres}}$

3. $\dfrac{12 \text{ gallons}}{275 \text{ miles}}$

4. $\dfrac{40 \text{ books}}{6 \text{ students}} = \dfrac{20 \text{ books}}{3 \text{ students}}$

5. $\dfrac{400 \text{ miles}}{8 \text{ hours}} = \dfrac{50 \text{ miles}}{1 \text{ hour}}$ or 50 miles/hour

6. $\dfrac{42 \text{ boxes}}{200 \text{ cookies}} = \dfrac{21 \text{ boxes}}{100 \text{ cookies}}$

7. $\dfrac{\$226}{40 \text{ hours}} = \$5.65 / \text{hour}$

8. $\dfrac{1000 \text{ students}}{45 \text{ teachers}} \approx 22 \text{ students/teacher}$

9. $\dfrac{\$1.99}{8 \text{ bagels}} \approx \$0.265 / \text{bagel}$

10. $\dfrac{65 \text{ pages}}{4 \text{ hours}} = 16.25 \text{ pages/hour}$

11. $\dfrac{\$14,000,000}{25 \text{ lottery winners}} = \$560,000$

12. $\dfrac{355 \text{ mL}}{12 \text{ fluid ounes}} \approx 29.6 \text{mL/fluid ounce}$

13. $\dfrac{\$0.69}{3 \text{ ounces}} = \$0.23/\text{ounce}$

    $\dfrac{\$2.99}{16 \text{ ounces}} \approx \$0.19/\text{ounce}$

    16 ounces for \$2.99 is the better deal

14. $\dfrac{\$1.79}{1 \text{ dozen}} = \$1.79/\text{dozen}$

    $\dfrac{\$2.88}{1\frac{1}{2} \text{ dozen}} = \$1.92/\text{dozen}$

    \$1.79 for one dozen is the better deal

15. $\dfrac{\$3.49}{32 \text{ ounces}} \approx \$0.11/\text{ounce}$

    $\dfrac{\$0.50}{6 \text{ ounces}} \approx \$0.08/\text{ounce}$

    \$0.50 for 6 ounces is the better deal

## 6.3 SOLUTIONS TO EXERCISES

1. $\dfrac{2\frac{1}{4}\text{cups of flour}}{36 \text{ cookies}} = \dfrac{15\frac{3}{4}\text{ cups of flour}}{252 \text{ cookies}}$

2. $\dfrac{2 \text{ pints}}{1 \text{ quart}} = \dfrac{46 \text{ pints}}{23 \text{ quarts}}$

3. $\dfrac{45 \text{ females}}{60 \text{ males}} = \dfrac{180 \text{ females}}{240 \text{ males}}$

4. $\dfrac{250 \text{ Cardinals fans}}{30 \text{ Rams fans}} = \dfrac{1000 \text{ Cardinals fans}}{120 \text{ Rams fans}}$

5. $\dfrac{1}{4} = \dfrac{25}{100}$

    $1 \cdot 100 = 4 \cdot 25$

    $100 = 100$

    True

    The proportion is true.

6. $\dfrac{30}{80} = \dfrac{300}{800}$

    $30 \cdot 800 = 80 \cdot 300$

    $24000 = 24000$

    True

    The proportion is true.

7. $\dfrac{6.25}{2.5} = \dfrac{7.1}{2.84}$

    $6.25(2.84) = 2.5(7.1)$

    $17.75 = 17.75$

    True

    The proportion is true.

8. $\dfrac{2.8}{1.7} = \dfrac{14}{9}$

    $2.8(9) = 1.7(14)$

    $25.2 = 23.8$

    False

    The proportion is false.

9. $\dfrac{\frac{3}{4}}{\frac{7}{3}} = \dfrac{\frac{9}{14}}{\frac{8}{5}}$

    $\dfrac{3}{4} \cdot \dfrac{8}{5} = \dfrac{7}{3} \cdot \dfrac{9}{14}$

    $\dfrac{6}{5} = \dfrac{3}{2}$

    False

    The proportion is false.

10. $\dfrac{3\frac{2}{3}}{\frac{9}{2}} = \dfrac{24}{29\frac{5}{11}}$

    $3\frac{2}{3} \cdot 29\frac{5}{11} = \dfrac{9}{2} \cdot 24$

    $\dfrac{11}{3} \cdot \dfrac{324}{11} = \dfrac{9}{2} \cdot \dfrac{24}{1}$

    $108 = 108$

    True

    The proportion is true.

11. $\dfrac{4}{3} = \dfrac{x}{33}$

    $4 \cdot 33 = 3 \cdot x$

    $132 = 3x$

    $\dfrac{132}{3} = \dfrac{3x}{3}$

    $44 = x$

12. $\dfrac{7}{y} = \dfrac{84}{132}$

$7 \cdot 132 = 84 \cdot y$

$924 = 84y$

$\dfrac{924}{84} = \dfrac{84y}{84}$

$11 = y$

13. $\dfrac{25}{80} = \dfrac{z}{16}$

$25 \cdot 16 = 80 \cdot z$

$400 = 80z$

$\dfrac{400}{80} = \dfrac{80z}{80}$

$5 = z$

14. $\dfrac{3}{5} = \dfrac{y}{55}$

$3 \cdot 55 = 5 \cdot y$

$165 = 5y$

$\dfrac{165}{5} = \dfrac{5y}{5}$

$33 = y$

15. $\dfrac{\frac{4}{9}}{18} = \dfrac{x}{9}$

$\dfrac{4}{9} \cdot 9 = 18 \cdot x$

$4 = 18x$

$\dfrac{4}{18} = \dfrac{18x}{18}$

$\dfrac{2}{9} = x$

16. $\dfrac{9.4}{3.2} = \dfrac{4.7}{y}$

$9.4(y) = 3.2(4.7)$

$9.4y = 15.04$

$\dfrac{9.4y}{9.4} = \dfrac{15.04}{9.4}$

$y = 1.6$

17. $\dfrac{\frac{8}{9}}{\frac{26}{27}} = \dfrac{2\frac{2}{3}}{z}$

$\dfrac{8}{9} \cdot z = \dfrac{26}{27} \cdot 2\dfrac{2}{3}$

$\dfrac{8}{9}z = \dfrac{26}{27} \cdot \dfrac{8}{3}$

$\dfrac{8}{9}z = \dfrac{208}{81}$

$\dfrac{9}{8} \cdot \dfrac{8}{9}z = \dfrac{208}{81} \cdot \dfrac{9}{8}$

$z = \dfrac{26}{9}$

18. $\dfrac{0.3}{x} = \dfrac{15}{400}$

$15(x) = 0.3(400)$

$15x = 120$

$\dfrac{15x}{15} = \dfrac{120}{15}$

$x = 8$

19. $\dfrac{x}{6.12} = \dfrac{0.91}{0.07}$

$x(0.07) = 6.12(0.91)$

$0.07x = 5.5692$

$\dfrac{0.07x}{0.07} = \dfrac{5.5692}{0.07}$

$x = 79.56$

20. $\dfrac{2036}{5694} = \dfrac{3122}{y}$

$2036 \cdot y = 5694 \cdot 3122$

$2036y = 17776668$

$\dfrac{2036y}{2036} = \dfrac{17776668}{2036}$

$y \approx 8731.17$

## 6.4 SOLUTIONS TO EXERCISES

1.　Let $x=$ number of free throws made

$$\frac{4 \text{ free throws made}}{9 \text{ free throws attempted}} = \frac{x}{45 \text{ free throws attempted}}$$
$$4 \cdot 45 = 9 \cdot x$$
$$180 = 9x$$
$$\frac{180}{9} = \frac{9x}{9}$$
$$20 = x$$

She would have made 20 free throws.

2.　Let $x=$ number of free throws attempted

$$\frac{4 \text{ free throws made}}{9 \text{ free throws attempted}} = \frac{24 \text{ free throws made}}{x \text{ free throws attempted}}$$
$$4 \cdot x = 24 \cdot 9$$
$$4x = 216$$
$$\frac{4x}{4} = \frac{216}{4}$$
$$x = 54$$

3.　Let $x=$ length of the wall
$$\frac{1 \text{ inch}}{8 \text{ feet}} = \frac{4\frac{3}{4} \text{ inches}}{x \text{ feet}}$$
$$1 \cdot x = 8 \cdot 4\frac{3}{4}$$
$$x = \frac{8}{1} \cdot \frac{19}{4} = 38$$
The wall is 38 feet long.

4.　Let $x=$ blueprint measurement
$$\frac{1 \text{ inch}}{8 \text{ feet}} = \frac{x \text{ inches}}{96 \text{ feet}}$$
$$1 \cdot 96 = 8 \cdot x$$
$$96 = 8x$$
$$\frac{96}{8} = \frac{8x}{8}$$
$$12 = x$$
The blueprint measurement is 12 inches.

5.　The area of the lawn is
$300 \times 150 = 45000$ square feet.
Let $x=$ number of bags of fertilizer
$$\frac{1 \text{ bag}}{5000 \text{ square feet}} = \frac{x \text{ bags}}{45000 \text{ square feet}}$$
$$1 \cdot 45000 = 5000 \cdot x$$
$$45000 = 5000x$$
$$\frac{45000}{5000} = \frac{5000x}{5000}$$
$$9 = x$$
9 bags of fertilizer should be purchased to cover a lawn that is 300 feet by 150 feet.

6.　The area of the lawn is
$175 \times 175 = 30625$ square feet.
Let $x=$ number of bags of fertilizer
$$\frac{1 \text{ bag}}{5000 \text{ square feet}} = \frac{x \text{ bags}}{30625 \text{ square feet}}$$
$$5000x = 30625$$
$$\frac{5000x}{5000} = \frac{30625}{5000}$$
$$x = 6.125$$
7 bags of fertilizer should be purchased to cover a square lawn 175 feet on each side.

7.　Let $x=$ number of hits
$$\frac{12 \text{ hits}}{39 \text{ times at bat}} = \frac{x \text{ hits}}{585 \text{ times at bat}}$$
$$39 \cdot x = 12 \cdot 585$$
$$39x = 7020$$
$$\frac{39x}{39} = \frac{7020}{39}$$
$$x = 180$$
He would make 180 hits

8.　Let $x=$ number of times at bat
$$\frac{12 \text{ hits}}{39 \text{ times at bat}} = \frac{60 \text{ hits}}{x \text{ times at bat}}$$
$$12 \cdot x = 39 \cdot 60$$
$$12x = 2340$$
$$\frac{12x}{12} = \frac{2340}{12}$$
$$x = 195$$
He had a 195 times at bat.

9.  Let $x$ = value of George's home
$$\frac{\$1.95 \text{ tax}}{\$100 \text{ house value}} = \frac{\$11,700 \text{ tax}}{x \text{ house value}}$$
$$1.95 \cdot x = 100 \cdot 11700$$
$$1.95x = 1170000$$
$$\frac{1.95x}{1.95} = \frac{1170000}{1.95}$$
$$x = 600,000$$
George's house value is $600,000.

10. Let $x$ = amount of tax
$$\frac{\$1.95 \text{ tax}}{\$100 \text{ house value}} = \frac{x \text{ tax}}{\$199,000}$$
$$1.95(199,000) = 100(x)$$
$$388050 = 100x$$
$$\frac{388050}{100} = \frac{100x}{100}$$
$$3880.50 = x$$
The property taxes are $3880.50.

11. Let $x$ = number of people who prefer chocolate
$$\frac{5 \text{ prefer chocolate}}{7 \text{ people}} = \frac{x \text{ prefer chocolate}}{84 \text{ people}}$$
$$5 \cdot 84 = 7 \cdot x$$
$$420 = 7x$$
$$\frac{420}{7} = \frac{7x}{7}$$
$$60 = x$$
60 of the people are likely to prefer chocolate.

12. Let $x$ = number of students who prefer vanilla
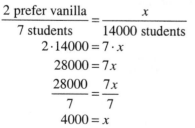
$$\frac{2 \text{ prefer vanilla}}{7 \text{ students}} = \frac{x}{14000 \text{ students}}$$
$$2 \cdot 14000 = 7 \cdot x$$
$$28000 = 7x$$
$$\frac{28000}{7} = \frac{7x}{7}$$
$$4000 = x$$
4000 of the students are likely to prefer vanilla.

13. Let $x$ = number of miles
$$\frac{275 \text{ miles}}{12 \text{ gallons}} = \frac{x \text{ miles}}{5 \text{ gallons}}$$
$$275 \cdot 5 = 12 \cdot x$$
$$1375 = 12x$$
$$\frac{1375}{12} = \frac{12x}{12}$$
$$114.583... = x$$
The Ford Taurus can travel about 115 miles on 5 gallons of gas.

14. Let $x$ = number of gallons
$$\frac{275 \text{ miles}}{12 \text{ gallons}} = \frac{1000 \text{ miles}}{x \text{ gallons}}$$
$$275 \cdot x = 12 \cdot 1000$$
$$275x = 12000$$
$$\frac{275x}{275} = \frac{12000}{275}$$
$$x \approx 43.6363...$$
The Ford Taurus needs about 44 gallons of gas to travel 1000 miles.

**6.5 SOLUTIONS TO EXERCISES**

1.  These triangles are congruent since they have two pairs of angles with equal measures and one pair of sides with equal measures; i.e. ASA

2.  These triangles are not congruent. They have only one pair of sides with the same measures.

3.  ratio of pair of corresponding sides =
$$\frac{38}{19} = \frac{2}{1}$$

4.  ratio of pair of corresponding sides =
$$\frac{12.5}{6.25} = \frac{15.3}{7.65} = \frac{20.1}{10.05} = \frac{2}{1}$$

5. $\dfrac{14}{91} = \dfrac{13}{x}$

    $14 \cdot x = 91 \cdot 13$

    $14x = 1183$

    $\dfrac{14x}{14} = \dfrac{1183}{14}$

    $x = 84.5$

6. $\dfrac{19.2}{3.2} = \dfrac{x}{1.2}$

    $3.2(x) = 19.2(1.2)$

    $3.2x = 23.04$

    $\dfrac{3.2x}{3.2} = \dfrac{23.04}{3.2}$

    $x = 7.2$

7. $\dfrac{12.5}{2.5} = \dfrac{30.5}{x}$

    $12.5(x) = 2.5(30.5)$

    $12.5x = 76.25$

    $\dfrac{12.5x}{12.5} = \dfrac{76.25}{12.5}$

    $x = 6.1$

8. $\dfrac{5}{3} = \dfrac{20}{x}$

    $5 \cdot x = 3 \cdot 20$

    $5x = 60$

    $\dfrac{5x}{5} = \dfrac{60}{5}$

    $x = 12$

9. Let $x =$ length of the shadow

    $\dfrac{100\text{-foot building}}{175\text{-foot shadow}} = \dfrac{6\text{-foot man}}{x\text{-foot shadow}}$

    $100 \cdot x = 175 \cdot 6$

    $100x = 1050$

    $\dfrac{100x}{100} = \dfrac{1050}{100}$

    $x = 10.5$

The shadow is 10.5 feet.

10. Let $x =$ length of the light pole

    $\dfrac{18\text{-foot light pole}}{25\text{-foot shadow}} = \dfrac{x\text{-foot light pole}}{20\text{-foot shadow}}$

    $18 \cdot 20 = 25 \cdot x$

    $360 = 25x$

    $\dfrac{360}{25} = \dfrac{25x}{25}$

    $14.4 = x$

The light pole is 14.4 feet tall.

## CHAPTER 6 PRACTICE TEST SOLUTIONS

1. $\dfrac{459 \text{ Gerber daisies}}{132 \text{ Gerber daisies}}$

2. $\dfrac{10\frac{3}{8} \text{ dollars}}{8\frac{1}{4} \text{ dollars}}$

3. $\dfrac{80}{25} = \dfrac{16}{5}$

4. $\dfrac{32}{50} = \dfrac{16}{25}$

5. $\dfrac{\$12}{\$90} = \dfrac{2}{15}$

6. $\dfrac{42 \text{ miles}}{84 \text{ miles}} = \dfrac{1}{2}$

7. $\dfrac{10 \text{ cars}}{3 \text{ miles}}$

8. $\dfrac{12 \text{ computers}}{82 \text{ students}} = \dfrac{6 \text{ computers}}{41 \text{ students}}$

9. $\dfrac{425 \text{ miles}}{5 \text{ hours}} = 85 \text{ miles/hour}$

10. $\dfrac{22 \text{ inches}}{30 \text{ days}} \approx 0.73 \text{ inches/day}$

11. $\dfrac{\$1.49}{8 \text{ cinnamon rolls}} = \$0.18625/\text{roll}$

    $\dfrac{\$2.28}{12 \text{ cinnamon rolls}} = \$0.19/\text{roll}$

    $\$1.49$ for 8 rolls is the better buy.

12. $\dfrac{\$0.99}{1 \text{ pound}} = \$0.99/\text{pound}$

$\dfrac{\$4.99}{5 \text{ pounds}} = \$0.998/\text{pound}$

The 1 pound bag for $0.99 is the better buy.

13. $\dfrac{1 \text{ cup of sugar}}{3 \text{ quarts of iced tea}} = \dfrac{4 \text{ cups of sugar}}{12 \text{ quarts of iced tea}}$

14. $\dfrac{36 \text{ inches}}{3 \text{ feet}} = \dfrac{198 \text{ inches}}{16.5 \text{ feet}}$

15. $\dfrac{20}{75} = \dfrac{80}{300}$

$20 \cdot 300 = 75 \cdot 80$

$6000 = 6000$

True

The proportion is true.

16. $\dfrac{\frac{2}{5}}{\frac{1}{3}} = \dfrac{\frac{4}{9}}{\frac{1}{4}}$

$\dfrac{2}{5} \cdot \dfrac{1}{4} = \dfrac{1}{3} \cdot \dfrac{4}{9}$

$\dfrac{1}{10} = \dfrac{4}{27}$

False

The proportion is false.

17. $\dfrac{x}{4} = \dfrac{35}{20}$

$20x = 140$

$x = 7$

18. $\dfrac{\frac{9}{5}}{\frac{7}{11}} = \dfrac{x}{\frac{5}{9}}$

$\dfrac{9}{5} \cdot \dfrac{5}{9} = \dfrac{7}{11} \cdot x$

$1 = \dfrac{7}{11}x$

$\dfrac{11}{7} = x$

19. $\dfrac{3.6}{4} = \dfrac{9}{y}$

$3.6y = 36$

$y = 10$

20. Let $x$ = number of miles

$\dfrac{1.5 \text{ inches}}{75 \text{ miles}} = \dfrac{2 \text{ inches}}{x \text{ miles}}$

$1.5x = 150$

$x = 100$

Wisconsin is 100 miles away.

21. Let $x$ = number of inches

$\dfrac{1.5 \text{ inches}}{75 \text{ miles}} = \dfrac{x \text{ inches}}{270 \text{ miles}}$

$75x = 405$

$x = 5.4$

Chicago would be 5.4 inches away from St. Louis on the map.

22. $\dfrac{22}{5.5} = \dfrac{13}{x}$

$22x = 71.5$

$x = 3.25$

23. Let $x$ = number of inches

$\dfrac{18.5 \text{ inches}}{1 \text{ set of curtains}} = \dfrac{x \text{ inches}}{12 \text{ sets of curtains}}$

$x = 222$

222 inches of lace is needed for 12 sets of curtains.

24. Let $x$ = height of tree

$\quad\quad$ Kelly $\quad\quad\quad\quad\quad$ tree

$\dfrac{3\frac{1}{2}\text{-foot shadow}}{5\frac{1}{4}\text{-foot tall}} = \dfrac{32\text{-foot shadow}}{x\text{-foot tall}}$

$3\frac{1}{2}x = 5\frac{1}{4} \cdot 32$

$3.5x = 168$

$x = 48$

The tree is 48 feet tall.

## 7.1 SOLUTION TO EXERCISES

1. $38\% = 0.38$

2. $3\% = 0.03$

3. $50.3\% = 0.503$

4. $125\% = 1.25$

5. $0.25 = 25\%$

6. $0.016 = 1.6\%$

7. $1.05 = 105\%$

8. $6 = 600\%$

9. $30\% = \dfrac{30}{100} = \dfrac{3}{10}$

10. $4.7\% = \dfrac{4.7}{100} \cdot \dfrac{10}{10} = \dfrac{47}{1000}$

11. $150\% = \dfrac{150}{100} = \dfrac{3}{2}$

12. $0.4\% = \dfrac{0.4}{100} \cdot \dfrac{10}{10} = \dfrac{4}{1000} = \dfrac{1}{250}$

13. $\dfrac{7}{25} = \dfrac{7}{25} \cdot 100\% = \dfrac{700}{25}\% = 28\%$

14. $\dfrac{7}{8} = \dfrac{7}{8} \cdot 100\% = \dfrac{700}{8}\% = 87.5\%$

15. $1\dfrac{1}{2} = \dfrac{3}{2} = \dfrac{3}{2} \cdot 100\% = \dfrac{300}{2}\% = 150\%$

16. $\dfrac{49}{50} = \dfrac{49}{50} \cdot 100\% = \dfrac{4900}{50}\% = 98\%$

17. $100\% = \dfrac{25 \text{ students attended}}{25 \text{ students enrolled}}$
    25 students attended.

18. $5\% = 0.05$

19. $0.0725 = 7.25\%$ or $7\dfrac{1}{4}\%$

20. $\dfrac{1}{2} \cdot 100\% = \dfrac{100}{2}\% = 50\%$

## 7.2 SOLUTIONS TO EXERCISES

1. 35% of 80 is what number?
   $35\% \cdot 80 = x$
   $0.35 \cdot 80 = x$

2. What percent of 10 is 20?
   $x \quad \cdot \quad 10 = 20$

3. 6.2 is 29% of what number?
   $6.2 = 29\% \cdot x$

4. 32% of 912 is what number?
   $32\% \cdot 912 = x$

5. $5\% \cdot 40 = x$
   $0.05 \cdot 40 = x$
   $2 = x$

6. $x = 25\% \cdot 71.1$
   $x = 0.25 \cdot 71.1$
   $x = 17.775$

7. $40 = 20\% \cdot x$
   $40 = 0.2x$
   $\dfrac{40}{0.2} = \dfrac{0.2x}{0.2}$
   $200 = x$

8. $0.22 = 40\% \cdot x$
   $0.22 = 0.4x$
   $\dfrac{0.22}{0.4} = \dfrac{0.4x}{0.4}$
   $0.55 = x$

9. $9 = x \cdot 36$
   $9 = 36x$
   $\dfrac{9}{36} = \dfrac{36x}{36}$
   $0.25 = x$
   $25\% = x$

10. $3.21 = x \cdot 32.1$

$3.21 = 32.1x$

$$\frac{3.21}{32.1} = \frac{32.1x}{32.1}$$

$0.1 = x$

$10\% = x$

11. $0.8 = 20\% \cdot x$

$0.8 = 0.2x$

$4 = x$

12. $16 = 125\% \cdot x$

$16 = 1.25x$

$12.8 = x$

13. $14.2 = 8\frac{1}{4}\% \cdot x$

$14.2 = 8.25\% \cdot x$

$14.2 = 0.0825x$

$172.12 \approx x$

14. $400 = x \cdot 50$

$400 = 50x$

$8 = x$

$800\% = x$

15. $21.3 = x \cdot 100$

$21.3 = 100x$

$0.213 = x$

$21.3\% = x$

16. $x = 15\% \cdot 25$

$x = 0.15 \cdot 25$

$x = 3.75$

## 7.3 SOLUTIONS TO EXERCISES

1. $\underbrace{\text{What percent}}_{\text{percent}}$ of $\underbrace{51}_{\text{base}}$ is $\underbrace{17}_{\text{amount}}$ ?

$$\frac{17}{51} = \frac{x}{100}$$

2. $\underbrace{9\%}_{\text{percent}}$ of $\underbrace{\text{what number}}_{\text{base}}$ is $\underbrace{10}_{\text{amount}}$ ?

$$\frac{10}{x} = \frac{9}{100}$$

3. $\underbrace{44}_{\text{amount}}$ is $\underbrace{22\%}_{\text{percent}}$ of $\underbrace{\text{what number}}_{\text{base}}$ ?

$$\frac{44}{x} = \frac{22}{100}$$

4. $\underbrace{65\%}_{\text{percent}}$ of $\underbrace{100}_{\text{base}}$ is $\underbrace{\text{what number}}_{\text{amount}}$ ?

$$\frac{x}{100} = \frac{65}{100}$$

5. $\dfrac{x}{200} = \dfrac{75}{100}$

$100x = 15000$

$x = 150$

75% of 200 is 150.

6. $\dfrac{x}{15} = \dfrac{4.5}{100}$

$100x = 67.5$

$x = 0.675$

0.675 is 4.5% of 15.

7. $\dfrac{60}{x} = \dfrac{8}{100}$

$8x = 6000$

$x = 750$

60 is 8% of 750.

8. $\dfrac{420}{x} = \dfrac{110}{100}$

$110x = 42000$

$x \approx 381.82$

420 is about 110% of 381.82.

9. $\dfrac{5}{50} = \dfrac{x}{100}$

$50x = 500$

$x = 10$

5 is 10% of 50.

10. $\dfrac{12}{112} = \dfrac{x}{100}$

$112x = 1200$

$x \approx 10.71$

12 is about 10.71% of 112.

11. $\dfrac{99}{x} = \dfrac{99}{100}$

$99x = 9900$

$x = 100$

99 is 99% of 100.

12. $\dfrac{3}{x} = \dfrac{100}{100}$

$100x = 300$

$x = 3$

3 is 100% of 3.

13. $\dfrac{15.5}{x} = \dfrac{5.5}{100}$

$5.5x = 1550$

$x \approx 281.82$

15.5 is about 5.5% of 281.82

14. $\dfrac{50}{40} = \dfrac{x}{100}$

$40x = 5000$

$x = 125$

50 is 125% of 40.

15. $\dfrac{27.6}{100} = \dfrac{x}{100}$

$100x = 2760$

$x = 27.6$

27.6 is 100% of 27.6.

16. $\dfrac{4}{x} = \dfrac{125}{100}$

$125x = 400$

$x = 3.2$

125% of 3.2 is 4.

## 7.4 SOLUTIONS TO EXERCISES

1. $4.5\% \cdot 1600 = x$

$0.045 \cdot 1600 = x$

$72 = x$

4.5% of $1600 is $72.

2. 625 is what percent of 2500?

$\dfrac{625}{2500} = \dfrac{x}{100}$

$2500x = 62500$

$x = 25$

The Smiths spend 25% of their monthly income on their mortgage.

3. What is 15.02% of 1250?

$\dfrac{x}{1250} = \dfrac{15.02}{100}$

$100x = 18775$

$x = 187.75$

The social security tax is $187.75.

4. 1000 is what percent of 45,500?

$\dfrac{1000}{45500} = \dfrac{x}{100}$

$45500x = 100000$

$x \approx 2.2$

Dave received about a 2.2% raise.

5. amount of increase = $26.2 - 22.4 = 3.8$

percent of increase = $\dfrac{3.8}{22.4} \approx 0.1696 \approx 17\%$

6. amount of decrease = $199 - 125 = 74$

percent of decrease = $\dfrac{74}{199} \approx 0.372 = 37.2\%$

7. amount of decrease = $2100 - 1600 = 500$

percent of decrease =

$\dfrac{500}{2100} \approx 0.238 = 23.8\%$

8. amount of increase = $150000 - 125000 = 25000$

percent of increase = $\dfrac{25000}{125000} = 0.2 = 20\%$

9. amount of increase = $1.32 - 1.16 = 0.16$

percent of increase = $\dfrac{0.16}{1.16} \approx 0.138 = 13.8\%$

10. amount of increase = $89 - 79 = 10$

percent of increase = $\dfrac{10}{79} \approx 0.127 = 12.7\%$

## 7.5 SOLUTIONS TO EXERCISES

1. sales tax = tax rate · purchase price
   $$= 6.5\% \cdot \$150$$
   $$= 0.065 \cdot \$150$$
   $$= \$9.75$$

2. sales tax = tax rate · purchase price
   $$= 5\% \cdot \$595$$
   $$= 0.05 \cdot \$595$$
   $$= \$29.75$$

3. sales tax = tax rate · purchase price
   $$= 7\% \cdot \$350$$
   $$= 0.07 \cdot \$350$$
   $$= \$24.50$$

4. sales tax = tax rate · purchase price
   $$= 7.5\% \cdot \$1200$$
   $$= 0.075 \cdot \$1200$$
   $$= \$90$$
   total price = purchase price + sales tax
   $$= \$1200 + \$90$$
   $$= \$1290$$

5. sales tax = tax rate · purchase price
   $$= 6.25\% \cdot \$23,900$$
   $$= 0.0625 \cdot \$23,900$$
   $$= \$1493.75$$
   total price = purchase price + sales tax
   $$= \$23,900 + \$1493.75$$
   $$= \$25393.75$$

6. total purchase price =
   $$\$45 + \$75 + \$120 = \$240$$
   sales tax = tax rate · purchase price
   $$= 5.5\% \cdot \$240$$
   $$= 0.055 \cdot \$240$$
   $$= \$13.20$$
   total price = purchase price + sales tax
   $$= \$240 + \$13.20$$
   $$= \$253.20$$

7. commission = commission rate · sales
   $$x = 1.2\% \cdot \$150,000,000$$
   $$x = 0.012 \cdot 150,000,000$$
   $$x = \$1,800,000$$

8. commission = commission rate · sales
   $$\$2675 = x \cdot \$29,722$$
   $$2576 = 29722x$$
   $$0.08666 \approx x$$
   $$8.7\% \approx x$$

9. commission = commission rate · sales
   $$\$1500 = 10\% \cdot x$$
   $$1500 = 0.1x$$
   $$\$15000 = x$$

10. discount = $\$800 \cdot 20\% = 800 \cdot 0.2 = \$160$

    new price = original price – discount
    $$= \$800 - \$160$$
    $$= \$640$$

11. discount = $\$25 \cdot 25\% = \$25 \cdot 0.25 = \$6.25$

    new price = original price – discount
    $$= \$25 - \$6.25$$
    $$= \$18.75$$

12. discount =
    $$\$25,000 \cdot 3.5\% = \$25,000 \cdot 0.035 = \$875$$

    new price = original price – discount
    $$= \$25,000 - \$875$$
    $$= \$24,125$$

## 7.6 SOLUTIONS TO EXERCISES

1. $I = P \cdot R \cdot T$
   $$= \$750 \cdot 4\% \cdot 5$$
   $$= \$750 \cdot 0.04 \cdot 5$$
   $$= \$150$$

2. $I = P \cdot R \cdot T$
   $$= \$80,000 \cdot 7.8\% \cdot 10$$
   $$= \$80,000 \cdot 0.078 \cdot 10$$
   $$= \$62,400$$

3. $I = P \cdot R \cdot T$
   $= \$400 \cdot 13\% \cdot 2.5$
   $= \$400 \cdot 0.13 \cdot 2.5$
   $= \$130$

4. $I = P \cdot R \cdot T$
   $= \$1650 \cdot 20\% \cdot 0.5$
   $= \$1650 \cdot 0.2 \cdot 0.5$
   $= \$165$

5. $I = P \cdot R \cdot T$
   $= \$1500 \cdot 6\frac{1}{4}\% \cdot 10$
   $= \$1500 \cdot 6.25\% \cdot 10$
   $= \$1500 \cdot 0.0625 \cdot 10$
   $= \$937.50$

6. $I = P \cdot R \cdot T$
   $= \$2500 \cdot 5\% \cdot 0.75$
   $= \$2500 \cdot 0.05 \cdot 0.75$
   $= \$93.75$

7. $I = P \cdot R \cdot T$
   $= \$17,300 \cdot 8.5\% \cdot 4$
   $= \$17,300 \cdot 0.085 \cdot 4$
   $= \$5882$

8. $I = P \cdot R \cdot T$
   $= \$3500 \cdot 8\frac{1}{2}\% \cdot 2$
   $= \$3500 \cdot 8.5\% \cdot 2$
   $= \$3500 \cdot 0.085 \cdot 2$
   $= \$595$

9. annually
   rate = 12%
   time = 10 years
   compound interest factor = 3.10585
   (from Appendix F in textbook)

   total amount = principal · compound interest factor
   $= \$9500 \cdot 3.10585$
   $= \$29,505.58$

10. semiannually
    rate = 12%
    time = 5 years
    compound interest factor = 1.79085

    total amount = principal · compound interest factor
    $= \$1500 \cdot 1.79085$
    $= \$2686.28$

11. quarterly
    rate = 8%
    time = 15
    compound interest factor = 3.28103

    total amount = principal · compound interest factor
    $= \$12000 \cdot 3.28103$
    $= \$39,372.36$

12. daily
    rate = 7%
    time = 20 years
    compound interest factor = 4.05466

    total amount = principal · compound interest factor
    $= \$25,000 \cdot 4.05466$
    $= \$101,366.50$

13. annually
    rate = 5%
    time = 15 years
    compound interest factor = 2.07893

    total amount = principal · compound interest factor
    $= \$950 \cdot 2.07893$
    $= \$1974.98$

14. quarterly
    rate = 17%
    time = 10 years
    compound interest factor = 5.28497

    total amount = principal · compound interest factor
    =$1250 · 5.28497
    =$6606.21

15. total amount = amount borrowed + interest
    = $30,000 + $14,578.42
    = $44,578.42

    number of payments
    = 5 years · 12 payments/year
    = 60 payments

    $$\text{monthly payment} = \frac{\text{total amount}}{\text{number of payments}}$$
    $$= \frac{\$44,578.42}{60}$$
    $$= \$742.97$$

16. total amount = amount borrowed + interest
    = $133,000 + $300,000
    = $433,000

    number of payments
    = 30 years · 12 payments/year
    = 360 payments

    $$\text{monthly payment} = \frac{\text{total amount}}{\text{number of payments}}$$
    $$= \frac{\$433,000}{360}$$
    $$= \$1202.78$$

## CHAPTER 7 PRACTICE TEST SOLUTIONS

1. $0.371 = 37.1\%$

2. $0.371\% = 0.00371$

3. $121\% = \frac{121}{100}$

4. $\frac{13}{25} = \frac{13}{25} \cdot 100\% = \frac{1300}{25}\% = 52\%$

5. $6.25\% = \frac{6.25}{100} = \frac{6.25}{100} \cdot \frac{100}{100} = \frac{625}{10000} = \frac{1}{16}$

6. $x = 35\% \cdot 90$
   $= 0.35 \cdot 90$
   $= 31.5$

   31.5 is 35% of 90.

7. $\frac{12}{x} = \frac{1.2}{100}$
   $1.2x = 1200$
   $x = 1000$

   1.2% of 1000 is 12.

8. $\frac{45}{90} = \frac{x}{100}$
   $90x = 4500$
   $x = 50$

   45 is 50% of 90.

9. $14 = 0.19x$

10. $\frac{14}{x} = \frac{19}{100}$

11. Let $x$ = number of pounds of copper
    $\frac{x}{180} = \frac{16}{100}$
    $100x = 2880$
    $x = 28.8$
    There are 28.8 pounds of copper in this alloy.

12. Let $x$ = number of pounds of candy corn
    $x = 0.12 \cdot 5$
    $= 0.6$
    There are 0.6 pounds of candy corn in this mixture.

13. Let $x$ = the commission
    $x = 0.015 \cdot 185,000$
    $= \$2775$

14. amount of tax $= = \$89.99 \cdot 6\frac{3}{4}\%$
$$= \$89.99 \cdot 6.75\%$$
$$= \$89.99 \cdot 0.0675$$
$$= \$6.07$$

total amount = original price + tax
$$= \$89.99 + \$6.07$$
$$= \$96.06$$

15. $I = P \cdot R \cdot T$
$$= \$600 \cdot 15.5\% \cdot \frac{9}{12}$$
$$= \$600 \cdot 0.155 \cdot 0.75$$
$$= \$69.75$$

16. $I = P \cdot R \cdot T$
$$= \$4250 \cdot 7\frac{1}{2}\% \cdot 6\frac{1}{4}$$
$$= \$4250 \cdot 7.5\% \cdot 6.25$$
$$= \$4250 \cdot 0.075 \cdot 6.25$$
$$= \$1992.19$$

17. amount of increase $= 16\% \cdot \$2.15$
$$= 0.16 \cdot \$2.15$$
$$= \$0.34$$

new price = old price + increase
$$= \$2.15 + \$0.34$$
$$= \$2.49$$

18. amount of increase $= \$7.25 - \$5.65 = \$1.60$

$$\frac{1.60}{5.65} = \frac{x}{100}$$
$$5.65x = 160$$
$$x \approx 28.3\%$$
The percent increase is about 28.3%.

19. quarterly
rate = 8%
time = 20 years
compound interest factor = 4.87544

total amount = principal · factor
$$= \$5 \cdot 4.87544$$
$$= \$24.38$$

20. semiannually
rate = 6%
time = 10 years
compound interest factor = 1.80611

total amount = principal · factor
$$= \$5260 \cdot 1.80611$$
$$= \$9500.14$$

21. amount of decrease $= 10.2\% - 8.5\% = 1.7\%$

percent of decrease $= \dfrac{1.7}{10.2} \approx 0.167 = 16.7\%$

22. total borrowed = \$8800 + \$620.35
$$= \$9420.35$$

number of payments
$$= 2\ \frac{1}{2}\ \text{years} \cdot 12\ \text{payments/year} = 30$$

monthly payment $= \dfrac{\$9420.35}{30} \approx \$314.01$

23. commission = commission rate · sales
$$12,000 = 0.03 \cdot x$$
$$\$400,000 = x$$
Her sales were \$400,000.

## 8.1 SOLUTIONS TO EXERCISES

1. $(\text{num. of houses}) \cdot (5 \text{ houses}) = 3 \cdot 5 \text{ houses}$
$$= 15 \text{ houses}$$

2. $(\text{num. houses}) \cdot (5 \text{ houses}) = 4 \cdot 5 \text{ houses}$
$$= 20 \text{ houses}$$

3. 1999 (this line contains the most symbols)

4. 1999: $6 \cdot 5 \text{ houses} = 30 \text{ houses}$
1997: $2 \cdot 5 \text{ houses} = 10 \text{ houses}$

   $30 \text{ houses} - 10 \text{ houses} = 20 \text{ houses}$

   There were 20 more renovations in 1999 than in 1997.

5. First add up the total number of symbols:
$2 + 4 + 6 + 4 + 3 + 4 = 23$
Now multiply by the number of houses each symbol represents.
$23 \cdot 5 \text{ houses} = 115 \text{ houses}$
The total number of renovations from 1997-2002 was 115.

6. $15 \text{ renovations} = \dfrac{15}{5} \text{ symbols} = 3 \text{ symbols}$

   2001 is the only year with 15 renovations.

7. Find the bar that corresponds to 1999, go to the top of the bar and then across to the vertical axis to identify the profit. The profit during 1999 was $125,000.

8. Find $200,000 on the vertical axis, then go horizontally to see if this corresponds to the top of a bar. There was a profit of $200,000 in 2001.

9. $2002: \quad \$275,000$
   $2000: \quad \underline{-\$150,000}$
   $\phantom{2000: } \quad \$125,000$
There was $125,000 more in profits in 2002 than in 2000.

10. Look at the top of consecutive bars, left to right and see where there is the greatest gap. The greatest increase in profit occurred between 2001 and 2002.

11. $1999: \quad \$125,000$
    $2000: \quad \$150,000$
    $2001: \quad \$200,000$
    $2002: \quad \underline{+\,\$275,000}$
    $\phantom{2002: } \quad \$750,000$
The total profit from 1999-2002 was $750,000.

12. The year with the tallest bar had the largest profit. The largest profit was in 2002.

13. The dot on the line graph corresponding to Tuesday appears to be halfway between 82 and 84. Thus, the high temperature reading for Tuesday was $83°F$.

14. Look for the lowest dot on the graph. The temperature was lowest on Friday.

15. Looking at consecutive days from left to right, locate the longest line segment that is rising. The greatest increase occurred between Friday and Saturday.

16. Find 82 on the vertical axis, then go horizontally across to the line graph to see if this temperature corresponds to a day. $82°F$ was the high temperature on Wednesday.

17. $\text{Sunday:} \quad 76°F$
    $\underline{\text{Saturday:} \quad 74°F}$
    $\text{difference:} \quad 2°F$

    There was a 2° difference in temperature readings on Sunday and Saturday.

18.

| Rating | Tally | Frequency |
|--------|-------|-----------|
| 1 | ||| | 3 |
| 2 | ||||| | 5 |
| 3 | |||| | 4 |
| 4 | || | 2 |
| 5 | | | 1 |

19. A rating of 2 had the largest frequency so it was reported the most.

20.

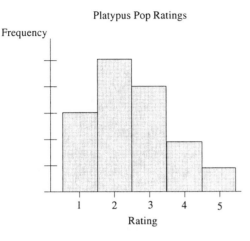

Platypus Pop Ratings

## 8.2 SOLUTIONS TO EXERCISES

1. amount = percent · base
$$= 8\% \cdot 500$$
$$= (0.08)(500)$$
$$= 40$$
40 students prefer horror movies.

2. sci-fi: amount = percent · base
$$= 10\% \cdot 500$$
$$= (0.1)(500)$$
$$= 50$$

   action: amount = percent · base
$$= 37\% \cdot 500$$
$$= (0.37)(500)$$
$$= 185$$

   $50 + 185 = 235$
   235 students prefer either sci-fi or action movies.

3. amount = percent · base
$$= 25\% \cdot 500$$
$$= (0.25)(500)$$
$$= 125$$
125 students prefer drama movies.

4. The percent of students preferring action movies is 37%.
$$\text{ratio} = \frac{37}{100}$$

5. $$\frac{\text{comedy }\%}{\text{drama }\%} = \frac{20\%}{25\%} = \frac{20}{25} = \frac{4}{5}$$

6. Look for the smallest sector. Horror movies were preferred the least.

7. Look for the largest sector. Swimming had the largest participation.

8. Look for the smallest sector. Crafts had the smallest participation.

9. $$\text{percent} = \frac{\text{number fishing}}{\text{total number}} = \frac{50}{200} = \frac{1}{4} = 0.25$$
25% of the campers went fishing.

10. $$\text{percent} = \frac{\text{number swimming}}{\text{total number}} = \frac{70}{200} = 0.35$$
35% of the campers went swimming.

11. $$\frac{\text{number canoeing}}{\text{number making crafts}} = \frac{40}{18} = \frac{20}{9}$$

12. $$\frac{\text{number swimming or hiking}}{\text{total number}} = \frac{92}{200} = \frac{23}{50}$$

13. Look for the second-largest sector. Fishing was the second-largest category.

14.

| Sector | Degrees in sector |
|--------|-------------------|
| Fenton | $40\% \cdot 360° = 144°$ |
| Smith | $5\% \cdot 360° = 18°$ |
| Mosser | $10\% \cdot 360° = 36°$ |
| Victorian | $20\% \cdot 360° = 72°$ |
| Westmoreland | $25\% \cdot 360° = 90°$ |

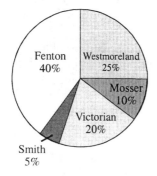

Glassware Collection

15. Look for the largest sector. Republicans make up the largest category in that county.

16. Look for the smallest sector. Other political parties combined to make the smallest category.

17. number = percent · base

$$= 15\% \cdot 20,000$$
$$= (0.15)(20,000)$$
$$= 3000$$

If the county had 20,000 registered voters, then 3000 of them would be Independents.

18. number = percent · base

$$= 50\% \cdot 20,000$$
$$= (0.5)(20,000)$$
$$= 10,000$$

If the county had 20,000 registered voters, then 10,000 of them would be Republicans.

19. number = percent · base

$$= 30\% \cdot 20,000$$
$$= (0.3)(20,000)$$
$$= 6000$$

If the county had 20,000 registered voters, then 6000 of them would be Democrats.

20. $\dfrac{\text{percent of Democrats}}{\text{percent of Republicans}} = \dfrac{30\%}{50\%} = \dfrac{30}{50} = \dfrac{3}{5}$

## 8.3 SOLUTIONS TO EXERCISES

1. – 6.

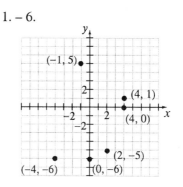

7. $A(-5,5)$; $B(6,3)$; $C(-3,-4)$;
   $D(4,0)$; $E(0,-6)$

8. Quadrant IV

9. y-axis

10. Quadrant III

11. x-axis

12. Quadrant II

13. $y = 4x$
    $4 = 4(-1)$
    $4 = -4$  False
    The order pair $(-1,4)$ is not a solution.

14. $x = -7y$
    $0 = -7(0)$
    $0 = 0$  True
    The ordered pair $(0,0)$ is a solution.

15. $3x + 2y = 7$
    $3(1) + 2(2) = 7$
    $3 + 4 = 7$
    $7 = 7$  True
    The ordered pair $(1,2)$ is a solution.

16.

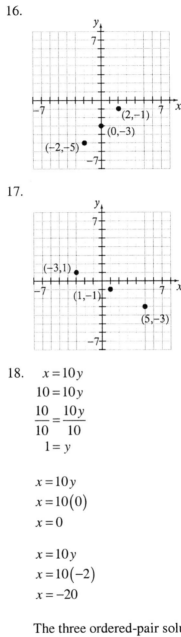

17.

18. $x = 10y$

$10 = 10y$

$$\frac{10}{10} = \frac{10y}{10}$$

$1 = y$

$x = 10y$

$x = 10(0)$

$x = 0$

$x = 10y$

$x = 10(-2)$

$x = -20$

The three ordered-pair solutions are $(10,1)$, $(0,0)$, and $(-20,-2)$.

19.   $4x - y = 8$

$4(2) - y = 8$

$8 - y = 8$

$8 - y - 8 = 8 - 8$

$-y = 0$

$$\frac{-y}{-1} = \frac{0}{-1}$$

$y = 0$

$4x - y = 8$

$4(3) - y = 8$

$12 - y = 8$

$12 - y - 12 = 8 - 12$

$-y = -4$

$$\frac{-y}{-1} = \frac{-4}{-1}$$

$y = 4$

$4x - y = 8$

$4x - 8 = 8$

$4x - 8 + 8 = 8 + 8$

$4x = 16$

$$\frac{4x}{4} = \frac{16}{4}$$

$x = 4$

The three ordered-pair solutions are $(2,0)$, $(3,4)$, and $(4,8)$.

20.   $x + 6y = 0$

$x + 6(1) = 0$

$x + 6 = 0$

$x + 6 - 6 = 0 - 6$

$x = -6$

$x + 6y = 0$

$x + 6(-2) = 0$

$x - 12 = 0$

$x - 12 + 12 = 0 + 12$

$x = 12$

$$x + 6y = 0$$
$$0 + 6y = 0$$
$$6y = 0$$
$$\frac{6y}{6} = \frac{0}{6}$$
$$y = 0$$

The three ordered-pair solutions are $(-6,1)$, $(12,-2)$, and $(0,0)$.

## 8.4 SOLUTIONS TO EXERCISES

1. $x + y = -5$
    Let $x = 0$:  $0 + y = -5$
    $$y = -5$$
    $$(0,-5)$$

    Let $y = 0$:  $x + 0 = -5$
    $$x = -5$$
    $$(-5,0)$$

    Let $x = -1$:  $-1 + y = -5$
    $$-1 + y + 1 = -5 + 1$$
    $$y = -4$$
    $$(-1,-4)$$

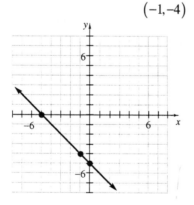

2. $x + 3y = 1$
    Let $x = 4$:  $4 + 3y = 1$
    $$4 + 3y - 4 = 1 - 4$$
    $$3y = -3$$
    $$\frac{3y}{3} = \frac{-3}{3}$$
    $$y = -1$$
    $$(4,-1)$$

    Let $y = 0$:  $x + 3(0) = 1$
    $$x = 1$$
    $$(1,0)$$

    Let $x = -2$:  $-2 + 3y = 1$
    $$-2 + 3y + 2 = 1 + 2$$
    $$3y = 3$$
    $$\frac{3y}{3} = \frac{3}{3}$$
    $$y = 1$$
    $$(-2,1)$$

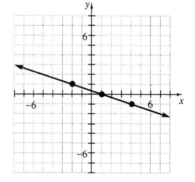

3. $3x - y = 6$
    Let $x = 0$:  $3(0) - y = 6$
    $$0 - y = 6$$
    $$-y = 6$$
    $$\frac{-y}{-1} = \frac{6}{-1}$$
    $$y = -6$$
    $$(0,-6)$$

Let $y = 0$: $\quad 3x - 0 = 6$

$$3x = 6$$

$$\frac{3x}{3} = \frac{6}{3}$$

$$x = 2$$

$$(2, 0)$$

Let $x = 1$: $\quad 3(1) - y = 6$

$$3 - y = 6$$

$$3 - y - 3 = 6 - 3$$

$$-y = 3$$

$$\frac{-y}{-1} = \frac{3}{-1}$$

$$y = -3$$

$$(1, -3)$$

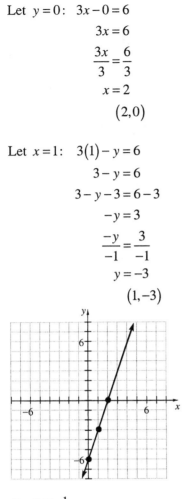

4. $y - x = -1$

Let $x = 0$: $\quad y - 0 = -1$

$$y = -1$$

$$(0, -1)$$

Let $y = 0$: $\quad 0 - x = -1$

$$-x = -1$$

$$\frac{-x}{-1} = \frac{-1}{-1}$$

$$x = 1$$

$$(1, 0)$$

Let $x = 2$: $\quad y - 2 = -1$

$$y - 2 + 2 = -1 + 2$$

$$y = 1$$

$$(2, 1)$$

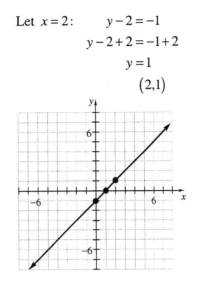

5. $y = 2x - 4$

| $x$ | $y = 2x - 4$ |
|---|---|
| 0 | $2(0) - 4 = -4$ |
| 1 | $2(1) - 4 = -2$ |
| 2 | $2(2) - 4 = 0$ |

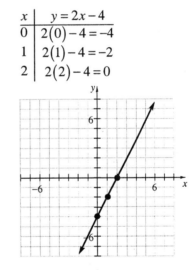

6. $x = 2y + 1$

Let $y = 0$: $\quad x = 2(0) + 1$

$$x = 0 + 1$$

$$x = 1$$

$$(1, 0)$$

Let $y = 1$: $\quad x = 2(1) + 1$

$$x = 2 + 1$$

$$x = 3$$

$$(3, 1)$$

Let $y = -2$: $x = 2(-2) + 1$

$\quad\quad\quad\quad x = -4 + 1$

$\quad\quad\quad\quad x = -3$

$\quad\quad\quad\quad\quad (-3, -2)$

Let $y = 6$: $x = 2(6) - 9$

$\quad\quad\quad\quad x = 12 - 9$

$\quad\quad\quad\quad x = 3$

$\quad\quad\quad\quad\quad (3, 6)$

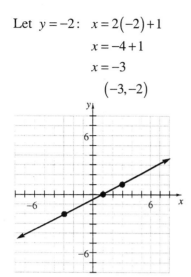

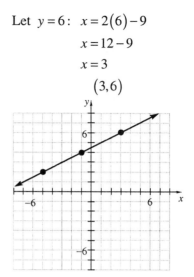

7. $y = x + 3$

| $x$ | $y = x + 3$ |
|-----|-------------|
| $-2$ | $-2 + 3 = 1$ |
| $0$ | $0 + 3 = 3$ |
| $2$ | $2 + 3 = 5$ |

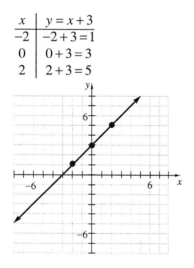

9. $x = 6$ is a vertical line that crosses the x-axis at 6.

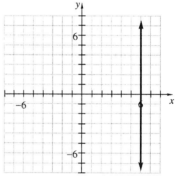

10. $y = 2$ is a horizontal line that crosses the y-axis at 2.

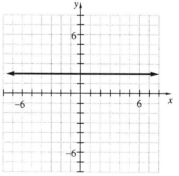

8. $x = 2y - 9$

Let $y = 2$: $x = 2(2) - 9$

$\quad\quad\quad\quad x = 4 - 9$

$\quad\quad\quad\quad x = -5$

$\quad\quad\quad\quad\quad (-5, 2)$

Let $y = 4$: $x = 2(4) - 9$

$\quad\quad\quad\quad x = 8 - 9$

$\quad\quad\quad\quad x = -1$

$\quad\quad\quad\quad\quad (-1, 4)$

11. $y = -7$ is a horizontal line that crosses the y-axis at $-7$.

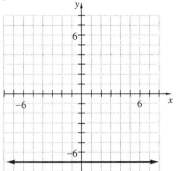

12. $x = -5$ is a vertical line that crosses the x-axis at $-5$.

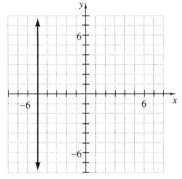

13. $\qquad x - 2 = 0$

$\qquad x - 2 + 2 = 0 + 2$

$\qquad\qquad x = 2$

This is a vertical line that crosses the x-axis at 2.

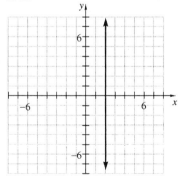

14. $\qquad y + 6 = 0$

$\qquad y + 6 - 6 = 0 - 6$

$\qquad\qquad y = -6$

This is a horizontal line that crosses the

y-axis at $-6$.

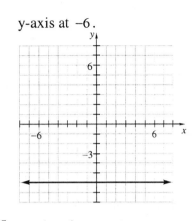

15. $x - 4y = 0$

Let $x = 0$: $\quad 0 - 4y = 0$

$\qquad\qquad\qquad -4y = 0$

$\qquad\qquad\qquad \dfrac{-4y}{-4} = \dfrac{0}{-4}$

$\qquad\qquad\qquad\quad y = 0$

$\qquad\qquad\qquad\quad (0,0)$

Let $y = 1$: $\quad x - 4(1) = 0$

$\qquad\qquad\qquad x - 4 = 0$

$\qquad\qquad x - 4 + 4 = 0 + 4$

$\qquad\qquad\qquad\quad x = 4$

$\qquad\qquad\qquad\quad (4,1)$

Let $y = -1$: $\quad x - 4(-1) = 0$

$\qquad\qquad\qquad x + 4 = 0$

$\qquad\qquad x + 4 - 4 = 0 - 4$

$\qquad\qquad\qquad\quad x = -4$

$\qquad\qquad\qquad\quad (-4,-1)$

16. $y - 2x = 0$

Let $x = 0$:   $y - 2(0) = 0$

$$y - 0 = 0$$
$$y = 0$$
$$(0, 0)$$

Let $x = 2$:   $y - 2(2) = 0$

$$y - 4 = 0$$
$$y - 4 + 4 = 0 + 4$$
$$y = 4$$
$$(2, 4)$$

Let $x = -2$:   $y - 2(-2) = 0$

$$y + 4 = 0$$
$$y + 4 - 4 = 0 - 4$$
$$y = -4$$
$$(-2, -4)$$

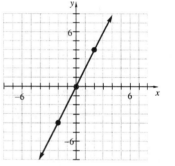

17. $y = -x - 4$

| $x$ | $y = -x - 4$ |
|---|---|
| $-6$ | $-(-6) - 4 = 2$ |
| $-3$ | $-(-3) - 4 = -1$ |
| $0$ | $-(0) - 4 = -4$ |

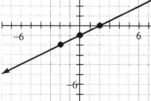

18. $\frac{1}{2}x - y = 1$

Let $x = -2$:   $\frac{1}{2}(-2) - y = 1$

$$-1 - y = 1$$
$$-1 - y + 1 = 1 + 1$$
$$-y = 2$$
$$\frac{-y}{-1} = \frac{2}{-1}$$
$$y = -2$$
$$(-2, -2)$$

Let $x = 0$:   $\frac{1}{2}(0) - y = 1$

$$0 - y = 1$$
$$-y = 1$$
$$\frac{-y}{-1} = \frac{1}{-1}$$
$$y = -1$$
$$(0, -1)$$

Let $x = 2$:   $\frac{1}{2}(2) - y = 1$

$$1 - y = 1$$
$$1 - y - 1 = 1 - 1$$
$$-y = 0$$
$$\frac{-y}{-1} = \frac{0}{-1}$$
$$y = 0$$
$$(2, 0)$$

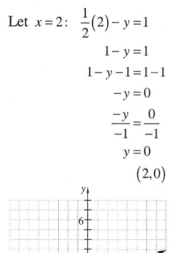

19. $x + y = -3$

     Let $x = -3$:    $-3 + y = -3$

                   $-3 + y + 3 = -3 + 3$

                       $y = 0$

                         $(-3, 0)$

     Let $x = 0$:   $0 + y = -3$

                   $y = -3$

                   $(0, -3)$

     Let $x = 3$:     $3 + y = -3$

                 $3 + y - 3 = -3 - 3$

                     $y = -6$

                     $(3, -6)$

20. $\frac{1}{2}x - \frac{1}{3}y = 1$

     Let $x = 0$:   $\frac{1}{2}(0) - \frac{1}{3}y = 1$

                    $0 - \frac{1}{3}y = 1$

                     $-\frac{1}{3}y = 1$

            $(-3)\left(-\frac{1}{3}y\right) = (-3)(1)$

                     $y = -3$

                     $(0, -3)$

Let $y = 0$:   $\frac{1}{2}x - \frac{1}{3}(0) = 1$

                  $\frac{1}{2}x - 0 = 1$

                    $\frac{1}{2}x = 1$

              $2 \cdot \frac{1}{2}x = 2 \cdot 1$

                    $x = 2$

                    $(2, 0)$

Let $x = 4$:   $\frac{1}{2}(4) - \frac{1}{3}y = 1$

                  $2 - \frac{1}{3}y = 1$

             $2 - \frac{1}{3}y - 2 = 1 - 2$

                  $-\frac{1}{3}y = -1$

        $(-3)\left(-\frac{1}{3}y\right) = (-3)(-1)$

                    $y = 3$

                    $(4, 3)$

## 8.5 SOLUTIONS TO EXERCISES

1.   mean $= \dfrac{18 + 24 + 16 + 31 + 19 + 26 + 30}{7}$

            $= \dfrac{164}{7}$

            $\approx 23.43$

2.  mean $= \dfrac{51+40+80+71+62+54+95+48}{8}$

$= \dfrac{501}{8}$

$= 62.625$

3.  mean $= \dfrac{9.4+8.6+11.2+17.8+10.1+3.4}{6}$

$= \dfrac{60.5}{6}$

$\approx 10.08$

4.  mean $= \dfrac{98.6+98.3+97.5+99.1+98.4+98.6}{6}$

$= \dfrac{590.5}{6}$

$\approx 98.42$

5.  mean $= \dfrac{-2+5+0+6+(-5)+7+9}{7}$

$= \dfrac{20}{7}$

$\approx 2.86$

6.  mean $= \dfrac{5.38+5.60+5.53+5.65+5.71+5.42}{6}$

$= \dfrac{33.29}{6}$

$\approx 5.55$

7.  0.1, 0.2, <u>0.3</u>, <u>0.6</u>, 0.7, 0.9

median: $\dfrac{0.3+0.6}{2} = \dfrac{0.9}{2} = 0.45$

8.  9, 11, 27, 54, <u>62</u>, 65, 71, 81, 90

median = 62

9.  328, 387, 419, <u>491</u>, 505, 576, 637

median = 491

10. 45, 58, 65, <u>69</u>, <u>70</u>, 70, 71, 89

median $= \dfrac{69+70}{2} = \dfrac{139}{2} = 69.5$

11. 0, 1, 2, <u>3</u>, <u>3</u>, 4, 7, 8

median =

12. 0.11, 0.12, 0.14, <u>0.16</u>, 0.17, 0.19, 0.20

median = 0.16

13. mode = 15 (it appears the most often)

14. mode = 122 (it appears the most often)

15. modes = 5.4 and 4.5 (bimodal)

16. mode = 3 (it appears the most often)

17. mode = 0.01 (it appears the most often)

18.

| Grade | Point Value (PV) | Credit Hours (CH) | (PV) · (CH) |
|-------|------|------|------|
| A | 4 | 4 | 16 |
| C | 2 | 3 | 6 |
| B | 3 | 3 | 9 |
| B | 3 | 4 | 12 |
| Totals | | 14 | 46 |

grade point average $= \dfrac{46}{14} = 3.29$

19.

| Grade | Point Value (PV) | Credit Hours (CH) | (PV) · (CH) |
|-------|------|------|------|
| C | 2 | 4 | 8 |
| B | 3 | 3 | 9 |
| B | 3 | 3 | 9 |
| A | 4 | 4 | 16 |
| D | 1 | 2 | 2 |
| Totals | | 16 | 44 |

grade point average $= \dfrac{44}{16} = 2.75$

20.

| Grade | Point Value (PV) | Credit Hours (CH) | (PV) · (CH) |
|-------|------------------|-------------------|-------------|
| A | 4 | 4 | 16 |
| A | 4 | 4 | 16 |
| B | 3 | 4 | 12 |
| A | 4 | 3 | 12 |
| B | 3 | 3 | 9 |
| | Totals | 18 | 65 |

$$\text{grade point average} = \frac{65}{18} = 3.61$$

## 8.6 SOLUTIONS TO EXERCISES

1.

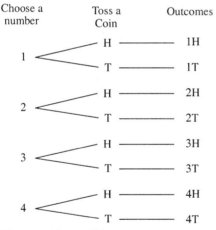

There are 8 possible outcomes.

2.

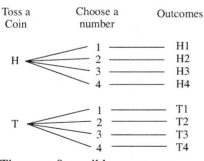

There are 8 possible outcomes.

3.

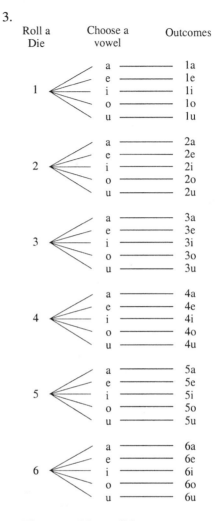

There are 30 possible outcomes.

4.

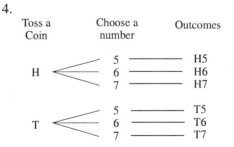

There are 6 possible outcomes.

5.   $\text{probability} = \dfrac{\text{number of ways event can occur}}{\text{number of outcomes}}$

$$= \frac{1}{8}$$

6. $\text{probability} = \dfrac{\text{number of ways event can occur}}{\text{number of outcomes}}$

$= \dfrac{1}{8}$

7. $\text{probability} = \dfrac{\text{number of ways event can occur}}{\text{number of outcomes}}$

$= \dfrac{1}{30}$

8. $\text{probability} = \dfrac{\text{number of ways event can occur}}{\text{number of outcomes}}$

$= \dfrac{1}{6}$

9. $\text{probability} = \dfrac{\text{number of white marbles}}{\text{total number of marbles}}$

$= \dfrac{3}{20}$

10. $\text{probability} = \dfrac{\text{number of pink marbles}}{\text{total number of marbles}}$

$= \dfrac{2}{20}$

$= \dfrac{1}{10}$

11. $\text{probability} = \dfrac{\text{number of purple marbles}}{\text{total number of marbles}}$

$= \dfrac{6}{20}$

$= \dfrac{3}{10}$

12. $\text{probability} = \dfrac{\text{number of blue marbles}}{\text{total number of marbles}}$

$= \dfrac{0}{20}$

$= 0$

13. $\text{probability} = \dfrac{\left(\begin{array}{c}\text{number of marbles that}\\ \text{are red or orange}\end{array}\right)}{\text{total number of marbles}}$

$= \dfrac{5+4}{20}$

$= \dfrac{9}{20}$

14. $\text{probability} = \dfrac{\left(\begin{array}{c}\text{number of marbles that}\\ \text{are purple or white}\end{array}\right)}{\text{total number of marbles}}$

$= \dfrac{6+3}{20}$

$= \dfrac{9}{20}$

15. $\text{probability} = \dfrac{\text{number of ways event can occur}}{\text{number of outcomes}}$

$= \dfrac{3}{5}$

16. $\text{probability} = \dfrac{\text{number of ways event can occur}}{\text{number of outcomes}}$

$= \dfrac{1}{5}$

17. $\text{probability} = \dfrac{\text{number of ways event can occur}}{\text{number of outcomes}}$

$= \dfrac{2}{5}$

18. $\text{probability} = \dfrac{\text{number of ways event can occur}}{\text{number of outcomes}}$

$= \dfrac{13}{52}$

$= \dfrac{1}{4}$

19. $\text{probability} = \dfrac{\text{number of ways event can occur}}{\text{number of outcomes}}$

$= \dfrac{1}{52}$

20. probability = $\dfrac{\text{number of ways event can occur}}{\text{number of outcomes}}$

$$= \frac{4}{52}$$

$$= \frac{1}{13}$$

## CHAPTER 8 PRACTICE TEST SOLUTIONS

1. Look for the largest sector. The 17-20 age group contains the most students.

2. amount = percent · base

$$= 10\% \cdot 600$$

$$= (0.1)(600)$$

$$= 60$$

There were 60 students in the 31-40 age group.

3. The 21-35 age group contained 28% of the students.

4. The price of the stock was $36 per share on Tuesday.

5. The price of the stock was highest on Thursday when it sold for $46 per share.

6. The price of the stock was lowest on Friday when it sold for $28 per share.

7. Monday:   $32
   Friday:    $28
   ─────────────────
   difference:  $4

   There was a $4 difference in the price of the stock from Monday to Friday.

8. Compare consecutive days and look for the longest increasing line segment. The largest price increase occurred from Wednesday to Thursday.

9. $A(3-5)$

10. $B(0,0)$

11. $C(2,4)$

12. $D(-5,0)$

13. $E(-3,3)$

14. $x+3y=1$
    $x+3(0)=1$
    $x+0=1$
    $x=1$

    $x+3y=1$
    $4+3y=1$
    $4+3y-4=1-4$
    $3y=-3$
    $\dfrac{3y}{3}=\dfrac{-3}{3}$
    $y=-1$

    $x+3y=1$
    $-5+3y=1$
    $-5+3y+5=1+5$
    $3y=6$
    $\dfrac{3y}{3}=\dfrac{6}{3}$
    $y=2$

The three ordered-pair solutions are $(1,0)$, $(4,-1)$, and $(-5,2)$.

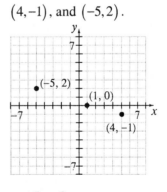

15. $y=5x-2$
    $y=5(0)-2$
    $y=0-2$
    $y=-2$

$$y = 5x - 2$$
$$y = 5(1) - 2$$
$$y = 5 - 2$$
$$y = 3$$

$$y = 5x - 2$$
$$-7 = 5x - 2$$
$$-7 + 2 = 5x - 2 + 2$$
$$-5 = 5x$$
$$\frac{-5}{5} = \frac{5x}{5}$$
$$-1 = x$$

The three ordered-pair solutions are $(0, -2)$, $(1, 3)$, and $(-1, -7)$.

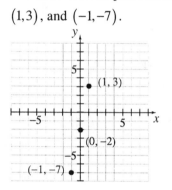

16. $y = x + 1$

| $x$ | $y = x + 1$ |
|-----|-------------|
| $-4$ | $-4 + 1 = -3$ |
| $0$ | $0 + 1 = 1$ |
| $4$ | $4 + 1 = 5$ |

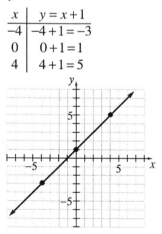

17. $x + 4 = 0$
$$x + 4 - 4 = 0 - 4$$
$$x = -4$$

This is a vertical line that crosses the x-axis at $-4$.

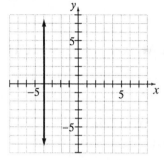

18. $y + 3 = 0$
$$y + 3 - 3 = 0 - 3$$
$$y = -3$$

This is a horizontal line that crosses the y-axis at $-3$.

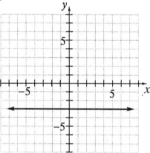

19. Let $x = 0$:
$$5x + 6y = 30$$
$$5(0) + 6y = 30$$
$$6y = 30$$
$$\frac{6y}{6} = \frac{30}{6}$$
$$y = 5$$
$$(0, 5)$$

Let $y = 0$:
$$5x + 6y = 30$$
$$5x + 6(0) = 30$$
$$5x = 30$$
$$\frac{5x}{5} = \frac{30}{5}$$
$$x = 6$$
$$(6, 0)$$

Let $x = 2$:    $5x + 6y = 30$

$$5(2) + 6y = 30$$
$$10 + 6y = 30$$
$$10 + 6y - 10 = 30 - 10$$
$$6y = 20$$
$$\frac{6y}{6} = \frac{20}{6}$$
$$y = \frac{10}{3}$$
$$\left(2, \frac{10}{3}\right)$$

20.   mean $= \dfrac{54 + 71 + 88 + 47 + 64 + 67}{6}$

$$= \frac{391}{6}$$
$$\approx 65.17$$

47, 54, $\underline{64}$, $\underline{67}$, 71, 88

median $= \dfrac{64 + 67}{2} = \dfrac{131}{2} = 65.5$

There is no mode.

21.   mean $= \dfrac{121 + 130 + 147 + 129 + 127 + 133 + 130}{7}$

$$= \frac{917}{7}$$
$$= 131$$

121, 127, 129, $\underline{130}$, 130, 133, 147

median $= 130$

mode $= 130$

22.

| Grade | Point Value (PV) | Credit Hours (CH) | (PV)·(CH) |
|-------|------|------|------|
| D | 1 | 3 | 3 |
| B | 3 | 5 | 15 |
| B | 3 | 3 | 9 |
| A | 4 | 4 | 16 |
| Totals | | 15 | 43 |

grade point average $= \dfrac{43}{15} = 2.87$

23.

| Grade | Point Value (PV) | Credit Hours (CH) | (PV)·(CH) |
|-------|------|------|------|
| C | 2 | 3 | 6 |
| C | 2 | 3 | 6 |
| A | 4 | 2 | 8 |
| B | 3 | 4 | 12 |
| Totals | | 12 | 32 |

grade point average $= \dfrac{32}{12} = 2.67$

24.   probability $= \dfrac{\text{number of ways event can occur}}{\text{number of outcomes}}$

$$= \frac{2}{6}$$
$$= \frac{1}{3}$$

25.   probability $= \dfrac{\text{number of ways event can occur}}{\text{number of outcomes}}$

$$= \frac{12}{52}$$
$$= \frac{3}{13}$$

**9.1 SOLUTIONS TO EXERCISES**

1. line segment

2. line

3. ray

4. angle

5. measure of $\angle ABD$ = measure of $\angle ABE$ + measure of $\angle EBD$
$$= 55° + 35°$$
$$= 90°$$

6. measure of $\angle ABC$ = measure of $\angle ABE$ + measure of $\angle EBD$ + measure of $\angle DBC$
$$= 55° + 35° + 15°$$
$$= 105°$$

7. measure of $\angle EBC$ = measure of $\angle EBD$ + measure of $\angle DBC$
$$= 35° + 15°$$
$$= 50°$$

8. measure of $\angle DBE = 35°$

9. obtuse angle

10. right angle

11. acute angle

12. straight angle

13. The supplement of a $43°$ angle is
$180° - 43° = 137°$

14. The complement of a $39°$ angle is
$90° - 39° = 51°$

15. The supplement of a $121°$ angle is
$180° - 121° = 59°$

16. measure of $\angle x = 62° - 40° = 22°$

17. The $53°$ angle and $\angle y$ are vertical angles so they have the same measure. Thus, the measure of $\angle y = 53°$.

   $\angle x$ and $\angle y$ are adjacent angles so the sum of their measures is $180°$. The measure of $\angle x = 180° - 53° = 127°$.

   $\angle x$ and $\angle z$ are vertical angles so they have the same measure. Thus, the measure of $\angle z = 127°$.

18. The $55°$ angle and $\angle z$ are vertical angles so they have the same measure. Thus, the measure of $\angle z = 55°$.

   $\angle z$ and $\angle y$ are alternate interior angles so they have the same measure. Thus, the measure of $\angle y = 55°$.

   $\angle y$ and $\angle x$ are vertical angles so they have the same measure. Thus, the measure of $\angle x = 55°$.

**9.2 SOLUTIONS TO EXERCISES**

1. $54 \text{ in} = 54 \text{ in} \cdot \dfrac{1 \text{ ft}}{12 \text{ in}} = \dfrac{54}{12} \text{ ft} = 4.5 \text{ ft}$

2. $17 \text{ yd} = 17 \text{ yd} \cdot \dfrac{3 \text{ ft}}{1 \text{ yd}} = \dfrac{51}{1} \text{ ft} = 51 \text{ ft}$

3. $29{,}040 \text{ ft} = 29{,}040 \text{ ft} \cdot \dfrac{1 \text{ mile}}{5280 \text{ ft}}$
$$= \dfrac{29{,}040}{5280} \text{ miles}$$
$$= 5.5 \text{ miles}$$

4. $2.6 \text{ mi} = 2.6 \text{ mi} \cdot \dfrac{5280 \text{ ft}}{1 \text{ mi}}$

   $= \dfrac{13,728}{1} \text{ ft}$

   $= 13,728 \text{ ft}$

5. $117 \text{ ft} = 117 \text{ ft} \cdot \dfrac{1 \text{ yd}}{3 \text{ ft}} = \dfrac{117}{3} \text{ yd} = 39 \text{ yd}$

6. $97 \text{ ft} = 97 \text{ ft} \cdot \dfrac{12 \text{ in.}}{1 \text{ ft}} = \dfrac{1164}{1} \text{ in.} = 1164 \text{ in.}$

7. 
```
    13 yd 2 ft
3)41
    3
   ──
   11
    9
   ──
    2
```

8. 
```
   4 ft 5 in.
12)53
   48
   ──
    5
```

9. 
```
       8 mi 2760 ft
5280)45,000
     42,240
     ──────
      2,760
```

10. $6 \text{ ft} = 6 \text{ ft} \cdot \dfrac{12 \text{ in.}}{1 \text{ ft}} = 6 \cdot 12 \text{ in.} = 72 \text{ in.}$

    $6 \text{ ft } 4 \text{ in.} = 72 \text{ in.} + 4 \text{ in.} = 76 \text{ in.}$

11. $6 \text{ yd} = 6 \text{ yd} \cdot \dfrac{3 \text{ ft}}{1 \text{ yd}} = 6 \cdot 3 \text{ ft} = 18 \text{ ft}$

    $6 \text{ yd } 1 \text{ ft} = 18 \text{ ft} + 1 \text{ ft} = 19 \text{ ft}$

12. m   dm   cm

    ———————↑

    2 units to the right.

    $65 \text{ m} = 65.00$
    
    ↑

    $= 6500 \text{ cm}$

13. m   dm   cm

    ↑———————

    2 units to the left

    $1300 \text{ cm} = 1300.$
    
    ↑

    $= 13 \text{ m}$

14. m   dm   cm   mm

    ↑——————

    2 units to the left

    $19.6 \text{ mm} = 19.6$
    
    ↑

    $= 0.196 \text{ dm}$

15. km   hm   dam   m   dm   cm   mm

    ————————————————————↑

    6 units to the right

    $2.1 \text{ km} = 2.100000$
    
    ↑

    $= 2,100,000 \text{ mm}$

16. 
```
    11 ft  6 in.
  + 8 ft  9 in.
    19 ft 15 in.
```
    $= 19 \text{ ft } 1 \text{ ft } 3 \text{ in.}$
    $= 20 \text{ ft } 3 \text{ in.}$

17. 
```
    30 ft 5 in.  =   29 ft 17 in.
  − 14 ft 7 in.    − 14 ft  7 in.
                    15 ft 10 in
```

18. 
```
     32 yd 2 ft
  ×        5
    160 yd 10 ft
```
    $= 160 \text{ yd } 3 \text{ yd } 1 \text{ ft}$
    $= 163 \text{ yd } 1 \text{ ft}$

19. $12 \text{ cm} = 120 \text{ mm}$

    ```
     120 mm
    − 37 mm
      83 mm
    ```

    or $18 \text{ mm} = 1.8 \text{ cm}$

$$\begin{array}{r} 12.0 \text{ cm} \\ -\ 3.7 \text{ cm} \\ \hline 8.3 \text{ cm} \end{array}$$

20.
$$\begin{array}{r} 3.2 \text{ m} \\ 4\overline{)12.8} \\ \underline{12} \\ 8 \\ \underline{8} \\ 0 \end{array}$$

21.
$$\begin{array}{r} 6 \text{ ft } 1 \text{ in.} = 5 \text{ ft } 13 \text{ in.} \\ -\ 2 \text{ ft } 5 \text{ in.} \quad -2 \text{ ft } 5 \text{ in.} \\ \hline 3 \text{ ft } 8 \text{ in.} \end{array}$$

22. $3 \text{ yd} \cdot 4 = 12 \text{ yd}$

$12 \text{ yd} = 12 \text{ yd} \cdot \dfrac{36 \text{ in.}}{1 \text{ yd}} = 432 \text{ in.}$

Payton would need 432 inches of cloth to make the 4 jackets.

## 9.3 SOLUTIONS TO EXERCISES

1. $P = 4s$
$= 4(23 \text{ meters})$
$= 92 \text{ meters}$

2. $P = a + b + c$
$= 3 \text{ inches} + 10 \text{ inches} + 9 \text{ inches}$
$= 22 \text{ inches}$

3. $P = 2l + 2w$
$= 2(18 \text{ feet}) + 2(4 \text{ feet})$
$= 36 \text{ feet} + 8 \text{ feet}$
$= 44 \text{ feet}$

4. $P = 28 \text{ cm} + 52 \text{ cm} + 28 \text{ cm} + 52 \text{ cm}$
$= 160 \text{ cm}$

5. $P = 11 \text{ ft} + 3 \text{ ft} + 9 \text{ ft} + 16 \text{ ft} + 5 \text{ ft}$
$= 44 \text{ ft}$

6. $P = 9 \text{ m} + 11 \text{ m} + 30 \text{ m} + 6 \text{ m} + 21 \text{ m} + 5 \text{ m}$
$= 82 \text{ m}$

7. $P = 20 \text{ ft} + 25 \text{ ft} + 8 \text{ ft} + 6 \text{ ft} + 4 \text{ ft}$
$= 63 \text{ ft}$

8. $P = a + b + c$
$= 20 \text{ cm} + 30 \text{ cm} + 50 \text{ cm}$
$= 100 \text{ cm}$

9. $P = 4s$
$= 4(3 \text{ miles})$
$= 12 \text{ miles}$

10. $P = 2l + 2w$
$= 2(37 \text{ yd}) + 2(29 \text{ yd})$
$= 74 \text{ yd} + 58 \text{ yd}$
$= 132 \text{ yd}$

11. $P = 2l + 2w$
$= 2(6 \text{ feet}) + 2(2 \text{ feet})$
$= 12 \text{ feet} + 4 \text{ feet}$
$= 16 \text{ feet}$
16 feet of stripping is needed.

12. $P = 2l + 2w$
$= 2(110 \text{ ft}) + 2(60 \text{ ft})$
$= 220 \text{ ft} + 120 \text{ ft}$
$= 340 \text{ ft}$
340 feet of fencing is needed.

13. Let $x = $ width of field. Then
$4x = $ length of field.
$$P = 2l + 2w$$
$$1200 = 2(4x) + 2(x)$$
$$1200 = 8x + 2x$$
$$1200 = 10x$$
$$\frac{1200}{10} = \frac{10x}{10}$$
$$120 = x$$
The length of the football field is
$4x = 4(120 \text{ meters}) = 480 \text{ meters}$.

14. Let $x$ = length of each equal side .

$$P = a + b + c$$
$$121 = x + x + 33$$
$$121 = 2x + 33$$
$$121 - 33 = 2x + 33 - 33$$
$$88 = 2x$$
$$\frac{88}{2} = \frac{2x}{2}$$
$$44 = x$$

The length of each equal side is 44 inches.

15. Let $x$ = length of rectangle . Then $2x - 11$ = width .

$$P = 2l + 2w$$
$$38 = 2(x) + 2(2x - 11)$$
$$38 = 2x + 4x - 22$$
$$38 = 6x - 22$$
$$38 + 22 = 6x - 22 + 22$$
$$60 = 6x$$
$$\frac{60}{6} = \frac{6x}{6}$$
$$10 = x$$

The width is $2x - 11 = 2(10) - 11 = 9$ meters .

16. $P = 4s$
$$= 4(9 \text{ inches})$$
$$= 36 \text{ inches}$$
The perimeter is 36 inches.

17. $P = a + b + c$
$$= 54 + 54 + 54$$
$$= 162$$
The perimeter of the leg's base is 162 feet.

18. $C = 2\pi r$
$$= 2\pi(25)$$
$$= 50\pi \approx 157.08 \text{ miles}$$
The perimeter of the mountain lion's territory is about 157.08 miles.

## 9.4 SOLUTIONS TO EXERCISES

1. $A = l \cdot w$
$$= (5.9 \text{ ft})(1.7 \text{ ft})$$
$$= 10.03 \text{ ft}^2$$

2. $A = \frac{1}{2}bh$
$$= \frac{1}{2}(5 \text{ cm})(3 \text{ cm})$$
$$= \frac{15}{2} \text{ cm}^2$$

3. $A = \frac{1}{2}bh$
$$= \frac{1}{2}(4 \text{ mi})(10 \text{ mi})$$
$$= 20 \text{ square miles}$$

4. $A = bh$
$$= (10 \text{ m})(4.5 \text{ m})$$
$$= 45 \text{ m}^2$$

5. $A = \pi r^2$
$$= \pi(17 \text{ in.})^2$$
$$= 289\pi \text{ square inches}$$
$$\approx 907.46 \text{ square inches}$$

6. $d = 7 \text{ ft}$
$$r = \frac{1}{2}d = \frac{1}{2}(7) = 3.5 \text{ ft}$$
$$A = \pi r^2$$
$$= \pi(3.5 \text{ ft})^2$$
$$= 12.25\pi \text{ square feet}$$
$$\approx 38.465 \text{ square feet}$$

7. $A = \frac{1}{2}(b + B)h$
$$= \frac{1}{2}(19 \text{ in.} + 12 \text{ in.})(3 \text{ in.})$$
$$= \frac{1}{2}(31 \text{ in.})(3 \text{ in.})$$
$$= 46.5 \text{ in.}^2$$

8. $A = \dfrac{1}{2}(b+B)h$

   $= \dfrac{1}{2}(7 \text{ cm} + 12 \text{ cm})(5 \text{ cm})$

   $= \dfrac{1}{2}(19 \text{ cm})(5 \text{ cm})$

   $= 47.5 \text{ cm}^2$

9. $A = $ area of large + area of small
   rectangle          rectangle

   $= (36 \text{ m})(22 \text{ m}) + (12 \text{ m})(30 \text{ m} - 22 \text{ m})$

   $= 792 \text{ m}^2 + (12 \text{ m})(8 \text{ m})$

   $= 792 \text{ m}^2 + 96 \text{ m}^2$

   $= 888 \text{ m}^2$

10. $V = l \cdot w \cdot h$

    $= (2 \text{ in.})(8 \text{ in.})(3 \text{ in.})$

    $= 48 \text{ in.}^3$

11. $V = \dfrac{4}{3}\pi r^3$

    $= \dfrac{4}{3}\pi (7.4 \text{ mi})^3$

    $\approx 1696.54$ cubic miles

12. $V = \pi r^2 h$

    $= \pi (2.2 \text{ ft})^2 (16 \text{ ft})$

    $= 77.44\pi$ cubic feet

    $\approx 243.16$ cubic feet

13. $V = \dfrac{1}{3}\pi r^2 h$

    $= \dfrac{1}{3}\pi (4 \text{ m})^2 (31 \text{ m})$

    $= \dfrac{496}{3}\pi \text{ m}^3$

    $\approx 519.15 \text{ m}^3$

14. $V = \dfrac{1}{3}s^2 h$

    $= \dfrac{1}{3}(4.7 \text{ in.})^2 (18.6 \text{ in.})$

    $= 136.958 \text{ in.}^3$

15. $A = l \cdot w$

    $= \left(12\dfrac{1}{4} \text{ ft}\right)(40 \text{ ft})$

    $= (12.25 \text{ ft})(40 \text{ ft})$

    $= 490 \text{ ft}^2$

    The wall has an area of 490 square feet.

16. $A = l \cdot w$

    $= (14 \text{ in.})\left(8\dfrac{1}{2} \text{ in.}\right)$

    $= (14 \text{ in.})(8.5 \text{ in.})$

    $= 119 \text{ in.}^2$

    The picture frame requires 119 square inches of glass.

17. $d = 16 \text{ in.}$

    $r = \dfrac{1}{2}d = \dfrac{1}{2}(16 \text{ in.}) = 8 \text{ in.}$

    $A = \pi r^2$

    $= \pi (8 \text{ in.})^2$

    $= 64\pi \text{ in.}^2$

    $\approx 200.96 \text{ in.}^2$

    The pizza has an area of about 200.96 square inches.

18. $V = s^3$

    $= \left(2\dfrac{3}{4} \text{ in.}\right)^3$

    $= (2.75 \text{ in.})^3$

    $\approx 20.8$ cubic inches

    The cube has a volume of about 20.8 cubic inches.

19. $V = l \cdot w \cdot h$

    $= (3 \text{ ft})\left(1\dfrac{1}{2} \text{ ft}\right)\left(\dfrac{1}{2} \text{ ft}\right)$

    $= (3 \text{ ft})(1.5 \text{ ft})(0.5 \text{ ft})$

    $= 2.25 \text{ ft}^3$

    The block of ice has a volume of 2.25 cubic feet.

20.   $V = \dfrac{1}{3}\pi r^2 h$

$\qquad = \dfrac{1}{3}\pi \left(45 \text{ ft}\right)^2 \left(30 \text{ ft}\right)$

$\qquad = 20{,}250\pi \text{ ft}^3$

$\qquad \approx 63{,}585 \text{ ft}^3$

The pile contains roughly 63,585 cubic feet of sand.

## 9.5 SOLUTIONS TO EXERCISES

1.   $17 \text{ lb} = 17 \text{ lb} \cdot \dfrac{16 \text{ oz}}{1 \text{ lb}}$

$\qquad = 17 \cdot 16 \text{ oz}$

$\qquad = 272 \text{ oz}$

2.   $6 \text{ tons} = 6 \text{ tons} \cdot \dfrac{2000 \text{ lbs}}{1 \text{ ton}}$

$\qquad = 6 \cdot 2000 \text{ lbs}$

$\qquad = 12{,}000 \text{ lbs}$

3.   $11{,}000 \text{ lbs} = 11{,}000 \text{ lbs} \cdot \dfrac{1 \text{ ton}}{2000 \text{ lbs}}$

$\qquad = \dfrac{11{,}000}{2000} \text{ tons}$

$\qquad = 5.5 \text{ tons}$

4.   $22.25 \text{ lbs} = 22.25 \text{ lbs} \cdot \dfrac{16 \text{ oz}}{1 \text{ lb}}$

$\qquad = 22.25 \cdot 16 \text{ oz}$

$\qquad = 356 \text{ oz}$

5.   $112 \text{ oz} = 112 \text{ oz} \cdot \dfrac{1 \text{ lb}}{16 \text{ oz}}$

$\qquad = \dfrac{112}{16} \text{ lb}$

$\qquad = 7.0 \text{ lb}$

6.   kg  hg  dag  g

  ↑   ˋ

  3 units left

$\quad 6000 \text{ g} = 6000.$

$\qquad\qquad\quad ↑$

$\qquad = 6.0 \text{ kg}$

7.   g  dg  cg  mg

               ↑

  3 units right

$\quad 38 \text{ g} = 38.000$

$\qquad\qquad\quad ↑$

$\qquad = 38{,}000 \text{ mg}$

8.   kg  hg  dag  g

  ↑

  3 units left

$\quad 7.2 \text{ g} = 007.2$

$\qquad\qquad ↑$

$\qquad = 0.0072 \text{ kg}$

9.   dag  g  dg  cg

  ↑

  2 units left

$\quad 741 \text{ dg} = 741.$

$\qquad\qquad\quad ↑$

$\qquad = 7.41 \text{ dag}$

10.   hg  dag  g  dg  cg

   ↑

  4 units left

$\quad 8025 \text{ cg} = 8025.$

$\qquad\qquad\quad ↑$

$\qquad = 0.8025 \text{ hg}$

11.      13 lb  5 oz

   + 18 lb 14 oz

     31 lb 19 oz

  $= 31 \text{ lb } 1 \text{ lb } 3 \text{ oz}$

  $= 32 \text{ lb } 3 \text{ oz}$

12.     1 ton  1905 lb

  + 5 tons  168 lb

    6 tons 2073 lb

  $= 6 \text{ tons } 1 \text{ ton } 73 \text{ lb}$

  $= 7 \text{ tons } 73 \text{ lb}$

13.  $\quad$ 12 lb 4 oz $\qquad$ 11 lb 20 oz

$\quad\underline{-\ 2\ \text{lb}\ 10\ \text{oz}}\quad\underline{-\ 2\ \text{lb}\ 10\ \text{oz}}$

$\qquad\qquad\qquad\qquad$ 9 lb 10 oz

14.  $\qquad$ 3 lb 7 oz

$\qquad\underline{\times\qquad 9}$

$\qquad$ 27 lb 63 oz

$\quad = 27$ lb 3 lb 15 oz

$\quad = 30$ lb 15 oz

15.
$$\begin{array}{r} 1\ \text{ton}\quad 1720\ \text{lbs} \\ 5\overline{)9\ \text{tons}\quad 600\ \text{lbs}} \\ \underline{5}\qquad\qquad \\ 4\ \text{tons} = \underline{8000\ \text{lbs}} \\ 8600\ \text{lbs} \end{array}$$

16.  $\qquad$ 89.7 g

$\qquad\underline{+\ 10.6\ \text{g}}$

$\qquad$ 100.3 g

17.  7 kg = 7000 g

$\qquad$ 7000 g

$\qquad\underline{-\ 4290\ \text{g}}$

$\qquad$ 2710 g

$\quad$ or 2710 g = 2.71 kg

18.  $\qquad$ 2.9 kg

$\qquad\underline{\times 8.6}$

$\qquad$ 174

$\qquad\underline{232}$

$\qquad$ 24.94 kg

19.  $\qquad$ 2.7 oz

$\qquad\underline{\times 36}$

$\qquad$ 162

$\qquad\underline{81}$

$\qquad$ 97.2 oz

$\quad$ 97.2 oz $= 97.2$ oz $\cdot\ \dfrac{1\ \text{lb}}{16\ \text{oz}}$

$\qquad\quad = \dfrac{97.2}{16}$ lb

$\qquad\quad \approx 6.1$ lb

The box would weigh 6.1 pounds.

20.  $\qquad$ 27 kg

$\qquad\underline{-18\ \text{kg}}$

$\qquad$ 9 kg

Shawn must remove 9 kg from his bag.

## 9.6 SOLUTIONS TO EXERCISES

1.  32 qt $= 32$ qt $\cdot \dfrac{1\ \text{gal}}{4\ \text{qt}} = \dfrac{32}{4}$ gal $= 8$ gal

2.  11 qt $= 11$ qt $\cdot \dfrac{2\ \text{pt}}{1\ \text{qt}} = 11 \cdot 2$ pt $= 22$ pt

3.  34 c $= 34$ c $\cdot \dfrac{1\ \text{pt}}{2\ \text{c}} = \dfrac{34}{2}$ pt $= 17$ pt

4.  50 c $= 50$ c $\cdot \dfrac{1\ \text{pt}}{2\ \text{c}} \cdot \dfrac{1\ \text{qt}}{2\ \text{pt}} \cdot \dfrac{1\ \text{gal}}{4\ \text{qt}}$

$\qquad = \dfrac{50}{16}$ gal

$\qquad = 3\dfrac{1}{8}$ gal

5.  $5\dfrac{3}{4}$ qt $= \dfrac{23}{4}$ qt $\cdot \dfrac{2\ \text{pt}}{1\ \text{qt}} \cdot \dfrac{2\ \text{c}}{1\ \text{pt}} = 23$ c

6.  $5\dfrac{7}{8}$ gal $= \dfrac{47}{8}$ gal $\cdot \dfrac{4\ \text{qt}}{1\ \text{gal}} \cdot \dfrac{2\ \text{pt}}{1\ \text{qt}} = 47$ pt

7.  L  dl  cl  ml

$\qquad\qquad\qquad\uparrow$

$\quad\overline{\qquad\qquad\qquad\quad}$

$\quad$ 3 units right

$\quad$ 11 L $= 11.000$

$\qquad\qquad\quad\uparrow$

$\quad\quad\overline{\qquad\qquad\quad}$

$\quad = 11{,}000$ ml

8.  L  dl  cl  ml

$\quad\uparrow$

$\quad\overline{\qquad\qquad\qquad}$

$\quad$ 3 units left

$\quad$ 3200 ml $= 3200.$

$\qquad\qquad\uparrow$

$\quad\quad\overline{\qquad\quad}$

$\quad = 3.2$ L

9. kl  hl  dal  L
↑ _____
3 units left

270 L = 270.
     ↑___
    = 0.27 kl

10.    5 gal 3 qt
  + 7 gal 1 qt
   12 gal 4 qt
  = 12 gal 1 gal
  = 13 gal

11.    7 c  4 fl oz
  + 3 c  6 fl oz
   10 c 10 fl oz
  = 10 c 1 c 2 fl oz
  = 11 c 2 fl oz

12.    2 gal 1 pt
  ×     5
   10 gal     5 pt
  = 10 gal 2 qt 1 pt

13.    3 pt       2 pt 2 c
  − 2 pt 1 c  − 2 pt 1 c
                     1 c

14.    20.2 L
  + 14.6 L
   34.8 L

15. 7920 ml = 7.92 L
    7.92 L
  − 0.20 L
    7.72 L

   or  0.2 L = 200 ml
    7920 ml
  −  200 ml
    7720 ml

16. $0.9\overline{)7.2}$ → $9\overline{)72.}$
$$\frac{\phantom{0}8.}{}$$
        72
         0

7.2 L ÷ 0.9 = 8 L

17.  125 ml
  × 7
  875 ml

18. $2\frac{1}{4}$ c = $\frac{9}{4}$ c · $\frac{8 \text{ fl oz}}{1 \text{ c}}$ = 18 fl oz
The recipe calls for 18 fluid ounces of milk.

19. $4\overline{)1.00}$   .25
      8
     20
     20
      0
Each friend will get 0.25 liters (250 ml).

20. 3 gal = 12 qt
   12 qt
  + 3 qt
   15 qt
They will have 15 quarts of coffee milk.

## 9.7 SOLUTIONS TO EXERCISES

1. 400 m ≈ 400 m · $\frac{3.28 \text{ ft}}{1 \text{ m}}$ = 1312 ft

2. 3 mi ≈ 3 mi · $\frac{1.61 \text{ km}}{1 \text{ mi}}$ = 4.83 km

3. 50 kg ≈ 50 kg · $\frac{2.20 \text{ lb}}{1 \text{ kg}}$ = 110 lb

4. 1.5 L ≈ 1.5 L · $\frac{1000 \text{ ml}}{1 \text{ L}}$ · $\frac{1 \text{ fl oz}}{29.57 \text{ ml}}$
   = $\frac{1500}{29.57}$ fl oz
   ≈ 50.73 fl oz.

5. $6 \text{ gal} \approx 6 \text{ gal} \cdot \dfrac{3.79 \text{ L}}{1 \text{ gal}} = 22.74 \text{ L}$

6. $27 \text{ in.} = 27 \text{ in.} \cdot \dfrac{2.54 \text{ cm}}{1 \text{ in.}} = 68.58 \text{ cm}$

7. $16 \text{ fl oz} = 16 \text{ fl oz} \cdot \dfrac{29.57 \text{ ml}}{1 \text{ fl oz}}$
$= 473.12 \text{ ml}$

8. $75 \text{ cm} \approx 75 \text{ cm} \cdot \dfrac{1 \text{ in.}}{2.54 \text{ cm}} \cdot \dfrac{1 \text{ yd}}{36 \text{ in}}$
$= \dfrac{75}{91.44} \text{ yd}$
$\approx 0.82 \text{ yd}$

9. $10 \text{ km} \approx 10 \text{ km} \cdot \dfrac{0.62 \text{ mi}}{1 \text{ km}} = 6.2 \text{ mi}$

10. $2 \text{ tons} \approx 2 \text{ tons} \cdot \dfrac{2000 \text{ lb}}{1 \text{ ton}} \cdot \dfrac{0.45 \text{ kg}}{1 \text{ lb}}$
$= 1800 \text{ kg}$

11. $8 \text{ oz} \approx 8 \text{ oz} \cdot \dfrac{28.35 \text{ g}}{1 \text{ oz}} \cdot \dfrac{1000 \text{ mg}}{1 \text{ g}}$
$= 226,800 \text{ mg}$

12. $2100 \text{ ml} \approx 2100 \text{ ml} \cdot \dfrac{1 \text{ L}}{1000 \text{ ml}} \cdot \dfrac{0.26 \text{ gal}}{1 \text{ L}}$
$= \dfrac{2100 \cdot (0.26)}{1000} \text{ gal}$
$\approx 0.55 \text{ gal}$

13. $5 \text{ gal} \approx 5 \text{ gal} \cdot \dfrac{3.79 \text{ L}}{1 \text{ gal}} = 19.85 \text{ L}$

Roughly 19.85 liters could be carried in a 5-gallon bucket.

14. $100 \text{ m} \approx 100 \text{ m} \cdot \dfrac{3.28 \text{ ft}}{1 \text{ m}} \cdot \dfrac{1 \text{ yd}}{3 \text{ ft}}$
$= \dfrac{328}{3} \text{ yd}$
$\approx 109.33 \text{ yd}$

The minimum length of a soccer field for international matches is roughly 109.33 yards.

15. $200 \text{ fl oz} \approx 200 \text{ fl oz} \cdot \dfrac{29.57 \text{ ml}}{1 \text{ fl oz}} \cdot \dfrac{1 \text{ L}}{1000 \text{ ml}}$
$= \dfrac{5914}{1000} \text{ L}$
$\approx 5.91 \text{ L}$

16. $1 \text{ lb} \approx 1 \text{ lb} \cdot \dfrac{0.45 \text{ kg}}{1 \text{ lb}} \cdot \dfrac{1000 \text{ g}}{1 \text{ kg}} = 450 \text{ g}$

17. $11 \text{ in.} = 11 \text{ in.} \cdot \dfrac{2.54 \text{ cm}}{1 \text{ in}} = 27.94 \text{ cm}$

18. $40 \text{ kg} = 40 \text{ kg} \cdot \dfrac{2.20 \text{ lb}}{1 \text{ kg}} = 88 \text{ lb}$

19. $310 \text{ mi} \approx 310 \text{ mi} \cdot \dfrac{1.61 \text{ km}}{1 \text{ mi}} = 499.1 \text{ km}$

20. $15 \text{ cm} = 15 \text{ cm} \cdot \dfrac{1 \text{ in}}{2.54 \text{ cm}}$
$= \dfrac{15}{2.54} \text{ in}$
$\approx 5.91 \text{ in.}$

## 9.8 SOLUTIONS TO EXERCISES

1. $F = \dfrac{9C}{5} + 32$
$= \dfrac{9(105)}{5} + 32$
$= 189 + 32$
$= 221$
$221°F$

2. $F = \dfrac{9C}{5} + 32$
$= \dfrac{9(30)}{5} + 32$
$= 54 + 32$
$= 86$
$86°F$

3. $C = \dfrac{5(F-32)}{9}$

    $= \dfrac{5(97-32)}{9}$

    $= \dfrac{5(65)}{9}$

    $\approx 36.1$

    $36.1°C$

4. $C = \dfrac{5(77-32)}{9}$

    $= \dfrac{5(45)}{9}$

    $= 25$

    $25°C$

5. $F = \dfrac{9C}{5} + 32$

    $= \dfrac{9(60)}{5} + 32$

    $= 108 + 32$

    $= 140$

    $140°F$

6. $C = \dfrac{5(F-32)}{9}$

    $= \dfrac{5(58-32)}{9}$

    $= \dfrac{5(26)}{9}$

    $\approx 14.4$

    $14.4°C$

7. $C = \dfrac{5(F-32)}{9}$

    $= \dfrac{5(81-32)}{9}$

    $= \dfrac{5(49)}{9}$

    $\approx 27.2$

    $27.2°C$

8. $F = \dfrac{9C}{5} + 32$

    $= \dfrac{9(80)}{5} + 32$

    $= 144 + 32$

    $= 176$

    $176°F$

9. $F = \dfrac{9C}{5} + 32$

    $= \dfrac{9(12.8)}{5} + 32$

    $= 23.04 + 32$

    $= 55.04$

    $55.04°F$

10. $C = \dfrac{5(F-32)}{9}$

    $= \dfrac{5(121.7-32)}{9}$

    $= \dfrac{5(89.7)}{9}$

    $\approx 49.8$

    $49.8°C$

11. $C = \dfrac{5(F-32)}{9}$

    $= \dfrac{5(92-32)}{9}$

    $= \dfrac{5(60)}{9}$

    $\approx 33.3$

    $33.3°C$

    The temperature outside is about $33.3°C$.

12. $C = \dfrac{5(F-32)}{9}$

    $= \dfrac{5(70-32)}{9}$

    $= \dfrac{5(38)}{9}$

    $\approx 21.1$

    $21.1°C$

    Dan's office is normally has a temperature of about $21.1°C$.

13. $F = \dfrac{9C}{5} + 32$

$= \dfrac{9(14)}{5} + 32$

$= 25.2 + 32$

$= 57.2$

$57.2°\text{F}$

The forecast temperature is $57.2°\text{F}$.

14. $F = \dfrac{9C}{5} + 32$

$= \dfrac{9(12)}{5} + 32$

$= 21.6 + 32$

$= 53.6$

$53.6°\text{F}$

The current temperature is $53.6°\text{F}$.

15. $C = \dfrac{5(F-32)}{9}$

$= \dfrac{5(160-32)}{9}$

$= \dfrac{5(128)}{9}$

$\approx 71.1$

$71.1°\text{C}$

To be safe, hamburger should be cooked to about $71.1°\text{C}$.

16. $C = \dfrac{5(F-32)}{9}$

$= \dfrac{5(-45-32)}{9}$

$= \dfrac{5(-77)}{9}$

$\approx -42.8$

$-42.8°\text{C}$

Dippin' Dots is kept at about $-42.8°\text{C}$.

## CHAPTER 9 PRACTICE TEST SOLUTIONS

1. complement:
   $90° - 41° = 59°$

   supplement:
   $180° - 41° = 139°$

2. $\angle x$ and the $70°$ angle are adjacent so they add to $180°$.
   $\angle x = 180° - 70° = 110°$

   $\angle x$ and $\angle z$ are vertical angles so they have the same measure.
   $\angle z = 110°$

   $\angle y$ and the $70°$ angle are vertical angles so they have the same measure.
   $\angle y = 70°$

3. The sum of the angles of a triangle must equal $180°$.
   $\angle x = 180° - (90° + 48°)$
   $\quad\ = 180° - 138°$
   $\quad\ = 42°$

4. $P = 2l + 2w$
   $= 2(30 \text{ ft}) + 2(19 \text{ ft})$
   $= 60 \text{ ft} + 38 \text{ ft}$
   $= 98 \text{ ft}$

5. $15 \text{ km} \approx 15 \text{ km} \cdot \dfrac{0.62 \text{ mi}}{1 \text{ km}} = 9.3 \text{ mi}$
   The race is about 9.3 miles long.

6. $A = l \cdot w$
   $= (11 \text{ in.})(4.5 \text{ in.})$
   $= 49.5 \text{ in.}^2$

7. $V = s^3$
   $= \left(5\dfrac{1}{3} \text{ m}\right)^3$
   $= \left(\dfrac{16}{5} \text{ m}\right)^3$
   $= \dfrac{4096}{125} \text{ m}^3$
   $= 32.768 \text{ m}^3$

8. $V = l \cdot w \cdot h$
   $= (3 \text{ ft})\left(1\dfrac{1}{2} \text{ ft}\right)\left(\dfrac{1}{2} \text{ ft}\right)$
   $= 3 \cdot \dfrac{3}{2} \cdot \dfrac{1}{2} \text{ ft}^3$
   $= 2.25 \text{ ft}^3$

9.
$$
\begin{array}{r}
7 \text{ ft } 11 \text{ in.} \\
12\overline{)95} \\
\underline{84} \\
11
\end{array}
$$

10. $26 \text{ qt} = 26 \text{ qt} \cdot \dfrac{1 \text{ gal}}{4 \text{ qt}} = \dfrac{26}{4} \text{ gal} = 6.5 \text{ gal}$

11. $52 \text{ in.} = 52 \text{ in.} \cdot \dfrac{2.54 \text{ cm}}{1 \text{ in}} = 132.08 \text{ cm}$

12. $4.6 \text{ tons} = 4.6 \text{ tons} \cdot \dfrac{2000 \text{ lbs}}{1 \text{ ton}} = 9200 \text{ lbs}$

13. $36 \text{ pt} = 36 \text{ pt} \cdot \dfrac{1 \text{ qt}}{2 \text{ pt}} \cdot \dfrac{1 \text{ gal}}{4 \text{ qt}}$
$\qquad = 4.5 \text{ gal}$

14. g   dg   cg   mg
$\uparrow$
3 units left

$62 \text{ mg} = 062.$
$\qquad\quad \uparrow$
$\qquad = 0.062 \text{ g}$

15. kg   hg   dag   g
$\qquad\qquad\qquad\uparrow$
3 units right

$4.8 \text{ kg} = 4.800$
$\qquad\qquad \uparrow$
$\qquad = 4800 \text{ g}$

16. cm      mm
$\qquad\qquad \uparrow$
1 unit right

$7.2 \text{ cm} = 7.2$
$\qquad\qquad \uparrow$
$\qquad = 72 \text{ mm}$

17. $7.1 \text{ gal} \approx 7.1 \text{ gal} \cdot \dfrac{3.79 \text{ L}}{1 \text{ gal}} \approx 26.91 \text{ L}$

18. L   dl   cl   ml
$\qquad\qquad\qquad\uparrow$
3 units right

$0.075 \text{ L} = 0.075$
$\qquad\qquad\quad \uparrow$
$\qquad = 75 \text{ ml}$

19.
$$
\begin{array}{r}
7 \text{ qt } 1 \text{ pt} \\
+\ \ 8 \text{ qt } 1 \text{ pt} \\
\hline
15 \text{ qt } 2 \text{ pt}
\end{array}
$$
$= 15 \text{ qt } 1 \text{ qt}$
$= 16 \text{ qt}$

20.
$$
\begin{array}{r}
10 \text{ lb } 5 \text{ oz} \\
-\ \ 3 \text{ lb } 7 \text{ oz} \\
\end{array}
\qquad
\begin{array}{r}
9 \text{ lb } 21 \text{ oz} \\
-\ \ 3 \text{ lb }\ \ 7 \text{ oz} \\
\hline
6 \text{ lb } 14 \text{ oz}
\end{array}
$$

21.
$$
\begin{array}{r}
5 \text{ ft } 7 \text{ in.} \\
\times \qquad 3 \\
\hline
15 \text{ ft } 21 \text{ in.}
\end{array}
$$
$= 15 \text{ ft } 1 \text{ ft } 9 \text{ in.}$
$= 16 \text{ ft } 9 \text{ in.}$

22.
$$
\begin{array}{r}
2 \text{ gal} \qquad 3 \text{ qt} \\
3\overline{)8 \text{ gal} \qquad 1 \text{ qt}} \\
\underline{6} \\
2 \text{ gal } = 8 \text{ qt} \\
9 \text{ qt}
\end{array}
$$

23. $12 \text{ cm} = 120 \text{ mm}$
$$
\begin{array}{r}
120 \text{ mm} \\
-\ \ 18 \text{ mm} \\
\hline
102 \text{ mm}
\end{array}
$$

or $18 \text{ mm} = 1.8 \text{ cm}$
$$
\begin{array}{r}
12.0 \text{ cm} \\
-\ \ 1.8 \text{ cm} \\
\hline
10.2 \text{ cm}
\end{array}
$$

24. $329 \text{ m} = 0.329 \text{ km}$

$$\begin{array}{r} 2.4 \quad \text{km} \\ + \, 0.329 \text{ km} \\ \hline 2.729 \text{ km} \end{array}$$

or $2.4 \text{ km} = 2400 \text{ m}$

$$\begin{array}{r} 2400 \text{ m} \\ + \; 329 \text{ m} \\ \hline 2729 \text{ m} \end{array}$$

25. $C = \dfrac{5(F-32)}{9}$

$= \dfrac{5(63-32)}{9}$

$= \dfrac{5(31)}{9}$

$\approx 17.2$

$17.2°\text{C}$

26. $F = \dfrac{9C}{5} + 32$

$= \dfrac{9(10.8)}{5} + 32$

$= 19.44 + 32$

$= 51.44$

$51.44°\text{F}$

## 10.1 SOLUTIONS TO EXERCISES

1. $(5t-3)+(-9t+21)=(5t-9t)+(-3+21)$
$$=-4t+18$$

2. $(18y+6)+(10y-22)$
$$=(18y+10y)+(6-22)$$
$$=28y-16$$

3. $(2x+8)+(6x^2-7x+3)$
$$=6x^2+(2x-7x)+(8+3)$$
$$=6x^2-5x+11$$

4. $(30x+5)-(25x-2)$
$$=(30x+5)+(-25x+2)$$
$$=(30x-25x)+(5+2)$$
$$=5x+7$$

5. $(-13a^2+6a-3)-(-5a+12)$
$$=(-13a^2+6a-3)+(5a-12)$$
$$=-13a^2+(6a+5a)+(-3-12)$$
$$=-13a^2+11a-15$$

6. $(10y^3+15y^2-y-2)-(8y^3+6y-12)$
$$=(10y^3+15y^2-y-2)+(-8y^3-6y+12)$$
$$=(10y^3-8y^3)+15y^2+(-y-6y)+(-2+12)$$
$$=2y^3+15y^2-7y+10$$

7. $(5.6b^3+15)+(-8.1b^2-4.9b+12.1)$
$$=5.6b^3-8.1b^2-4.9b+(15+12.1)$$
$$=5.6b^3-8.1b^2-4.9b+27.1$$

8. $(-9t-7)-(16t-7)=(-9t-7)+(-16t+7)$
$$=(-9t-16t)+(-7+7)$$
$$=-25t$$

9. $(17x^2+4x-10)-(4x^2-9x+17)$
$$=(17x^2+4x-10)+(-4x^2+9x-17)$$
$$=(17x^2-4x^2)+(4x+9x)+(-10-17)$$
$$=13x^2+13x-27$$

10. $\left(-3x^2+\dfrac{5}{8}x\right)-\left(4x^2-\dfrac{3}{8}x\right)$
$$=\left(-3x^2+\dfrac{5}{8}x\right)+\left(-4x^2+\dfrac{3}{8}x\right)$$
$$=(-3x^2-4x^2)+\left(\dfrac{5}{8}x+\dfrac{3}{8}x\right)$$
$$=-7x^2+x$$

11. $-11x-6=-11(3)-6=-33-6=-39$

12. $4x+13=4(3)+13=12+13=25$

13. $x^2-4x+8=(3)^2-4(3)+8$
$$=9-12+8$$
$$=5$$

14. $-x^2-x-1=-(3)^2-3-1$
$$=-9-3-1$$
$$=-13$$

15. $\dfrac{8x^2}{6}-12=\dfrac{8(3)^2}{6}-12$
$$=\dfrac{8(9)}{6}-12$$
$$=\dfrac{72}{6}-12$$
$$=12-12$$
$$=0$$

16. $\dfrac{x^3}{9}-x-11=\dfrac{(3)^3}{9}-3-11$
$$=\dfrac{27}{9}-3-11$$
$$=3-3-11$$
$$=-11$$

17. $6x+5=6(-4)+5=-24+5=-19$

18. $x^2=(-4)^2=16$

19. $2x^3=2(-4)^3=2(-64)=-128$

20. $x^3-x^2+x+1=(-4)^3-(-4)^2+(-4)+1$
$$=-64-16-4+1$$
$$=-83$$

## 10.2 SOLUTIONS TO EXERCISES

1. $x^4 \cdot x^9 = x^{4+9} = x^{13}$

2. $a^{15} \cdot a = a^{15+1} = a^{16}$

3. $2y^3 \cdot 6y^4 = (2 \cdot 6)\left(y^3 \cdot y^4\right) = 12y^{3+4} = 12y^7$

4. $-6x \cdot 13x = (-6 \cdot 13)(x \cdot x) = -78x^2$

5. $\left(-10a^2 b\right)\left(-2a^6 b^5\right)$
   $= (-10)(-2)\left(a^2 \cdot a^6\right)\left(b^1 \cdot b^5\right)$
   $= 20a^{2+6} b^{1+5}$
   $= 20a^8 b^6$

6. $\left(-x^4 y z^7\right)\left(-4x^3 y^3 z^5\right)$
   $= (-1)(-4)\left(x^4 \cdot x^3\right)\left(y^1 \cdot y^3\right)\left(z^7 \cdot z^5\right)$
   $= 4x^{4+3} y^{1+3} z^{7+5}$
   $= 4x^7 y^4 z^{12}$

7. $2x \cdot 6x \cdot x^2 = (2 \cdot 6)\left(x \cdot x \cdot x^2\right)$
   $= 12x^{1+1+2}$
   $= 12x^4$

8. $4t \cdot 8t^{12} \cdot 7t^6 = (4 \cdot 8 \cdot 7)\left(t \cdot t^{12} \cdot 6^6\right)$
   $= 224t^{1+12+6}$
   $= 224t^{19}$

9. $\left(x^{10}\right)^9 = x^{10 \cdot 9} = x^{90}$

10. $\left(n^{12}\right)^7 = n^{12 \cdot 7} = n^{84}$

11. $(2m)^4 = 2^4 m^4 = 16m^4$

12. $\left(r^4\right)^5 \cdot \left(r^3\right)^2 = r^{4 \cdot 5} \cdot r^{3 \cdot 2}$
    $= r^{20} \cdot r^6$
    $= r^{20+6}$
    $= r^{26}$

13. $\left(x^3 y^8\right)^7 = \left(x^3\right)^7 \left(y^8\right)^7 = x^{3 \cdot 7} y^{8 \cdot 7} = x^{21} y^{56}$

14. $\left(7w^4 z^{13}\right)^3 = 7^3 \left(w^4\right)^3 \left(z^{13}\right)^3$
    $= 343w^{4 \cdot 3} z^{13 \cdot 3}$
    $= 343w^{12} z^{39}$

15. $(-4z)\left(2z^9\right)^4 = -4 \cdot z \cdot 2^4 \cdot \left(z^9\right)^4$
    $= -4 \cdot z \cdot 16 \cdot z^{9 \cdot 4}$
    $= -4 \cdot 16 \cdot z^{1+36}$
    $= -64z^{37}$

16. $\left(3x^2 y^3\right)^5 \left(2x^4 y^2\right)^3$
    $= 3^5 \left(x^2\right)^5 \left(y^3\right)^5 \cdot 2^3 \left(x^4\right)^3 \left(y^2\right)^3$
    $= 243x^{2 \cdot 5} y^{3 \cdot 5} \cdot 8x^{4 \cdot 3} y^{2 \cdot 3}$
    $= 243x^{10} y^{15} \cdot 8x^{12} y^6$
    $= (243 \cdot 8)\left(x^{10} \cdot x^{12}\right)\left(y^{15} \cdot y^6\right)$
    $= 1944x^{10+12} y^{15+6}$
    $= 1944x^{22} y^{21}$

17. $\left(14y^{12} z^8\right)^2 = 14^2 \left(y^{12}\right)^2 \left(z^8\right)^2$
    $= 196y^{12 \cdot 2} z^{8 \cdot 2}$
    $= 196y^{24} z^{16}$

18. $\left(6a^5 b^7\right)^4 \left(2a^{13} b\right)^5$
    $= 6^4 \left(a^5\right)^4 \left(b^7\right)^4 \cdot 2^5 \left(a^{13}\right)^5 b^5$
    $= 1296a^{5 \cdot 4} b^{7 \cdot 4} \cdot 32a^{13 \cdot 5} b^5$
    $= 1296a^{20} b^{28} \cdot 32a^{65} b^5$
    $= (1296 \cdot 32)\left(a^{20} \cdot a^{65}\right)\left(b^{28} \cdot b^5\right)$
    $= 41,472a^{20+65} b^{28+5}$
    $= 41,472a^{85} b^{33}$

19. $A = s^2 = \left(3x^5\right)^2 = 3^2 \left(x^5\right)^2 = 9x^{5 \cdot 2} = 9x^{10}$

    The area is $9x^{10}$ square feet.

20. $A = l \cdot w = 7y^5 \cdot 8y^2 = 7 \cdot 8 \cdot y^{5+2} = 56y^7$

    The area is $56y^7$ square meters.

## 10.3 SOLUTIONS TO EXERCISES

1. $5x(9x^2 + 11) = 5x \cdot 9x^2 + 5x \cdot 11$
   $= 45x^3 + 55x$

2. $3y(9y^4 - y) = 3y \cdot 9y^4 + 3y \cdot y$
   $= 27y^5 + 3y^2$

3. $-7m(4m^2 - m - 6)$
   $= -7m \cdot 4m^2 - 7m(-m) - 7m(-6)$
   $= -28m^3 + 7m^2 + 42m$

4. $8t^3(-2t^2 + t + 6)$
   $= 8t^3 \cdot (-2t^2) + 8t^3 \cdot t + 8t^3 \cdot 6$
   $= -16t^5 + 8t^4 + 48t^3$

5. $(p-5)(p-8) = p(p-8) - 5(p-8)$
   $= p \cdot p - p \cdot 8 - 5 \cdot p - 5(-8)$
   $= p^2 - 8p - 5p + 40$
   $= p^2 - 13p + 40$

6. $(y+10)(y+1) = y(y+1) + 10(y+1)$
   $= y \cdot y + y \cdot 1 + 10 \cdot y + 10 \cdot 1$
   $= y^2 + y + 10y + 10$
   $= y^2 + 11y + 10$

7. $(t-7)(t+7) = t(t+7) - 7(t+7)$
   $= t \cdot t + t \cdot 7 - 7 \cdot t - 7 \cdot 7$
   $= t^2 + 7t - 7t - 49$
   $= t^2 - 49$

8. $(3x+5)(x-11)$
   $= 3x(x-11) + 5(x-11)$
   $= 3x \cdot x + 3x(-11) + 5 \cdot x + 5(-11)$
   $= 3x^2 - 33x + 5x - 55$
   $= 3x^2 - 28x - 55$

9. $(3m+8)(3m+4)$
   $= 3m(3m+4) + 8(3m+4)$
   $= 3m \cdot 3m + 3m \cdot 4 + 8 \cdot 3m + 8 \cdot 4$
   $= 9m^2 + 12m + 24m + 32$
   $= 9m^2 + 36m + 32$

10. $(4y-5)^2 = (4y-5)(4y-5)$
    $= 4y(4y-5) - 5(4y-5)$
    $= 4y \cdot 4y + 4y(-5) - 5 \cdot 4y - 5(-5)$
    $= 16y^2 - 20y - 20y + 25$
    $= 16y^2 - 40y + 25$

11. $(4y+9)^2 = (4y+9)(4y+9)$
    $= 4y(4y+9) + 9(4y+9)$
    $= 4y \cdot 4y + 4y \cdot 9 + 9 \cdot 4y + 9 \cdot 9$
    $= 16y^2 + 36y + 36y + 81$
    $= 16y^2 + 72y + 81$

12. $\left(z + \dfrac{1}{4}\right)\left(z - \dfrac{3}{4}\right)$
    $= z\left(z - \dfrac{3}{4}\right) + \dfrac{1}{4}\left(z - \dfrac{3}{4}\right)$
    $= z \cdot z + z\left(-\dfrac{3}{4}\right) + \dfrac{1}{4} \cdot z + \dfrac{1}{4}\left(-\dfrac{3}{4}\right)$
    $= z^2 - \dfrac{3}{4}z + \dfrac{1}{4}z - \dfrac{3}{16}$
    $= z^2 - \dfrac{1}{2}z - \dfrac{3}{16}$

13. $(5a+11)(5a-11)$
    $= 5a(5a-11) + 11(5a-11)$
    $= 5a \cdot 5a + 5a(-11) + 11 \cdot 5a + 11(-11)$
    $= 25a^2 - 55a + 55a - 121$
    $= 25a^2 - 121$

14. $(x+7)^2 = (x+7)(x+7)$
    $= x(x+7) + 7(x+7)$
    $= x \cdot x + x \cdot 7 + 7 \cdot x + 7 \cdot 7$
    $= x^2 + 7x + 7x + 49$
    $= x^2 + 14x + 49$

15. $(n-8)(4n^2 + 3n + 14)$
    $= n(4n^2 + 3n + 14) - 8(4n^2 + 3n + 14)$
    $= n \cdot 4n^2 + n \cdot 3n + n \cdot 14 - 8 \cdot 4n^2 - 8 \cdot 3n - 8 \cdot 14$
    $= 4n^3 + 3n^2 + 14n - 32n^2 - 24n - 112$
    $= 4n^3 - 29n^2 - 10n - 112$

16. $(x+5)(x^2-5x+25)$

$= x(x^2-5x+25)+5(x^2-5x+25)$

$= x\cdot x^2 + x(-5x)+x\cdot 25+5\cdot x^2$
$\qquad\qquad +5(-5x)+5\cdot 25$

$= x^3-5x^2+25x+5x^2-25x+125$

$= x^3+125$

17. $(b^2+3)(4b^2-b+6)$

$= b^2(4b^2-b+6)+3(4b^2-b+6)$

$= b^2\cdot 4b^2+b^2(-b)+b^2\cdot 6+3\cdot 4b^2$
$\qquad\qquad +3(-b)+3\cdot 6$

$= 4b^4-b^3+6b^2+12b^2-3b+18$

$= 4b^4-b^3+18b^2-3b+18$

18. $(x^2+2x+3)(x^3-x^2+4)$

$= x^2(x^3-x^2+4)+2x(x^3-x^2+4)$
$\qquad\qquad +3(x^3-x^2+4)$

$= x^2\cdot x^3+x^2(-x^2)+x^2\cdot 4+2x\cdot x^3$
$\qquad\quad +2x(-x^2)+2x\cdot 4+3\cdot x^3$
$\qquad\quad +3(-x^2)+3\cdot 4$

$= x^5-x^4+4x^2+2x^4-2x^3+8x+3x^3$
$\qquad\qquad\qquad\qquad\qquad -3x^2+12$

$= x^5+x^4+x^3+x^2+8x+12$

19. $A=s^2$

$=(6x+13)^2$

$=(6x+13)(6x+13)$

$=6x(6x+13)+13(6x+13)$

$=6x\cdot 6x+6x\cdot 13+13\cdot 6x+13\cdot 13$

$=36x^2+78x+78x+169$

$=36x^2+156x+169$

The area is $(36x^2+156x+169)$ sq. meters.

20. $A=l\cdot w$

$=(y+5)(y^2+3y+7)$

$= y(y^2+3y+7)+5(y^2+3y+7)$

$= y\cdot y^2+y\cdot 3y+y\cdot 7+5\cdot y^2+5\cdot 3y+5\cdot 7$

$= y^3+3y^2+7y+5y^2+15y+35$

$= y^3+8y^2+22y+35$

The area is $(y^3+8y^2+22y+35)$ sq. inches.

## 10.4 SOLUTIONS TO EXERCISES

1. $75=5\cdot 15$
   $90=6\cdot 15$

   $GCF=15$

2. $72=2\cdot 36$
   $180=5\cdot 36$

   $GCF=36$

3. $x^9=x^5\cdot x^4$
   $x^4=x^4$
   $x^7=x^3\cdot x^4$

   $GCF=x^4$

4. The GCF of 4, 6, and 8 is 2.
   The GCF of $y^3$, $y^2$, and $y$ is $y$.
   Thus, the GCF of $4y^3$, $6y^2$, and $8y$ is $2y$.

5. The GCF of $a^2$, $a^3$, and $a$ is $a$.
   The GCF of $b^3$, $b^2$, and $b^2$ is $b^2$.
   Thus, the GCF of $a^2b^3$, $a^3b^2$, and $ab^2$ is $ab^2$.

6. The GCF of 14, 21, and 35 is 7.
   The GCF of $y$, $y^2$, and $y^3$ is $y$.
   The GCF of $z$, $z$, and $z^2$ is $z$.
   Thus, the GCF of $14yz$, $21y^2z$, and $35y^3z^2$ is $7yz$.

7. The GCF of 24, 18, and 42 is 6.
   The GCF of $a^5$, $a^6$, and $a^3$ is $a^3$.
   The GCF of $b^7$, $b^4$, and $b^6$ is $b^4$.
   Thus, the GCF of $24a^5b^7$, $18a^6b^4$, and
   $42a^3b^6$ is $6a^3b^4$.

8. The GCF of 9, 15, and 12 is 3.
   The GCF of $x^2$, $x^3$, and $x^5$ is $x^2$.
   The GCF of $y^5$, $y^2$, and $y^4$ is $y^2$.
   The GCF of $z^3$, $z^4$, and $z^2$ is $z^2$.
   Thus, the GCF of $9x^2y^5z^3$, $15x^3y^2z^4$, and
   $12x^5y^4z^2$ is $3x^2y^2z^2$.

9. $4x^3 + 8x^2 = 4x^2 \cdot x + 4x^2 \cdot 2$
   $= 4x^2(x+2)$

10. $16y^2 - 40y^4 = 8y^2 \cdot 2 - 8y^2 \cdot 5y^2$
    $= 8y^2(2 - 5y^2)$

11. $20z^4 + 10z^2 = 10z^2 \cdot 2z^2 + 10z^2 \cdot 1$
    $= 10z^2(2z^2 + 1)$

12. $20m^2 - 15m^4 = 5m^2 \cdot 4 - 5m^2 \cdot 3m^2$
    $= 5m^2(4 - 3m^2)$

13. $b^{12} - 2b^8 = b^8 \cdot b^4 - b^8 \cdot 2$
    $= b^8(b^4 - 2)$

14. $m^9 + 7m^5 = m^5 \cdot m^4 + m^5 \cdot 7$
    $= m^5(m^4 + 7)$

15. $13x^6 - 26x^4 + 39x^2$
    $= 13x^2 \cdot x^4 - 13x^2 \cdot 2x^2 + 13x^2 \cdot 3$
    $= 13x^2(x^4 - 2x^2 + 3)$

16. $12y^6 - 8y^4 + 16y^3$
    $= 4y^3 \cdot 3y^3 - 4y^3 \cdot 2y + 4y^3 \cdot 4$
    $= 4y^3(3y^3 - 2y + 4)$

17. $3a^4 - 6b^2 + 9 = 3 \cdot a^4 - 3 \cdot 2b^2 + 3 \cdot 3$
    $= 3(a^4 - 2b^2 + 3)$

18. $26m^5 + 13m^4 - 39m^2$
    $= 13m^2 \cdot 2m^3 + 13m^2 \cdot m^2 - 13m^2 \cdot 3$
    $= 13m^2(2m^3 + m^2 - 3)$

19. $20b^{12} - 30b^8 + 50b^6$
    $= 10b^6 \cdot 2b^6 - 10b^6 \cdot 3b^2 + 10b^6 \cdot 5$
    $= 10b^6(2b^6 - 3b^2 + 5)$

20. $x^2y^3 + 5x^3y^4 + 7x^2y^5$
    $= x^2y^3 \cdot 1 + x^2y^3 \cdot 5xy + x^2y^3 \cdot 7y^2$
    $= x^2y^3(1 + 5xy + 7y^2)$

**CHAPTER 10 PRACTICE TEST SOLUTIONS**

1. $(13x - 12) + (4x + 7) = (13x + 4x) + (-12 + 7)$
   $= 17x - 5$

2. $(15x - 7) - (2x + 8) = (15x - 7) + (-2x - 8)$
   $= (15x - 2x) + (-7 - 8)$
   $= 13x - 15$

3. $(6.1y^2 + 8) + (2.3y^2 - 6.1y - 13.4)$
   $= (6.1y^2 + 2.3y^2) - 6.1y + (8 - 13.4)$
   $= 8.4y^2 - 6.1y - 5.4$

4. $(4b^2 - 4b - 1) - (6b^2 - 5)$
   $= (4b^2 - 4b - 1) + (-6b^2 + 5)$
   $= (4b^2 - 6b^2) - 4b + (-1 + 5)$
   $= -2b^2 - 4b + 4$

5. $x^2 + 5x - 3 = (-4)^2 + 5(-4) - 3$
   $= 16 - 20 - 3$
   $= -7$

6. $m^3 - 4m^2 + 9 = 3^3 - 4 \cdot 3^2 + 9$
   $= 27 - 4 \cdot 9 + 9$
   $= 27 - 36 + 9$
   $0$

7. $y^6 \cdot y^8 = y^{6+8} = y^{14}$

8. $\left(m^9\right)^7 = m^{9\cdot7} = m^{63}$

9. $\left(3x^6\right)^3 = 3^3\left(x^6\right)^3 = 27x^{6\cdot3} = 27x^{18}$

10. $\left(-12a^4\right)\left(-3a^{12}\right) = (-12)(-3)a^{4+12} = 36a^{16}$

11. $\left(b^{12}\right)^5\left(b^2\right)^3 = b^{12\cdot5}\cdot b^{2\cdot3}$
$$= b^{60}\cdot b^6$$
$$= b^{60+6}$$
$$= b^{66}$$

12. $\left(3x^4y\right)^3\left(4x^2y^2\right)^2 = 3^3\left(x^4\right)^3 y^3\cdot 4^2\left(x^2\right)^2\left(y^2\right)^2$
$$= 27x^{4\cdot3}y^3\cdot16x^{2\cdot2}y^{2\cdot2}$$
$$= 27x^{12}y^3\cdot16x^4y^4$$
$$= (27\cdot16)\left(x^{12}\cdot x^4\right)\left(y^3\cdot y^4\right)$$
$$= 432x^{12+4}y^{3+4}$$
$$= 432x^{16}y^7$$

13. $6x\left(9x^3 - 2.6\right) = 6x\cdot9x^3 - 6x\cdot2.6$
$$= 54x^4 - 15.6x$$

14. $-7m\left(m^4 - 11m^3 + 4\right)$
$$= -7m\cdot m^4 - 7m\left(-11m^3\right) - 7m\cdot4$$
$$= -7m^5 + 77m^4 - 28m$$

15. $(x-6)(x-7) = x(x-7) - 6(x-7)$
$$= x\cdot x + x(-7) - 6\cdot x - 6(-7)$$
$$= x^2 - 7x - 6x + 42$$
$$= x^2 - 13x + 42$$

16. $(6x+7)^2 = (6x+7)(6x+7)$
$$= 6x(6x+7) + 7(6x+7)$$
$$= 6x\cdot6x + 6x\cdot7 + 7\cdot6x + 7\cdot7$$
$$= 36x^2 + 42x + 42x + 49$$
$$= 36x^2 + 84x + 49$$

17. $(y-7)\left(y^2 + 7y + 49\right)$
$$= y\left(y^2 + 7y + 49\right) - 7\left(y^2 + 7y + 49\right)$$
$$= y\cdot y^2 + y\cdot7y + y\cdot49 - 7\cdot y^2 - 7\cdot7y - 7\cdot49$$
$$= y^3 + 7y^2 + 49y - 7y^2 - 49y - 343$$
$$= y^3 - 343$$

18. $(4x-9)(4x+9)$
$$= 4x(4x+9) - 9(4x+9)$$
$$= 4x\cdot4x + 4x\cdot9 - 9\cdot4x - 9\cdot9$$
$$= 16x^2 + 36x - 36x - 81$$
$$= 16x^2 - 81$$

19. $P = 2l + 2w$
$$= 2(5x+3) + 2(6x)$$
$$= 2\cdot5x + 2\cdot3 + 12x$$
$$= 10x + 6 + 12x$$
$$= 22x + 6$$
The perimeter is $(22x+6)$ feet.

$A = lw$
$$= (5x+3)\cdot6x$$
$$= 5x\cdot6x + 3\cdot6x$$
$$= 30x^2 + 18x$$
The area is $\left(30x^2 + 18x\right)$ sq. feet.

20. $75 = 5\cdot15$
$90 = 6\cdot15$

$GCF = 15$

21. The GCF of 8, 20, and 24 is 4.
The GCF of $x^7$, $x^5$, and $x^{12}$ is $x^5$.
Thus, the GCF of $8x^7$, $20x^5$, and $24x^{12}$ is $4x^5$.

22. $7x^2 - 35 = 7\cdot x^2 - 7\cdot5 = 7\left(x^2 - 5\right)$

23. $y^9 - 7y^5 = y^5\cdot y^4 - y^5\cdot7 = y^5\left(y^4 - 7\right)$

24. $3x^2 - 6x + 30 = 3\cdot x^2 - 3\cdot2x + 3\cdot10$
$$= 3\left(x^2 - 2x + 10\right)$$

25. $-16(3)^2 + 400 = -16\cdot9 + 400$
$$= -144 + 400$$
$$= 256$$
When $t = 3$ seconds, the height of the rock is 256 feet.

## SOLUTIONS TO PRACTICE FINAL A

1.
$$
\begin{array}{r}
62 \\
+57 \\
\hline
119
\end{array}
$$

2.
$$
\begin{array}{r}
8\ 14 \\
8\,\cancel{9}\,\cancel{4} \\
-63\ 8 \\
\hline
25\ 6
\end{array}
$$

3.
$$
\begin{array}{r}
127 \\
\times\ 13 \\
\hline
381 \quad \leftarrow 3(127) \\
1270 \quad \leftarrow 10(127) \\
\hline
1651 \quad \text{Add.}
\end{array}
$$

4.
$$
\begin{array}{r}
92 \\
49\overline{)4508} \\
441 \\
\hline
98 \\
98 \\
\hline
0
\end{array}
$$

5. $\left(3^2 - 4\right) \cdot 8 = (9 - 4) \cdot 8 = 5 \cdot 8 = 40$

6. $31 + 48 \div 4 \cdot 2 - 10 = 31 + 12 \cdot 2 - 10$
$$
\begin{aligned}
&= 31 + 24 - 10 \\
&= 55 - 10 \\
&= 45
\end{aligned}
$$

7. $2{,}13\underline{7}{,}\boxed{5}46$ rounds to $2{,}138{,}000$.

8. $5\left(x^3 - 7\right) = 5\left(3^3 - 7\right)$
$$
\begin{aligned}
&= 5(27 - 7) \\
&= 5(20) \\
&= 100
\end{aligned}
$$

9. Price per can = (total cost) $\div$ (no. of cans)
$$
\begin{aligned}
&= \quad 312 \quad \div \quad 26 \\
&= \quad 12
\end{aligned}
$$
Each can of varnish costs \$12.

10. $19 - 53 = 19 + (-53) = -34$

11. $-22 + 17 = -5$

12. $(-5)(-71) = 355$

13. $\dfrac{-57}{3} = -19$

14. $(-6)^2 - 30 \div (-5) = 36 - 30 \div (-5)$
$$
\begin{aligned}
&= 36 - (-6) \\
&= 36 + 6 \\
&= 42
\end{aligned}
$$

15. $\dfrac{|39 - 57|}{6} = \dfrac{|-18|}{6} = \dfrac{18}{6} = 3$

16. $\dfrac{7(-12) + 16}{-2(9 - 26)} = \dfrac{-84 + 16}{-2(-17)} = \dfrac{-68}{34} = -2$

17. $\dfrac{25}{-5} - \dfrac{4^3}{8} = \dfrac{25}{-5} - \dfrac{64}{8} = -5 - 8 = -13$

18. $4x - y = 4(-6) - (-7) = -24 + 7 = -17$

19. $|x - y| + |x| = |-8 - 10| + |-8|$
$$
\begin{aligned}
&= |-18| + |-8| \\
&= 18 + 8 \\
&= 26
\end{aligned}
$$

20. $8x - 14 - 15x + 29 = 8x - 15x - 14 + 29$
$$
= -7x + 15
$$

21. $-10(2x + 9) = -10 \cdot 2x - 10 \cdot 9$
$$
= -20x - 90
$$

22. $P = 4s$
$$
\begin{aligned}
&= 4 \cdot 29 \\
&= 116
\end{aligned}
$$
The perimeter is 116 feet.

23. $8x + x = 81$
$$
\begin{aligned}
9x &= 81 \\
\dfrac{9x}{9} &= \dfrac{81}{9} \\
x &= 9
\end{aligned}
$$

24.
$$
\begin{aligned}
24 &= 5x - 17x \\
24 &= -12x \\
\dfrac{24}{-12} &= \dfrac{-12x}{-12} \\
-2 &= x
\end{aligned}
$$

25. $19x + 12 - 18x - 30 = 20$
$$x - 18 = 20$$
$$x - 18 + 18 = 20 + 18$$
$$x = 38$$

26. $\quad 7(x-3) = 0$
$$7x - 21 = 0$$
$$7x - 21 + 21 = 0 + 21$$
$$7x = 21$$
$$\frac{7x}{7} = \frac{21}{7}$$
$$x = 3$$

27. $10 + 6(2y - 1) = 28$
$$10 + 12y - 6 = 28$$
$$12y + 4 = 28$$
$$12y + 4 - 4 = 28 - 4$$
$$12y = 24$$
$$\frac{12y}{12} = \frac{24}{12}$$
$$y = 2$$

28. $\quad 6(5x - 7) = 8(4x + 1)$
$$30x - 42 = 32x + 8$$
$$30x - 42 + 42 = 32x + 8 + 42$$
$$30x = 32x + 50$$
$$30x - 32x = 32x + 50 - 32x$$
$$-2x = 50$$
$$\frac{-2x}{-2} = \frac{50}{-2}$$
$$x = -25$$

29. Let $x$ represent the number.
$$3x + 7x = 90$$
$$10x = 90$$
$$\frac{10x}{10} = \frac{90}{10}$$
$$x = 9$$
The number is 9.

30. Let $s$ represent the side length of the porch.
$$4s = 152$$
$$\frac{4s}{4} = \frac{152}{4}$$
$$s = 38$$
The side length is 38 feet.

31. $\dfrac{4}{5} \cdot \dfrac{35}{8} = \dfrac{4 \cdot 35}{5 \cdot 8} = \dfrac{\boxed{4} \cdot \boxed{5} \cdot 7}{\boxed{5} \cdot \boxed{4} \cdot 2} = \dfrac{7}{2}$ or $3\dfrac{1}{2}$

32. $\dfrac{6x}{7} - \dfrac{4x}{7} = \dfrac{6x - 4x}{7} = \dfrac{2x}{7}$

33. $\dfrac{xy^3}{z^2} \cdot \dfrac{z^3}{x^4 y} = \dfrac{\boxed{x} \cdot \boxed{y} \cdot y \cdot y \cdot \boxed{z} \cdot \boxed{z} \cdot z}{\boxed{z} \cdot \boxed{z} \cdot \boxed{x} \cdot x \cdot x \cdot x \cdot \boxed{y}} = \dfrac{y^2 z}{x^3}$

34. $\dfrac{6y}{17} + \dfrac{5}{34} = \dfrac{6y \cdot 2}{17 \cdot 2} + \dfrac{5}{34}$
$$= \dfrac{12y}{34} + \dfrac{5}{34}$$
$$= \dfrac{12y + 5}{34}$$

35. $4\dfrac{1}{5} \div \dfrac{7}{25} = \dfrac{21}{5} \div \dfrac{7}{25}$
$$= \dfrac{21}{5} \cdot \dfrac{25}{7}$$
$$= \dfrac{3 \cdot \cancel{7}}{\cancel{5}} \cdot \dfrac{\cancel{5} \cdot 5}{\cancel{7}}$$
$$= 15$$

36. 
$$5\dfrac{2}{3} = \quad 5\dfrac{12}{18}$$
$$4\dfrac{1}{6} = \quad 4\dfrac{3}{18}$$
$$+\, 8\dfrac{7}{9} = \quad +\, 8\dfrac{14}{18}$$
$$17\dfrac{29}{18} = 17 + 1\dfrac{11}{18} = 18\dfrac{11}{18}$$

37. $18 \div 3\dfrac{4}{9} = 18 \div \dfrac{31}{9} = \dfrac{18}{1} \cdot \dfrac{9}{31} = \dfrac{162}{31}$ or $5\dfrac{7}{31}$

38. $40y^2 \div \dfrac{y}{8} = \dfrac{40y^2}{1} \cdot \dfrac{8}{y} = \dfrac{40 \cdot \cancel{y} \cdot y \cdot 8}{\cancel{y}} = 320y$

39. $-\dfrac{8}{7} \div \dfrac{64}{21} = -\dfrac{8}{7} \cdot \dfrac{21}{64} = -\dfrac{\cancel{8} \cdot 3 \cdot \cancel{7}}{\cancel{7} \cdot \cancel{8} \cdot 8} = -\dfrac{3}{8}$

40. $\left(\dfrac{16}{7}\cdot\dfrac{42}{8}\right)\div 8 = \left(\dfrac{2\cdot\cancel{8}}{\cancel{7}}\cdot\dfrac{6\cdot\cancel{7}}{\cancel{8}}\right)\div 8$

$\qquad\qquad\quad = 12\div 8$

$\qquad\qquad\quad = \dfrac{12}{1}\cdot\dfrac{1}{8}$

$\qquad\qquad\quad = \dfrac{3\cdot\cancel{4}}{2\cdot\cancel{4}}$

$\qquad\qquad\quad = \dfrac{3}{2}$ or $1\dfrac{1}{2}$

41. $\dfrac{6+\dfrac{3}{5}}{4-\dfrac{7}{10}} = \dfrac{10\left(6+\dfrac{3}{5}\right)}{10\left(4-\dfrac{7}{10}\right)}$

$\qquad = \dfrac{10\cdot 6+10\left(\dfrac{3}{5}\right)}{10\cdot 4+10\left(\dfrac{7}{10}\right)}$

$\qquad = \dfrac{60+6}{40+7}$

$\qquad = \dfrac{66}{47}$ or $1\dfrac{19}{47}$

42. $\qquad\dfrac{x}{4}+x = -\dfrac{15}{8}$

$\qquad 8\left(\dfrac{x}{4}+x\right) = 8\left(-\dfrac{15}{8}\right)$

$\qquad 8\left(\dfrac{x}{4}\right)+8(x) = 8\left(-\dfrac{15}{8}\right)$

$\qquad\quad 2x+8x = -15$

$\qquad\qquad 10x = -15$

$\qquad\qquad \dfrac{10x}{10} = \dfrac{-15}{10}$

$\qquad\qquad\quad x = -\dfrac{3}{2}$ or $-1\dfrac{1}{2}$

43. $\qquad\dfrac{5}{9}+\dfrac{x}{6} = \dfrac{2}{3}-\dfrac{x}{12}$

$\qquad 36\left(\dfrac{5}{9}+\dfrac{x}{6}\right) = 36\left(\dfrac{2}{3}-\dfrac{x}{12}\right)$

$\qquad 36\left(\dfrac{5}{9}\right)+36\left(\dfrac{x}{6}\right) = 36\left(\dfrac{2}{3}\right)-36\left(\dfrac{x}{12}\right)$

$$20+6x = 24-3x$$
$$20+6x-20 = 24-3x-20$$
$$6x = -3x+4$$
$$6x+3x = -3x+4+3x$$
$$9x = 4$$
$$\dfrac{9x}{9} = \dfrac{4}{9}$$
$$x = \dfrac{4}{9}$$

44. $xy = 3\dfrac{3}{4}\cdot 2\dfrac{2}{9}$

$\qquad = \dfrac{15}{4}\cdot\dfrac{20}{9}$

$\qquad = \dfrac{\cancel{3}\cdot 5\cdot\cancel{4}\cdot 5}{\cancel{4}\cdot\cancel{3}\cdot 3}$

$\qquad = \dfrac{25}{3}$ or $8\dfrac{1}{3}$

45. $\quad\overset{\scriptstyle 12\ \ \ 1}{11.654}$
$\qquad\ \ 3.71$
$\qquad +\ 9.827$
$\qquad\overline{\ 25.191}$

46. $-48.7-8.36 = -48.7+(-8.36) = -57.06$

47. $\qquad 14.6$
$\qquad\times 3.25$
$\qquad\overline{\quad 730}$
$\qquad\ 2920$
$\qquad 43800$
$\qquad\overline{47.450}$

48. $(-1.4)^2+3.9 = 1.96+3.9 = 5.86$

49. $\dfrac{0.11-3.75}{0.2} = \dfrac{-3.64}{0.2} = -18.2$

50. $1358.63\boxed{5}9$ rounds to $1358.64$

51. $0.72 = \dfrac{72}{100} = \dfrac{4\cdot 18}{4\cdot 25} = \dfrac{18}{25}$

52.
$$\begin{array}{r} 0.0375 \\ 400\overline{)15.0000} \\ \underline{12\ 00} \\ 3\ 000 \\ \underline{2\ 800} \\ 2000 \\ \underline{2000} \\ 0 \end{array}$$

$$\frac{15}{400} = 0.0375$$

53. $-2\sqrt{36} + \sqrt{25} = -2\cdot 6 + 5 = -12 + 5 = -7$

54. $V = s^3$

$$= \left(3\frac{5}{8}\right)^3$$

$$= 3\frac{5}{8}\cdot 3\frac{5}{8}\cdot 3\frac{5}{8}$$

$$= \frac{29}{8}\cdot\frac{29}{8}\cdot\frac{29}{8}$$

$$= \frac{24{,}389}{512} \quad \text{or} \quad 47\frac{325}{512}$$

The volume is $47\dfrac{325}{512}$ cubic centimeters.

55. $A = l\cdot w = 9\cdot 2.7 = 24.3$
The area is 24.3 square feet.

56. $4x + 3y = 24$

Let $x = 0$: $4(0) + 3y = 24$
$$3y = 24$$
$$y = 8$$

Let $y = 0$: $4x + 3(0) = 24$
$$4x = 24$$
$$x = 6$$

Let $y = 4$: $4x + 3(4) = 24$
$$4x + 12 = 24$$
$$4x = 12$$
$$x = 3$$

The ordered pairs are (0, 8), (6, 0), and (3, 4).

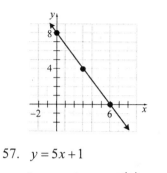

57. $y = 5x + 1$

Let $x = 0$: $y = 5(0) + 1$
$$y = 1$$

Let $x = 1$: $y = 5(1) + 1$
$$y = 5 + 1$$
$$y = 6$$

Let $y = -4$: $-4 = 5x + 1$
$$-5 = 5x$$
$$-1 = x$$

The ordered pairs are (0, 1), (1, 6), and (−1 , −4).

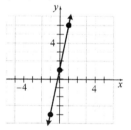

58. $x + y = 6$

Let $x = 0$: $0 + y = 6$
$$y = 6$$

Let $y = 0$: $x + 0 = 6$
$$x = 6$$

Let $x = 3$: $3 + y = 6$
$$y = 3$$

The ordered pairs (0, 6), (6, 0), and (3, 3) are on the graph.

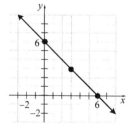

59. $x - 5 = 0$

    $x = 5$

This is a vertical line that crosses the $x$-axis at 5.

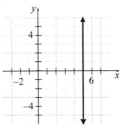

60. $y + 6 = 0$

    $y = -6$

This is a horizontal line that crosses the $y$-axis at $-6$.

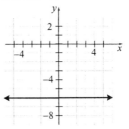

61. $4x - 5y = 20$

Let $x = 0$: $4(0) - 5y = 20$

                 $-5y = 20$

                    $y = -4$

Let $y = 0$: $4x - 5(0) = 20$

                  $4x = 20$

                   $x = 5$

Let $x = -5$: $4(-5) - 5y = 20$

                $-20 - 5y = 20$

                  $-5y = 40$

                    $y = -8$

The ordered pairs $(0, -4)$, $(5, 0)$, and $(-5, -8)$ are on the graph

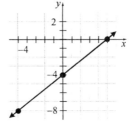

62. $\text{mean} = \dfrac{57 + 42 + 69 + 74 + 47 + 56 + 61}{7}$

           $= \dfrac{406}{7}$

           $= 58$

63. 16, 16, 21, 28, $\boxed{37}$, 47, 75, 83, 92

    median $= 37$

64. 20, 20, 20, 21, 34, 35, 35, 49, 84, 85, 94

    mode $= 20$

65. $\text{GPA} = \dfrac{3 \cdot 4 + 4 \cdot 4 + 5 \cdot 3 + 3 \cdot 2}{3 + 4 + 5 + 3}$

        $= \dfrac{12 + 16 + 15 + 6}{15}$

        $= \dfrac{49}{15}$

        $\approx 3.27$

66. $\dfrac{270 \text{ bushels}}{432 \text{ bushels}} = \dfrac{270}{432} = \dfrac{5}{8}$

67. $\dfrac{972 \text{ miles}}{18 \text{ hour}} = 54$ miles per hour

68. $\dfrac{18}{x} = \dfrac{135}{210}$

    $18 \cdot 210 = x \cdot 135$

    $\dfrac{3780}{135} = \dfrac{135x}{135}$

       $28 = x$

69. $\dfrac{\frac{9}{5}}{\frac{3}{4}} = \dfrac{x}{25}$    

$\dfrac{\frac{9}{5}}{\frac{3}{4}} = \dfrac{x}{\frac{25}{18}}$

    $\dfrac{9}{5} \cdot \dfrac{25}{18} = x \cdot \dfrac{3}{4}$

        $\dfrac{5}{2} = \dfrac{3}{4}x$

    $\dfrac{4}{3} \cdot \dfrac{5}{2} = \dfrac{4}{3} \cdot \dfrac{3}{4}x$

        $\dfrac{10}{3} = x$

70.
$$\begin{array}{r} 52 \text{ R } 6 \\ 12\overline{)630} \\ \underline{60} \\ 30 \\ \underline{24} \\ 6 \end{array}$$

630 inches = 52 ft 6 in

71. $7\dfrac{1}{2}$ gal $= \dfrac{15}{2}$ gal $\times \dfrac{4 \text{ qt}}{1 \text{ gal}} = 30$ qt

72. $38$ g $= \dfrac{38 \text{ g}}{1} \times \dfrac{1000 \text{ mg}}{1 \text{ g}} = 38,000$ mg

73. $5700$ ml $= \dfrac{5700 \text{ ml}}{1} \times \dfrac{1 \text{ L}}{1000 \text{ ml}}$
$= \dfrac{5700 \text{ L}}{1000}$
$= 5.7$ L

74. $C = \dfrac{5}{9}(F - 32) = \dfrac{5}{9}(77 - 32) = \dfrac{5}{9}(45) = 25$

Thus, $77°F = 25°C$.

75.
$$\begin{array}{r} 12 \text{ lb} \quad 6 \text{ oz} \\ + 10 \text{ lb } 14 \text{ oz} \\ \hline 22 \text{ lb } 20 \text{ oz} \end{array}$$
$= 22$ lb 1 lb 4 oz
$= 23$ lb 4 oz

76. $3.4$ km $= 3400$ m

$3.4$ km $+ 346$ m $= 3400$ m $+ 346$ m
$= 3746$ m

77. $9$ cm $= 90$ mm

$9$ cm $- 15$ mm $= 90$ mm $- 15$ mm
$= 75$ mm

78. $0.0037 = 0.0037 \cdot 100\% = 0.37\%$

79. $32.8\% = \dfrac{32.8\%}{100\%} = 0.328$

80. $\dfrac{3}{40} = \dfrac{3}{40} \cdot 100\% = \dfrac{300\%}{40} = 7.5\%$

81. $x = 68\% \cdot 900$
$x = 0.68 \cdot 900$
$x = 612$

82. $203 = 35\% \cdot x$
$203 = 0.35x$
$\dfrac{203}{0.35} = \dfrac{0.35x}{0.35}$
$580 = x$

83. $40.32 = x \cdot 96$
$\dfrac{40.32}{96} = \dfrac{96x}{96}$
$0.42 = x$
$42\% = x$

84. What is 24% of 350?
$x = 24\% \cdot 350$
$x = 0.24 \cdot 350$
$x = 84$

There are 84 pounds of sunflower seeds in the birdfeed.

85. Total amount $= 375 + 0.065 \cdot 375$
$\approx 375 + 24.38$
$\approx 399.38$

The total charge is $399.38.

86. Compounding quarterly
rate = 8%
time = 5 years
compounding factor = 1.48595
(See Appendix F in the textbook)
Total amount $= 8300 \cdot 1.48595 \approx 12,333.39$

The amount in the account after five years will be $12,333.39.

87. Commission $= 2.6\% \cdot 18,700$
$= 0.025 \cdot 18,700$
$= 467.5$

Dolores' commission was $467.50.

88. $(10y + 3) + (-8y + 15) = (10y - 8y) + (3 + 15)$
$= 2y + 18$

89. $(12x - 5) - (x - 1) = (12x - 5) + (-x + 1)$
$= (12x - x) + (-5 + 1)$
$= 11x - 4$

90. $x^2 - x + 10 = (-4)^2 - (-4) + 10$
$$= 16 + 4 + 10$$
$$= 30$$

91. $y^{15} \cdot y^{16} = y^{15+16} = y^{31}$

92. $\left(x^6\right)^8 = x^{6 \cdot 8} = x^{48}$

93. $\left(a^3\right)^5 \left(a^{10}\right)^6 = a^{3 \cdot 5} \cdot a^{10 \cdot 6}$
$$= a^{15} \cdot a^{60}$$
$$= a^{15+60}$$
$$= a^{75}$$

94. $-4y\left(y^2 - 5y + 7\right)$
$$= -4y \cdot y^2 - 4y(-5y) - 4y \cdot 7$$
$$= -4y^3 + 20y^2 - 28y$$

95. $(x+11)(x-9)$
$$= x(x-9) + 11(x-9)$$
$$= x \cdot x + x \cdot (-9) + 11 \cdot x + 11(-9)$$
$$= x^2 - 9x + 11x - 99$$
$$= x^2 + 2x - 99$$

96. $(3x+7)^2 = (3x+7)(3x+7)$
$$= 3x(3x+7) + 7(3x+7)$$
$$= 3x \cdot 3x + 3x \cdot 7 + 7 \cdot 3x + 7 \cdot 7$$
$$= 9x^2 + 21x + 21x + 49$$
$$= 9x^2 + 42x + 49$$

97. $(b-8)\left(b^2 + 8b + 64\right)$
$$= b\left(b^2 + 8b + 64\right) - 8\left(b^2 + 8b + 64\right)$$
$$= b \cdot b^2 + b \cdot 8b + b \cdot 64 - 8 \cdot b^2 - 8 \cdot 8b - 8 \cdot 64$$
$$= b^3 + 8b^2 + 64b - 8b^2 - 64b - 512$$
$$= b^3 - 512$$

98. The GCF of 16, 24, and 32 is 8.
The GCF of $x^5$, $x^3$, and $x^7$ is $x^3$.
Thus, the GCF of $16x^5$, $24x^3$, and $32x^7$ is $8x^3$.

99. $8x^3 - 64x^5 = 8x^3 \cdot 1 - 8x^3 \cdot 8x^2 = 8x^3\left(1 - 8x^2\right)$

100. $15y^2 - 20y = 5y \cdot 3y - 5y \cdot 4 = 5y(3y - 4)$

**SOLUTIONS TO PRACTICE FINAL B**

1. $\overset{1}{5}7$
$\underline{+98}$
$155$

2. $\overset{12}{\underset{}{}}$
$6\ \overset{12}{\cancel{7}}\ 12$
$\cancel{7}\ \cancel{3}\ \cancel{2}$
$\underline{-4\ 6\ 8}$
$2\ 6\ 4$

3. $315$
$\underline{\times\ 17}$
$2205 \quad \leftarrow 7(315)$
$\underline{3150} \quad \leftarrow 10(315)$
$5355 \quad$ Add.

4. $\begin{array}{r} 91 \\ 65\overline{)5915} \\ \underline{585} \\ 65 \\ \underline{65} \\ 0 \end{array}$

5. $\left(2^4 - 9\right) \cdot 8 = (16 - 9) \cdot 8 = 7 \cdot 8 = 56$

6. $13 + 18 \div 9 \cdot 5 - 10 = 13 + 2 \cdot 5 - 10$
$$= 13 + 10 - 10$$
$$= 23 - 10$$
$$= 13$$

7. $83\underline{7},\boxed{9}51$ rounds to 838,000.

8. $9\left(x^2 - 12\right) = 9\left(7^2 - 12\right)$
$$= 9(49 - 12)$$
$$= 9(37)$$
$$= 333$$

9. Price per case = (total cost) ÷ (no. of cases)
$$= \quad 86.22 \quad \div \quad 18$$
$$= \quad 4.79$$
Each case of soda costs $4.79.

10. $21 - 58 = 21 + (-58) = -37$

11. $-43 + 17 = -26$

12. $(-10)(8) = -80$

13. $\dfrac{-68}{-4} = 17$

14. $(-9)^2 - 35 \div (-5) = 81 - 35 \div (-5)$
$$= 81 - (-7)$$
$$= 81 + 7$$
$$= 88$$

15. $\dfrac{|8 - 60|}{-13} = \dfrac{|-52|}{-13} = \dfrac{52}{-13} = -4$

16. $\dfrac{4(-12) + 8}{-1(-2 - 6)} = \dfrac{-48 + 8}{-1(-8)} = \dfrac{-40}{8} = -5$

17. $\dfrac{42}{-7} - \dfrac{2^3}{4} = \dfrac{42}{-7} - \dfrac{8}{4} = -6 - 2 = -8$

18. $5x - y = 5(-9) - (-4) = -45 + 4 = -41$

19. $|x + y| - |y| = |-3 + 10| - |10|$
$$= |7| - |10|$$
$$= 7 - 10$$
$$= -3$$

20. $14x + 21 - 8x - 49 = 14x - 8x + 21 - 49$
$$= 6x - 28$$

21. $-12(3x + 8) = -12 \cdot 3x - 12 \cdot 8$
$$= -36x - 96$$

22. $P = 4s$
$$= 4 \cdot 19$$
$$= 76$$
The perimeter is 76 feet.

23. $15x - 4x = 33$
$$11x = 33$$
$$\dfrac{11x}{11} = \dfrac{33}{11}$$
$$x = 3$$

24. $32 = 7x - 15x$
$$32 = -8x$$
$$\dfrac{32}{-8} = \dfrac{-8x}{-8}$$
$$-4 = x$$

25. $17x + 41 - 15x + 5 = 14$
$$2x + 46 = 14$$
$$2x + 46 - 46 = 14 - 46$$
$$2x = -32$$
$$\dfrac{2x}{2} = \dfrac{-32}{2}$$
$$x = -16$$

26. $6(x - 8) = 0$
$$6x - 48 = 0$$
$$6x - 48 + 48 = 0 + 48$$
$$6x = 48$$
$$\dfrac{6x}{6} = \dfrac{48}{6}$$
$$x = 8$$

27. $7 + 5(5y - 3) = 42$
$$7 + 25y - 15 = 42$$
$$25y - 8 = 42$$
$$25y - 8 + 8 = 42 + 8$$
$$25y = 50$$
$$\dfrac{25y}{25} = \dfrac{50}{25}$$
$$y = 2$$

28. $8(2x - 6) = 4(3x + 5)$
$$16x - 48 = 12x + 20$$
$$16x - 48 + 48 = 12x + 20 + 48$$
$$16x = 12x + 68$$
$$16x - 12x = 12x + 68 - 12x$$
$$4x = 68$$
$$\dfrac{4x}{4} = \dfrac{68}{4}$$
$$x = 17$$

29. Let $x$ represent the number.
$$6x + 9x = 60$$
$$15x = 60$$
$$\dfrac{15x}{15} = \dfrac{60}{15}$$
$$x = 4$$
The number is 9.

30. Let $s$ represent the side length of the porch.
$$4s = 84$$
$$\dfrac{4s}{4} = \dfrac{84}{4}$$
$$s = 21$$
The side length is 21 feet.

31. $\dfrac{5}{6} \cdot \dfrac{27}{45} = \dfrac{5 \cdot 27}{6 \cdot 45} = \dfrac{\boxed{5} \cdot \boxed{3} \cdot \boxed{3} \cdot \boxed{3}}{2 \cdot \boxed{3} \cdot \boxed{3} \cdot \boxed{3} \cdot \boxed{5}} = \dfrac{1}{2}$

32. $\dfrac{7x}{5} - \dfrac{2x}{5} = \dfrac{7x - 2x}{5} = \dfrac{5x}{5} = x$

33. $\dfrac{xy^3}{z^2} \cdot \dfrac{z}{x^3y} = \dfrac{\boxed{x} \cdot \boxed{y} \cdot y \cdot y \cdot \boxed{z}}{\boxed{z} \cdot z \cdot \boxed{x} \cdot x \cdot x \cdot \boxed{y}} = \dfrac{y^2}{x^2z}$

34. $\dfrac{5y}{13} + \dfrac{7}{52} = \dfrac{5y \cdot 4}{13 \cdot 4} + \dfrac{7}{52}$

$\qquad = \dfrac{20y}{52} + \dfrac{7}{52}$

$\qquad = \dfrac{20y + 7}{52}$

35. $3\dfrac{3}{8} \div \dfrac{6}{7} = \dfrac{27}{8} \div \dfrac{6}{7}$

$\qquad = \dfrac{27}{8} \cdot \dfrac{7}{6}$

$\qquad = \dfrac{9 \cdot \cancel{3}}{8} \cdot \dfrac{7}{2 \cdot \cancel{3}}$

$\qquad = \dfrac{63}{16} \quad \text{or} \quad 3\dfrac{15}{16}$

36. $\begin{array}{r} 7\dfrac{1}{2} = \\[2mm] 4\dfrac{3}{8} = \\[2mm] + 9\dfrac{5}{6} = \\ \hline \end{array} \quad \begin{array}{r} 7\dfrac{12}{24} \\[2mm] 4\dfrac{9}{24} \\[2mm] + 9\dfrac{20}{24} \\ \hline 20\dfrac{41}{24} = 20 + 1\dfrac{17}{24} = 21\dfrac{17}{24} \end{array}$

37. $24 \div 6\dfrac{3}{7} = 24 \div \dfrac{45}{7}$

$\qquad = \dfrac{24}{1} \cdot \dfrac{7}{45}$

$\qquad = \dfrac{\cancel{3} \cdot 8}{1} \cdot \dfrac{7}{\cancel{3} \cdot 15}$

$\qquad = \dfrac{56}{15} \quad \text{or} \quad 3\dfrac{11}{15}$

38. $10y^3 \div \dfrac{y}{4} = \dfrac{10y^3}{1} \cdot \dfrac{4}{y} = \dfrac{10 \cdot \cancel{x} \cdot y^2 \cdot 4}{\cancel{x}} = 40y^2$

39. $-\dfrac{5}{9} \div \left(-\dfrac{20}{27}\right) = \dfrac{5}{9} \cdot \dfrac{27}{20} = \dfrac{\cancel{5} \cdot 3 \cdot \cancel{9}}{\cancel{9} \cdot \cancel{5} \cdot 4} = \dfrac{3}{4}$

40. $4 \div \left(\dfrac{2}{3} \cdot \dfrac{9}{16}\right) = 4 \div \left(\dfrac{\cancel{2}}{\cancel{3}} \cdot \dfrac{\cancel{3} \cdot 3}{\cancel{2} \cdot 8}\right)$

$\qquad = 4 \div \dfrac{3}{8}$

$\qquad = \dfrac{4}{1} \cdot \dfrac{8}{3}$

$\qquad = \dfrac{32}{3} \quad \text{or} \quad 10\dfrac{2}{3}$

41. $\dfrac{\dfrac{1}{4} + \dfrac{5}{6}}{\dfrac{7}{8} - \dfrac{2}{3}} = \dfrac{24\left(\dfrac{1}{4} + \dfrac{5}{6}\right)}{24\left(\dfrac{7}{8} - \dfrac{2}{3}\right)}$

$\qquad = \dfrac{24\left(\dfrac{1}{4}\right) + 24\left(\dfrac{5}{6}\right)}{24\left(\dfrac{7}{8}\right) + 24\left(-\dfrac{2}{3}\right)}$

$\qquad = \dfrac{6 + 20}{21 - 16}$

$\qquad = \dfrac{26}{5} \quad \text{or} \quad 5\dfrac{1}{5}$

42. $\dfrac{x}{6} + x = -\dfrac{5}{12}$

$\qquad 12\left(\dfrac{x}{6} + x\right) = 12\left(-\dfrac{5}{12}\right)$

$\qquad 12\left(\dfrac{x}{6}\right) + 12(x) = 12\left(-\dfrac{5}{12}\right)$

$\qquad 2x + 12x = -5$

$\qquad 14x = -5$

$\qquad \dfrac{14x}{14} = \dfrac{-5}{14}$

$\qquad x = -\dfrac{5}{14}$

43.
$$\frac{5}{6} + \frac{x}{12} = \frac{1}{3} - \frac{x}{2}$$
$$12\left(\frac{5}{6} + \frac{x}{12}\right) = 12\left(\frac{1}{3} - \frac{x}{2}\right)$$
$$12\left(\frac{5}{6}\right) + 12\left(\frac{x}{12}\right) = 12\left(\frac{1}{3}\right) - 12\left(\frac{x}{2}\right)$$
$$10 + x = 4 - 6x$$
$$10 + x - 10 = 4 - 6x - 10$$
$$x = -6x - 6$$
$$x + 6x = -6x - 6 + 6x$$
$$7x = -6$$
$$\frac{7x}{7} = \frac{-6}{7}$$
$$x = -\frac{6}{7}$$

44.
$$\frac{x}{y} = \frac{-\frac{3}{7}}{1\frac{1}{9}} = \frac{-\frac{3}{7}}{\frac{10}{9}} = -\frac{3}{7} \cdot \frac{9}{10} = -\frac{27}{70}$$

45.
$$\overset{2}{6}.91$$
$$3.805$$
$$+\ 2.8$$
$$\overline{13.515}$$

46. $-18.6 - 31.5 = -18.6 + (-31.5) = -50.1$

47.
$$10.46$$
$$\times\ 3.4$$
$$\overline{4184}$$
$$31380$$
$$\overline{35.564}$$

48. $(-2.3)^2 + 4.1 = 5.29 + 4.1 = 9.39$

49. $\dfrac{0.9 - 2.58}{-0.3} = \dfrac{-1.68}{-0.3} = 5.6$

50. $29.057\boxed{2}$ rounds to $29.057$

51. $0.86 = \dfrac{86}{100} = \dfrac{2 \cdot 43}{2 \cdot 50} = \dfrac{43}{50}$

52.
$$\begin{array}{r} 0.214 \\ 500\overline{)107.000} \\ \underline{100\ 0}\phantom{00} \\ 7\ 00 \\ \underline{5\ 00} \\ 2\ 000 \\ \underline{2\ 000} \\ 0 \end{array}$$
$$\frac{107}{500} = 0.214$$

53. $-4\sqrt{121} - \sqrt{64} = -4 \cdot 11 - 8 = -44 - 8 = -52$

54. $V = s^3$
$$= \left(1\frac{3}{7}\right)^3$$
$$= 1\frac{3}{7} \cdot 1\frac{3}{7} \cdot 1\frac{3}{7}$$
$$= \frac{10}{7} \cdot \frac{10}{7} \cdot \frac{10}{7}$$
$$= \frac{1000}{343} \quad \text{or} \quad 2\frac{314}{343}$$

The volume is $2\dfrac{314}{343}$ cubic inches.

55. $A = l \cdot w = 5.6 \cdot 2.5 = 14$
The area is 14 square feet.

56. $4x - 7y = 28$

Let $x = 0$: $4(0) - 7y = 28$
$$-7y = 28$$
$$y = -4$$

Let $y = 0$: $4x - 7(0) = 28$
$$4x = 28$$
$$x = 7$$

Let $x = -1$: $4(-1) - 7y = 28$
$$-4 - 7y = 28$$
$$-7y = 32$$
$$y = -\frac{32}{7} \quad \text{or} \quad -4\frac{4}{7}$$

The ordered pairs are (0, –4), (7, 0), and $\left(-1, -4\frac{4}{7}\right)$.

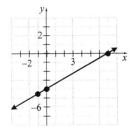

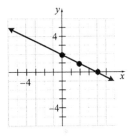

57. $y = 3x - 5$

Let $x = 0$: $y = 3(0) - 5$
$y = -5$

Let $y = 0$: $0 = 3x - 5$
$-3x = -5$
$x = \dfrac{5}{3}$ or $1\dfrac{2}{3}$

Let $x = 2$: $y = 3(2) - 5$
$y = 6 - 5$
$y = 1$

The ordered pairs are $(0, -5)$, $\left(1\dfrac{2}{3}, 0\right)$, and

$(2, 1)$.

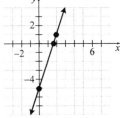

58. $x + 2y = 4$

Let $x = 0$: $0 + 2y = 4$
$2y = 4$
$y = 2$

Let $y = 0$: $x + 2(0) = 4$
$x = 4$

Let $x = 2$: $2 + 2y = 4$
$2y = 2$
$y = 1$

The ordered pairs $(0, 2)$, $(4, 0)$, and $(2, 1)$ are on the graph.

59. $x - 3 = 0$
$x = 3$

This is a vertical line that crosses the $x$-axis at 3.

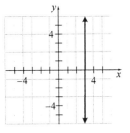

60. $2y - 3 = 0$
$2y = 3$
$y = \dfrac{3}{2}$

This is a horizontal line that crosses the $y$-axis at $\dfrac{3}{2}$.

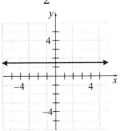

61. $4x + 5y = 20$

Let $x = 0$: $4(0) + 5y = 20$
$5y = 20$
$y = 4$

Let $y = 0$: $4x + 5(0) = 20$
$4x = 20$
$x = 5$

Let $x = -5$: $4(-5) + 5y = 20$

$$-20 + 5y = 20$$
$$5y = 40$$
$$y = 8$$

The ordered pairs $(0, 4)$, $(5, 0)$, and $(-5, 8)$ are on the graph

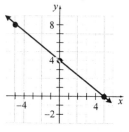

62.  mean
$$= \frac{108 + 112 + 137 + 142 + 98 + 156 + 110 + 118}{8}$$
$$= \frac{981}{8}$$
$$= 122.625$$

63.  10, 12, 14, 15, 23, $\boxed{30, 34}$, 47, 55, 57, 59, 78

median $= \dfrac{30 + 34}{2} = \dfrac{64}{2} = 32$

64.  10, 10, 10, 28, 29, 37, 37, 49, 51, 52, 52, 52, 52, 91

mode $= 52$

65.  $\text{GPA} = \dfrac{3 \cdot 3 + 3 \cdot 4 + 4 \cdot 2 + 5 \cdot 3}{3 + 3 + 4 + 5}$

$= \dfrac{9 + 12 + 8 + 15}{15}$

$= \dfrac{44}{15}$

$\approx 2.93$

66.  $\dfrac{62 \text{ marbles}}{248 \text{ marble}} = \dfrac{62}{248} = \dfrac{1}{4}$

67.  $\dfrac{624 \text{ miles}}{24 \text{ gallons}} = 26$ miles per gallon

68.  $\dfrac{9}{60} = \dfrac{x}{20}$

$$9 \cdot 20 = 60 \cdot x$$
$$180 = 60x$$
$$\dfrac{180}{60} = \dfrac{60x}{60}$$
$$3 = x$$

69.  $\dfrac{4.8}{x} = \dfrac{30}{115}$

$$4.8 \cdot 115 = x \cdot 30$$
$$552 = 30x$$
$$\dfrac{552}{30} = \dfrac{30x}{30}$$
$$18.4 = x$$

70.
$$\begin{array}{r} 91 \\ 12\overline{)1092} \\ \underline{108} \\ 12 \\ \underline{12} \\ 0 \end{array}$$

1092 inches = 91 feet

71.  $78 \text{ qt} = \dfrac{78 \text{ qt}}{1} \times \dfrac{1 \text{ gal}}{4 \text{ qt}} = \dfrac{78}{4}$ gal $= 19.5$ gal

72.  $12{,}000 \text{ mg} = \dfrac{12{,}000 \text{ mg}}{1} \times \dfrac{1 \text{ g}}{1000 \text{ mg}}$

$= \dfrac{12{,}000}{1000}$ g

$= 12$ g

73.  $13 \text{ L} = \dfrac{13 \text{ L}}{1} \times \dfrac{1000 \text{ ml}}{1 \text{ L}} = 13{,}000$ ml

74.  $F = \dfrac{9}{5}C + 32 = \dfrac{9}{5}(20) + 32 = 36 + 32 = 68$

Thus, $20°C = 68°F$.

75.
$$\begin{array}{r} 10 \text{ ft } 6 \text{ in} = 9 \text{ ft } 18 \text{ in} \\ -4 \text{ ft } 9 \text{ in} = -4 \text{ ft } 9 \text{ in} \\ \hline 5 \text{ ft } 9 \text{ in} \end{array}$$

76.  $3.8 \text{ kg} = 3800$ g

$3.8 \text{ kg} + 160 \text{ g} = 3800 \text{ g} + 160$ g

$= 3960$ g

77. $(9 \text{ lb } 3 \text{ oz}) \times 6 = 54 \text{ lb } 18 \text{ oz}$
$= 54 \text{ lb } 1 \text{ lb } 2 \text{ oz}$
$= 55 \text{ lb } 2 \text{ oz}$

78. $0.126 = 0.126 \cdot 100\% = 12.6\%$

79. $0.37\% = \dfrac{0.37\%}{100\%} = 0.0037$

80. $\dfrac{6}{75} = \dfrac{6}{75} \cdot 100\% = \dfrac{600\%}{75} = 8\%$

81. $x = 4.2\% \cdot 950$
$x = 0.042 \cdot 950$
$x = 39.9$

82. $172.2 = x \cdot 820$
$\dfrac{172.2}{820} = \dfrac{820x}{820}$
$.21 = x$
$21\% = x$

83. $39.8 = 40\% \cdot x$
$39.8 = 0.40x$
$\dfrac{39.8}{0.40} = \dfrac{0.40x}{0.40}$
$99.5 = x$

84. $\text{interest} = \text{principal} \cdot \text{rate} \cdot \text{time}$
$= 1600 \cdot 8.75\% \cdot 2.5$
$= 1600 \cdot 0.0875 \cdot 2.5$
$= 350$
The interest earned is $350.

85. $5 \text{ years} = 5 \text{ years} \cdot \dfrac{12 \text{ months}}{1 \text{ year}} = 60 \text{ months}$

$\text{payment} = \dfrac{8500 + 1275}{60} = \dfrac{9775}{60} \approx 162.92$

The monthly payment will be approximately $162.92.

86. $\text{commission} = 4.5\% \cdot 283{,}000$
$= 0.045 \cdot 283{,}000$
$= 12{,}735$

Suzanna's commission is $12,735.

87. $(6x^2 - 8x + 5) + (3x^2 - 4x - 9)$
$= (6x^2 + 3x^2) + (-8x - 4x) + (5 - 9)$
$= 9x^2 - 12x - 4$

88. $(9x^3 - x + 5) - (4x^2 - 7x + 6)$
$= (9x^3 - x + 5) + (-4x^2 + 7x - 6)$
$= 9x^3 - 4x^2 + (-x + 7x) + (5 - 6)$
$= 9x^3 - 4x^2 + 6x - 1$

89. $3x^2 - 2x + 7 = 3(2)^2 - 2(2) + 7$
$= 3 \cdot 4 - 4 + 7$
$= 12 - 4 + 7$
$= 15$

90. $y^{16} \cdot y^{21} = y^{16+21} = y^{37}$

91. $\left(m^5\right)^{13} = m^{5 \cdot 13} = m^{65}$

92. $\left(b^7\right)^3 \left(b^3\right)^7 = b^{7 \cdot 3} \cdot b^{3 \cdot 7}$
$= b^{21} \cdot b^{21}$
$= b^{21+21}$
$= b^{42}$

93. $6x\left(x^2 - 5x - 12\right)$
$= 6x \cdot x^2 + 6x(-5x) + 6x(-12)$
$= 6x^3 - 30x^2 - 72x$

94. $(x+8)(x+3) = x(x+3) + 8(x+3)$
$= x \cdot x + x \cdot 3 + 8 \cdot x + 8 \cdot 3$
$= x^2 + 3x + 8x + 24$
$= x^2 + 11x + 24$

95. $(x-5)(x+5) = x(x+5) - 5(x+5)$
$= x \cdot x + x \cdot 5 - 5 \cdot x - 5 \cdot 5$
$= x^2 + 5x - 5x - 25$
$= x^2 - 25$

96. $(3y-1)^2 = (3y-1)(3y-1)$
$$= 3y(3y-1) - 1(3y-1)$$
$$= 3y \cdot 3y + 3y(-1) - 1 \cdot 3y - 1(-1)$$
$$= 9y^2 - 3y - 3y + 1$$
$$= 9y^2 - 6y + 1$$

97. $(b-6)(b^2 + 6b + 36)$
$$= b(b^2 + 6b + 36) - 6(b^2 + 6b + 36)$$
$$= b \cdot b^2 + b \cdot 6b + b \cdot 36 - 6 \cdot b^2 - 6 \cdot 6b - 6 \cdot 36$$
$$= b^3 + 6b^2 + 36b - 6b^2 - 36b - 216$$
$$= b^3 - 216$$

98. The GCF of 21, 49, and 98 is 7.
The GCF of $y^5$, $y^4$, and $y^{10}$ is $y^4$.
Thus, the GCF of $21y^5$, $49y^4$, and $98y^{10}$ is $7y^4$.

99. $12x^5 - 36x^3 = 12x^3 \cdot x^2 - 12x^3 \cdot 3$
$$= 12x^3(x^2 - 3)$$

100. $10a^4 - 30a^3 - 20a^2$
$$= 10a^2 \cdot a^2 - 10a^2 \cdot 3a - 10a^2 \cdot 2$$
$$= 10a^2(a^2 - 3a - 2)$$